The Sand Dunes of the Sef

Proceedings of the *Sefton Coast Research Seminar*, Liverpool 31st May 1991.

Edited by David Atkinson and John Houston

NATIONAL MUSEUMS & GALLERIES
· ON MERSEYSIDE ·

The Sand Dunes of the Sefton Coast

Edited by David Atkinson[1] and John Houston[2]

1   Department of Environmental and Evolutionary Biology, The
     University of Liverpool, PO Box 147, Liverpool L69 3BX

2   Sefton Metropolitan Borough Council, Planning Department,
     Vermont House, 375 Stanley Road, Bootle L20 3RY

First Published 1993

British Library Cataloguing in Publication Data.

A Catalogue Record for this book is available from the
British Library.

Published by National Museums & Galleries on
Merseyside in association with Sefton Metropolitan
Borough Council.

Printed by Eaton Press Ltd, England 1993

ISBN 0 906367 62 X

CONTENTS

Foreword

Pat Doody

A dune landscape probably began to form on of the Sefton Coast about 4000 years ago when man's ability to control the forces of nature was minimal. Since then the area has been progressively changed as interference with the natural dune processes has taken place. Attempts to control instability, in part probably the result of insensitive management and overuse, have taken place for centuries. In more recent years housing and roads and recreational developments have stopped sand movement altogether, by covering the dune surface. Today some 2100 ha of dune survives out of a total area of blown sand, which was probably in excess of 3000 ha. Despite this loss this is still the largest area of open dune landscape in England and one of only six sites in Great Britain with more than 1000 ha of dune habitat (Doody 1991).

Throughout Europe management and use of the coastline has been approached on a piecemeal basis with little regard to its natural value or to the inter-relationships between the processes which operate there. Paradoxically at the same time its importance for recreation has grown, though individuals have not always recognised their own impact on the survival of coastal systems, particularly dunes. The importance of the Sefton Coast for nature conservation is recognised by the designation of virtually the whole dune system as a Site of Special Scientific Interest. This recognition is further strengthened by the presence of two National Nature Reserves, two Local Nature Reserves and National Trust land. These protective measures go some way to prevent the damage and destruction which continues to occur elsewhere. However, problems still remain, notably in relation to the development of appropriate techniques for management and monitoring.

In 1987 the GB Coastal Research and Management Group (CRMG) was established in response to a recognition of the need for better communication and integration between coastal research workers and site managers. It was hoped that this would help the research worker direct his or her activities towards more practical problems. A UK-wide coastal newsletter provides a mechanism for communication and a number of excursions have been held to look at particular problems: sea level rise in East Anglia, sand dune management and recreation in Cumbria and sand dune water relationships in South Wales.

The Sefton Coast Research Seminar held on May 31st 1991 brought together local and national research workers and local dune managers to review the conservation problems of the coastline of a specific site. The fact that this seminar took place in an area where the local council, Sefton Metropolitan Borough Council has already been instrumental in developing a coordinated approach to coastal management is of great significance.

The value of the wide-ranging nature of the papers presented here, which partly arose from the seminar, and their relevance to the coastal management and conservation issues is particularly important. The historical context, both over the longer Holocene timescale and in relation to man's more recent impact on the coastal zone is a significant starting point in setting the context for management decisions.

Understanding the underlying geomorphological processes and the soil, water and nutrient regimes is also essential for interpreting changes in the plant and animal communities. At the same time it is important to monitor uses and management of the dunes and relate these to observed changes, so that where necessary appropriate remedial action can be taken.

The identification of research needs in the light of a review of conservation issues, is exactly the type of approach that the Coastal Research and Management Group aimed to foster and it is hoped that the initiative taken here will be followed elsewhere in the UK. For its part the newly formed Joint Nature Conservation Committee (JNCC), whose remit includes providing a UK- and European-wide perspective on conservation issues, has agreed to continue to publish the Coastal Group's newsletter. In its co-ordination and communication role, encouraging the development of more integrated approaches to coastal management is seen as being of major importance to coastal conservation. The way in which these initiatives link with the wider European scene will be especially important as our ties grow ever stronger. In this context the affiliation of the CRMG and its development as the UK branch of the European Union for Coastal Conservation (EUCC) is an important step towards better understanding and integration on a European scale.

Introduction to the Volume

David Atkinson

This book brings together for the first time information from many disciplines relating to the sand dunes of the Sefton Coast in Merseyside, north-west England. Thirty-nine specialists have contributed to the fourteen chapters and to a bibliography containing many references to both published and unpublished work.

The book is organised into six main sections, each starting with a review chapter. These reviews have been designed to introduce the reader to each subject area. Technical terms, when included, have generally been explained either in the text, as footnotes, or by reference to figures or other illustrations in the book. In addition to these reviews are shorter more specialised chapters which examine certain topics in greater detail.

Factual information has been fully referenced, and guidance is given in the reference list at the end of the volume on the location, where known, of unpublished information. Information on the Sefton Coast is stored in a number of databases and a guide to their use is given in Appendix 1.

Names of animal and plant species include the English name, if one is in common usage, and, when the species is first mentioned in each chapter, also the scientific name followed by the name or initial of the person or 'authority' who gave it the name. Thus creeping willow (*Salix repens* L.) for example, was given its scientific name by Linnaeus (often abbreviated to L.)

Wherever possible the most up-to-date references are used to name animal and plant species. Flowering plants are named according to the *New Flora of the British Isles* (Stace 1991).

Two main types of dating have been employed. For recent human history the AD system is used, whereas for geomorphological and prehistoric timescales the BP system is generally used. Years BP are years 'before present' and present is taken conventionally to be 1950 AD. Other dating techniques, when used, are described by the authors.

The Sefton Coast is conveniently divided up by a series of landownerships (see figure iii, page xi) and most of the text can be related to these broad areas. Where a more detailed location is thought necessary a six figure British National Grid reference has been given (all these begin with the prefix SD).

A GUIDE TO THE SECTIONS

SECTION 1: History

This section comprises a single review chapter (Chapter 1) by Jones *et al.* It reviews the development of human settlement in the coastal area of Sefton. The authors mention evidence of hunting in what is now coastal Lancashire and Merseyside as far back as the Mesolithic period (*c* 9500 - 5300 BP) when sea level was rising after the low levels at the end of the last Ice Age. Jones *et al.* use sources of information of many different kinds to construct a picture of landscape development. Changes in climate and sea level, the occurrence of wars and plague, controls on land tenure and the ability to manage the land all played a part in the changing pattern of occupation of the area over the centuries.

The draining of the mosslands in the eighteenth century, the growing importance of Liverpool as a port and the increasing value attached to seaside resorts for recreation led to a major change in the area in the nineteenth century, continuing to the present century. The population and human activity grew enormously, tourism increased, asparagus farming was at its peak, and attempts were made at large-scale dune afforestation.

By the early 1960s pressures from new housing and uncontrolled access were leading to environmental degradation. In 1978, four years after local government reorganisation, the Sefton Coast Management Scheme was established. This Scheme encourages an integrated approach to land management between several landowners and agencies. This management work is introduced here and described in more detail in Chapter 12 by Wheeler *et al.* An appendix to this Section provides a chronology of the Sefton Coast.

SECTION 2: Geomorphology

The review of coastal and sea-level changes by Plater *et al.* (Chapter 2) describes both past and current views of how landforms and coastline have changed during the last 10,000 years. They describe four inundations by the sea (marine transgressions) between about 8000 years BP (first transgression) and 4800 to 4545 years BP (fourth transgression). A fifth, less well confirmed transgression may have occurred around 2330 years BP. They also describe how the main source of sand appears to be glacial outwash sediments found on the floor of the Irish Sea, and that there is a net movement of this in an easterly direction. Patterns of erosion, at Formby Point for example, are also explained. Suggested future areas for research are related to the prediction of effects caused by changes in climate, sea-level and storm activity, as well as their interactions with human influences on the coast. Innes and Tooley (Chapter 3) outline the evidence for their conclusion that the initial period of dune building on the Sefton coast was between 4600 and 4000 BP, and identify later periods of interruptions in sand accumulation. Recent field-drilling investigations by Pye and Neal (Chapter 4) also indicate periods of dune stability and instability. They warn too, that some coastal changes may be due to local variations in beach sediment budget and wave exposure, rather than coast-wide effects.

SECTION 3: Soils, Nutrient Cycling and Hydrology

James (Chapter 5) describes the development of different dune soil types from the original raw alkaline sands. Much of the soils of dry duneland can be described as 'pararendzinas' in which an organic layer has developed on the alkaline sand. Soils under the pinewoods have lost bases and other constituents of the upper soil horizons through the process of leaching. The upper mineral horizon of these (podzolized) soils thus have become acid. The chemical nature of dune slack soils is shown to depend critically on their wetness and hence the amount of oxidation occurring. Fluxes of plant nutrients such as nitrogen (very important for plant growth) and the cations (atoms with a positive electrical charge) of the elements calcium, magnesium, sodium and potassium are also described. Possible soil responses to a hypothetical change in climate and sea-level, described by James, depend greatly on hydrological processes such as those outlined by Clarke and Pegg (Chapter 6) who show how levels of standing water are almost totally dependent upon effective rainfall in the preceding months and that very rapid changes can occur such as between the low levels in August 1976 and the high levels in February 1977. The importance of hydrological processes in controlling vegetational composition has been revealed by studies in many different dune systems, and is reviewed by Jones (Chapter 7).

SECTION 4: Vegetation Studies

Results of recent surveys of dune and slack vegetation using techniques adopted in the National Vegetation Classification are used by Edmondson *et al.* (Chapter 8) to describe the great variation in vegetation types. Areas much modified by tree planting, asparagus farming and the dumping of tobacco waste are also included.

Some of the semi-natural vegetation types reflect different stages in dune succession, but the vegetation at any one time and place is affected by the history of the physical, biological and human factors that have operated through time at that particular place. These influences on vegetation communities are also discussed in this review chapter, and a detailed study of vegetation recovery following the clear-felling of dune plantations is described by Sturgess (Chapter 9).

SECTION 5: Animal and Plant Groups

Information on all the major animal and plant groups obtained by naturalists and biologists over a period of more than 150 years is reviewed by Atkinson *et al.* (Chapter 10). Particularly well studied species include the natterjack toad (*Bufo calamita* L.), the sand lizard (*Lacerta agilis* L.; whose habitat is described also by Cooke, Chapter 11) and some rare plants such as the baltic rush (*Juncus balticus* Willd) and its hybrids. But this review also revealed eight species of bryophyte (mosses and liverworts) sufficiently rare to be included in the appropriate British Red Data Book, including one species (*Petalophyllum ralfsii* Wils.) protected under the Bern Convention. Eight beetle species are included in the Red Data Books, several of which are coastal and dune specialists. Atkinson *et al.* (Chapter 10) also suggest future research which would aid the effective management of the dune system. Attention should be paid, they suggest, not just to rare species, but also those which are indicators of habitat quality and which have an important role in the ecology of the dunes such as rabbits, creeping willow and species sensitive to particular types of environmental change such as water table levels, climate and grazing.

SECTION 6: Dune Use and Management

The management work of the three main agencies on the coast: Sefton Council, English Nature and the National Trust, is summarised by Wheeler *et al.* (Chapter 12). This includes dune conservation and management, woodland and other vegetation management (including the control of birch and sea buckthorn scrub) and the conservation of individual species. They describe also how management addresses the demands of recreation and the use of the dunes as an educational resource. Educational demand and provision on the coast is evaluated by Huddart (Chapter 14).

To assess the rate of change and impact of management practices it is necessary to monitor land use. Mackay (Chapter 14) discusses alternative ways of doing this. Land utilisation surveys, detailed vegetation surveys and aerial photography and other remote sensing methods are all evaluated.

When referencing authors in this volume the following format should be used eg **James, P. A. (1993).** Soils and Nutrient Cycling. In: *The Sand Dunes of the Sefton Coast.* eds. D. Atkinson and J. A. Houston, Liverpool Museum, Liverpool. In Chapter 10, Animal and Plant Groups, individual contributors are cross-referenced to each entry and should be referenced as eg **Gunn, A.S. (1993).** Lichens. In: *The Sand Dunes of the Sefton Coast.* eds. D. Atkinson and J. A. Houston, National Museums & Galleries on Merseyside, Liverpool.

Introduction to the Coast

John Houston

Sefton is a Metropolitan Authority, one of five Boroughs which make up the former County of Merseyside in north-west England. Sefton's 32km long coastline is part of a large coastal system, with high tidal range, which includes the Ribble and Mersey estuaries (Figure i). The area known as the Sefton Coast features one of the largest sand flat and dune complexes in Britain (Ratcliffe 1977) and includes the estuary of the River Alt. The 2109ha area of dunes (Doody 1991) is approximately 17km long with an average width of 1.5km. Behind the protective dune barrier lies a low-lying hinterland of rich agricultural land. Much of the farmland has been reclaimed from wet mossland and meres and water levels are maintained by pumped drainage.

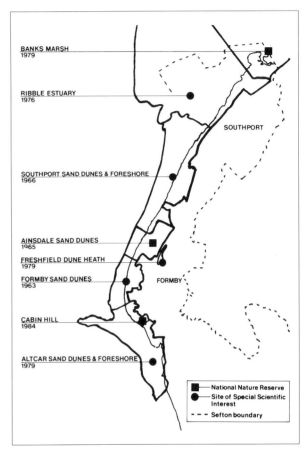

Figure ii. Nature Conservation Designations on the Sefton Coast. The Banks Marsh (now Ribble Marshes) National Nature Reserve and Ribble Estuary SSSI are both partly within Sefton but are not sand-dune areas.

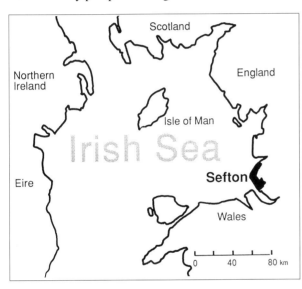

Figure i. the Sefton Coast in the context of the north Irish Sea.

The Sefton coast was well known and visited by pioneering naturalists and geomorphologists in the nineteenth century. Both Ainsdale and Freshfield dunes featured in the 1915 Survey of 'areas worthy of protection' carried out by the Society for the Promotion of Nature Reserves and Ainsdale was one of the top 22 sites in the U.K. listed by the Nature Reserves Investigation Committee in 1944 (Sheail 1976). But it was not until 1965 that the first fully protected reserve, the Ainsdale Sand Dunes National Nature Reserve was established by the Nature Conservancy.

Since 1963 English Nature (formerly the Nature Conservancy 1949-73 and the Nature Conservancy Council 1973-91) has scheduled a chain of Sites of Special Scientific Interest along the coast (Figure ii) and

declared a second duneland National Nature Reserve at Cabin Hill. In 1967 the National Trust purchased land at Formby Point, lying within the Formby Sand Dunes and Foreshore SSSI. The third main conservation agency is Sefton Council itself. Sefton Council are the lead agency in the Sefton Coast Management Scheme and the largest landowner on the coast. Since 1980 Sefton Council has designated two duneland Local Nature Reserves, a third is proposed, and has established a permanent team of countryside rangers.

The dune coast today is managed almost entirely for conservation, amenity, formal recreation and military training. Land ownership and land-uses create a useful pattern of zonation (Figure iii) ranging from restricted to open access. The three main managing agencies, English Nature, the National Trust and Sefton Council follow the aims of the Sefton Coast Management Scheme and adopt co-ordinated coastwide strategies for species and habitat management. The scheme has contact with the other dune landowners, notably the five golf courses and the military training area at Altcar to maintain an integrated approach to the management of the whole system. Farming is no longer a major land use although increasingly grazing is being re-introduced on reserves. There is no commercial hunting or warrening and the pine plantations are managed principally for amenity and nature conservation.

Recreation pressures are high, considerably higher and more extensive than on most dune systems and active management is essential to control and direct these pressures (Figure iv). The Sefton Coast Management Scheme has been able to integrate as far as possible the needs of recreation and conservation. Recreation pressure is no longer perceived as the greatest threat to the dunes, and the attention of managers has switched to long term habitat management. Future management decisions must be founded on a solid research base and the purpose of the Sefton Coast Research Seminar and this volume is to bring together the known information on the sand-dunes and to stimulate discussion on their future management.

Figure iv. Formby Point is an area which requires active management. The dune system is under pressure from the large local population at Formby, from residential caravan sites and day-visitors. Car parks and footpath networks direct this pressure. The relationship between the foreshore, dune system and mossland is shown in this photograph. The town of Formby lies across the boundary between the dune sands and the peats of the mossland. Photograph by John Mills Photography Ltd.

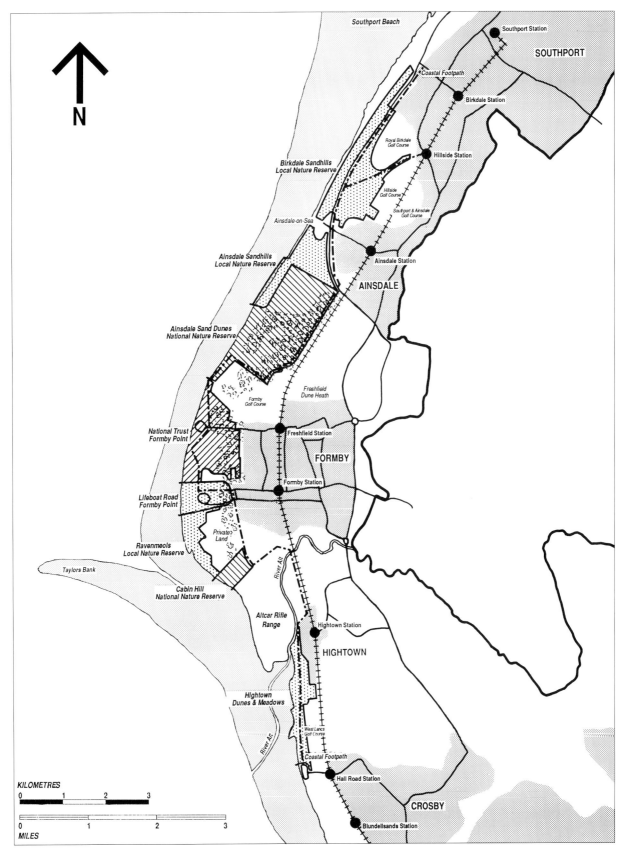

Figure iii. The divisions of landownership and management on the Sefton Coast, as referred to in the text.

Figure v. The Sefton Coast, looking north from Formby Point. Photograph by
John Mills Photography Ltd.

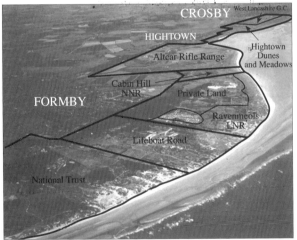

Figure vi. The Sefton Coast, looking south from Formby Point. Photograph by John Mills Photography Ltd.

Acknowledgements

The editors would like to thank firstly the review organisers and other authors who have contributed to the chapters in this volume. That 39 individuals are credited in the contents pages is a reflection of the enthusiasm and support that we received for the research seminar held at Liverpool University in May 1991. To all those who have given up their time voluntarily and have borne with us through the process of editing and checking we hope that you are satisfied with the results.

We would also like to thank the Managers of the North West Biological Field Data Bank, the Joint Countryside Advisory Service and Ainsdale National Nature Reserve for putting up with a stream of researchers rifling through their files.

We are particularly grateful to the staff of National Museums and Galleries on Merseyside for their encouragement and to the Museum for publishing the volume. We would like to thank Angus Gunn from Liverpool Museum for his advice, and input in updating many of the species names mentioned in the text. The research seminar and this volume reflects a growing partnership between site managers, academic researchers, the Museum and naturalists.

Many people have helped put this volume together and we would like to thank Les Coleman and Anne Malone of Cox & Cairney for initial word processing, Paul Sutton of Sefton's Planning Department for the document's layout, Bob McFadyen of the same department for artwork and figures, David Woodfall for the cover photographs and colour photographs (pages 74 & 75), Tom Eccles for line drawings of beetles (pages 100 & 101) and Anthony Smith for line drawings of other animals and plants (pages 103 - 107, 113 & 116).

The financial contributions of English Nature and the Joint Nature Conservation Committee towards the production of this volume are gratefully acknowledged.

THE JOINT NATURE CONSERVATION COMMITTEE is the statutory body constituted by the Environmental Protection Act 1990 to be responsible for research and advice on nature conservation at both UK and international levels. It is established by English Nature, Scottish Natural Heritage and the Countryside Council for Wales, together with representatives from the Countryside Commission and Northern Ireland, and is supported by specialist staff.

ENGLISH NATURE is the statutory advisor to the Government on nature conservation in England and promotes the conservation of England's wildlife and natural features. Its work includes the selection, establishment and management of National Nature Reserves and Marine Nature Reserves; the identification and notification of Sites of Specific Scientific Interest; the provision of advice and information about nature conservation; and the support and conduct of research to these functions.

SECTION 1

HISTORY

CHAPTER ONE

A History of Human Influence on the Coastal Landscape

C. R. Jones, J. A. Houston and D. Bateman

INTRODUCTION

This section attempts to provide a short review of the development of human settlement in the coastal area of Sefton, and how people have interacted with the changing coastal environment to create the present landscape.

Sefton is a modern administrative unit dating from 1974 but nevertheless incorporates a belt of coastal settlements within a distinct and coherent geographic unit stretching between the Mersey and Ribble estuaries forming the seaward margin of the Hundred of West Derby, one of the six hundredal manors of the area 'inter Ripam et Mersham' recorded in medieval documents. Its relative isolation afforded a degree of protection from the storms of history and it is perhaps possible to focus on the relationship between people and land to a greater extent than in areas subject to 'significant' historical events.

EARLY HISTORY TO LATE EIGHTEENTH CENTURY

Early settlement may have occurred in an environment that was not only different in vegetation and climate but radically different in geographic shape. In addition to any influence of people on the shape of the coast, high energy forces (tides, wind, waves and storm surges) act on a gently sloping or almost flat zone composed of thick glacial and post glacial deposits with no inherent structural strength, creating the possibility of both large and small-scale changes in landform in addition to ecological changes. The coastal zone, and human settlement within it, has therefore evolved through a highly complex and constantly changing mosaic of landforms and habitats. Figure 1.1 illustrates this interaction in schematic form and further explanation is given in Section 2.

After the ablation of the ice about 15000 years ago sea levels were very low leaving the East Irish Sea Basin as part of a much larger drainage area extending to the Pennines. This is when the Shirdley Hill sands are likely to have been deposited as wind-driven coversands under polar desert conditions. A major change in sea level occurred about 10000 years ago and a scrub/steppe tundra vegetation developed over the variety of glacial deposits. There is evidence of Mesolithic hunting at this time from the Fylde (Megaw

& Simpson 1979) and further evidence for the period is now also emerging at Little Crosby following field-walking surveys conducted by the Field Archaeology Unit at Liverpool Museum.

Climatic warming resumed after the sharp reversal to cold conditions in the Loch Lomond Stadial (Figure 1.1). This allowed the development of birch/pine woodland over most of the area, but slight increases in sea level would have engulfed large tracts of the almost flat plain, and marine influences began to be felt in the region of the present coast about 7000 years ago. The sea probably moved furthest inland during the late Mesolithic and early Neolithic period when Downholland silts were deposited.

Pollen analysis of peat deposits in north-west England and particularly the coastal belt indicates woodland clearance usually associated with fire in the late Mesolithic (c.8500-5300 BP), concentrated in the Flandrian II period (Figure 1.1). There is evidence that cereals were cultivated locally prior to the elm decline which has previously been regarded as marking the change from Mesolithic foraging society to sedentary Neolithic (Edwards & Hierons 1984).

Deposition of sediment derived from plant and animal remains then followed the extensive marine/estuarine deposition of the Downholland silts. An analysis of these beds, among which are the 'submerged forests' for which Altmouth is noted, shows a succession from saltmarsh through reed-swamp to eutrophic (nutrient rich) fen.

Thus it is possible that there were exploitable environments well seaward of the present shoreline before dune formation began and artefacts of the Neolithic period have been found at Altmouth and North Meols (Lewis 1983) although in circumstances which have not enabled accurate dating.

Cooler, drier conditions coupled with extended periods of lower sea-level tendencies in the early Bronze Age possibly led to the exposure of extensive sand flats and the initiation of dune building at the coast about 4000 years ago. Some clues to the form this took may lie in the present landscapes of the Waddensee where similar processes are occurring albeit on a much vaster scale. Thus the Bronze Age coast may have been an extensive system of sand bars, lagoons, estuarine creeks and marshes with fen-carr woodlands at their landward edges.

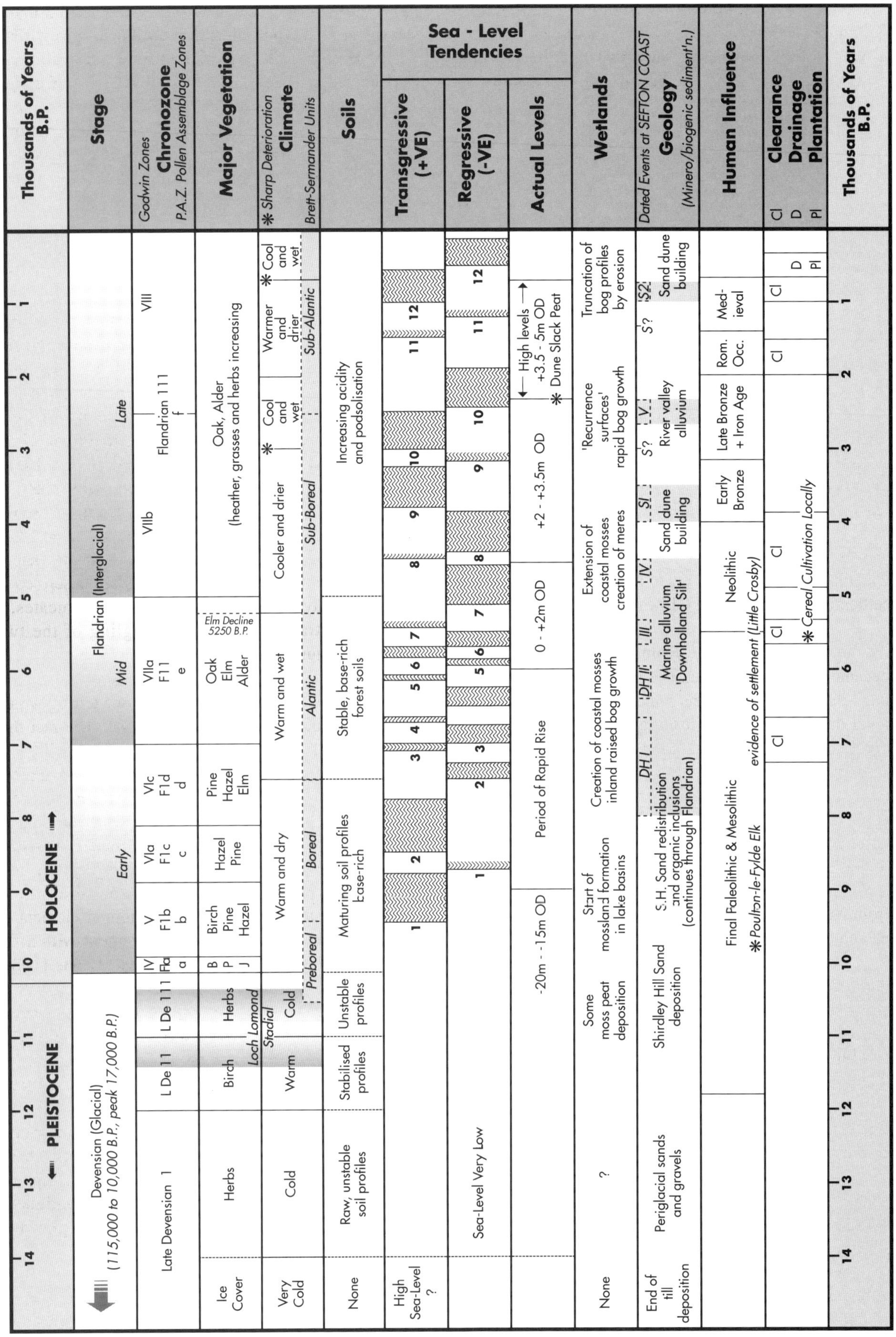

Figure 1.1 — Major events in the sub-region over the last 15,000 years

Column headings (left to right):
- Thousands of Years B.P.
- Stage
- Chronozone — *Godwin Zones* / *P.A.Z. Pollen Assemblage Zones*
- Major Vegetation
- Climate — *Sharp Deterioration* / *Brett-Sermander Units*
- Soils
- Sea-Level Tendencies — Transgressive (+VE) / Regressive (-VE) / Actual Levels
- Wetlands
- Geology — *Dated Events at SEFTON COAST* (*Minero/biogenic sediment'n.*)
- Human Influence
- Clearance / Drainage / Plantation (Cl, D, Pl)
- Thousands of Years B.P.

Stage column:
- PLEISTOCENE ⟸
- Devensian (Glacial) (115,000 to 10,000 B.P., peak 17,000 B.P.)
- HOLOCENE ⟹
- Flandrian (Interglacial) — Late / Mid / Early

Chronozone (Godwin Zones / P.A.Z.):
- VIII
- Flandrian 111 — f
- VIIb — F11 e
- VIIa — F11 e
- VIc / F1d — d
- VIa / F1c — c
- V / F1b — b
- IV / Fa — a
- L De 111
- L De 11 — Birch / Herbs (Loch Lomond Stadial)
- Late Devensian 1 — Herbs

Major Vegetation:
- Oak, Alder (heather, grasses and herbs increasing)
- Oak Elm Alder
- Pine Hazel Elm
- Hazel Pine
- Birch Pine Hazel
- Birch / Herbs
- Elm Decline 5250 B.P.

Climate (Brett-Sermander Units):
- Warmer and drier / Cool and wet — Sub-Atlantic
- Cool and wet
- Cooler and drier — Sub-Boreal
- Warm and wet — Atlantic
- Warm and dry — Boreal
- Warm and dry — Preboreal
- Cold
- Warm
- Cold
- Very Cold / Ice Cover

Soils:
- Increasing acidity and podsolisation
- Stable, base-rich forest soils
- Maturing soil profiles base-rich
- Unstable profiles
- Stabilised profiles
- Raw, unstable soil profiles
- None

Sea-Level — Actual Levels:
- High levels +3.5 - 5m OD / Dune Slack Peat
- +2 - +3.5m OD
- 0 - +2m OD
- Period of Rapid Rise
- -20m - -15m OD
- Sea-Level Very Low
- High Sea-Level?

Wetlands:
- Truncation of bog profiles by erosion
- 'Recurrence surfaces' rapid bog growth
- Extension of coastal mosses creation of meres
- Creation of coastal mosses inland raised bog growth
- Start of mossland formation in lake basins
- Some moss peat deposition
- None

Geology (Sefton Coast):
- Sand dune building — S2?
- River valley alluvium — S? V
- Sand dune building — S1
- Marine alluvium 'Downholland Silt' — DH I, II, III, IV
- S.H. Sand redistribution and organic inclusions (continues through Flandrian)
- Shirdley Hill Sand deposition
- Periglacial sands and gravels
- End of till deposition

Human Influence:
- Medieval
- Rom. Occ.
- Late Bronze + Iron Age
- Early Bronze
- Neolithic
- Cereal Cultivation Locally
- Final Paleolithic & Mesolithic
- evidence of settlement (Little Crosby)
- Poulton-le-Fylde Elk

Clearance / Drainage / Plantation:
- Cl, D, Pl

Figure 1.1 Major events in the sub-region over the last 15,000 years in context (Courtesy of J.B. Innes). Dating is in years BP (Years Before Present; present taken conventionally to be 1950AD). The table shows some of the inter-relationships between climate, vegetation, sea-level trends and human activity over the Holocene period. Further explanation of the table is given in the chapters by Plater *et al.*, Innes and Tooley and Pye and Neal (this volume).

4

There are striking similarities in the evolution of the Sefton and Netherlands coast and comparison may well provide clues as to the pattern of occupation and settlement in the prehistoric periods (Louwe Kooijmans 1980, 1987).

As the Bronze Age progressed, soils deteriorated and there was an increasing intensity of clearance with possible expansion as technology improved with a possible concentration of cultivation in the sandier areas of the coastal lowlands. There was a reduced marine influence during the period but the climate was becoming cooler and wetter towards the opening of the Iron Age, with a rapid deterioration after about 3000 BP. This period is also marked by a marine transgression with relatively high sea-levels. However there is no evidence for inundation in the coastal belt and it is likely therefore that the dune system was beginning to act as a natural sea defence. These conditions probably led to a high inland water table and the formation of mosslands as well as flooding of rivers and extensive alluvial deposits (Lewis 1983). There is little evidence of human occupation of the area during this period, which mirrors the situation in north-west England as a whole, with the exception of the settlements on the Wirral (Howard-Davies *et al.* 1988).

At the beginning of the Roman period the climate became warmer and drier. The increasing warmth may have influenced sea levels which again rose to a high level during the period, leading to waterlogged inland conditions and rendering the area marginal from the Roman point of view. For the Romans the Irish Sea province was strategically important but the trade routes passed through the ports of Chester and Lancaster, perhaps avoiding the tidal rips and treacherous shoals of the Mersey and Sefton Coast. Landward the main road north passed through Wigan from Northwich to Lancaster and thus the area was by-passed by sea and on land.

Nevertheless the improving climate (natural and economic) may have made the area more attractive for permanent settlement than in the previous millenium. Scattered finds of coins and other artefacts from the Altmouth area and elsewhere in north Merseyside are starting to suggest that the coast was not devoid of settlement during the Roman period (J. Lewis pers. comm.).

The climate began to deteriorate again during the middle of the Anglo-Saxon period (see Table 1.1), with increasing storminess accompanied by relatively high sea-level tendencies (Lewis 1983). This may have initiated the dune building period from 800 - 900 AD in which erosional processes may have led to the build-up of a dune ridge and sand-hills.

The six hundredal manors identified 'inter Ripam et Mersham' by the Domesday Survey, sub-divided into vills and manors illustrates a well-established Anglian system of land tenure, lordship and local government. No evidence has yet been found for the survival of any earlier systems (e.g. Romano-British or Celtic). However the marginality of the area and the location of Lancashire at the 'hinge point' of several cultural provinces - Celtic, Germanic and Scandinavian - suggests that the possibility of such discoveries should not be discounted.

Place names in the coastal belt certainly indicate a Scandinavian/Anglo-Saxon mix (Mills 1976), but with only one or two British names. The Scandinavian influence probably reflects the colonisation of the Irish Sea province by Norwegian settlers from about 850 AD onwards and it has been suggested that the low-lying coastal belt, less attractive to Anglo-Saxon farmers occupying the higher land around Lydiate and Melling, was exploited by people better able to make use of the seaboard location and its rich potential (Lewis 1983). The new colonists may also have taken advantage of the general abandonment of Anglo-Saxon settlement during the seventh and eighth centuries (Taylor 1983) perhaps brought about by the period of climate change mentioned above. Local landholdings are described in the Domesday Book in both hides and carucates, a further illustration of the intermingling of the two dominant cultures.

Fourteen vills are identified in Sefton, ten of which occupy the coastal belt (see Figure 1.2). The fact that these vills still form recognisable units within the present administrative system shows the remarkable resilience of the Anglo-Saxon system of local government (Blair 1984). It is likely that the vills or townships represent 'resource territories' possibly reinforced and stabilised by the tithing system and manorial duties (Taylor 1983) and that these boundaries may well be the oldest human element in the landscape. As such their arrangement within the coastal belt is of considerable interest. Lewis (1983) notes three categories. Firstly, those within the belt of blown sand north of the Alt, representing what may be termed 'strip' territories with roughly parallel boundaries dividing the coastal belt into territories between sea and moss; secondly those south and west of the Alt such as Little Crosby (Crosebi) and Ince (Hinne) which may be regarded as 'core-periphery' territories centred on safe higher land surrounded by river valley, moss or sea; and thirdly townships on generally higher ground east of the Alt, contiguous with other territories on the boulder clay platform extending inland.

There has been no systematic archaeological investigation of any settlement in the district to date and therefore the form that early settlement might have taken within these territories can only be inferred from evidence available elsewhere.

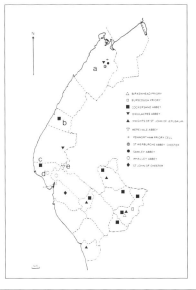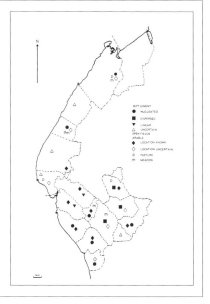

Figure 1.2 a) Vills (Townships) in Sefton named in the Domesday Survey, b) Monastic lands in Sefton ((a) North Meols, (b) Ainsdale, (c) Ravenmeols, (d) Altmouth, (e) Great Altcar), c) Medieval Settlement and agriculture in Sefton (After Lewis 1983).

Scandinavian or Anglo-Saxon settlements comprised dispersed hamlets and farmsteads not much different from settlements of earlier periods (Taylor 1983). Very little of this early medieval settlement would have survived into the present landscape. The scattered buildings were mostly of wood and thatch and it is highly unlikely that any of the present coastal settlements date back to this period. The present pattern of settlement with dispersed hamlets and farms, which does bear some resemblance to the Anglo-Saxon model, can in many cases be dated to later periods (Lewis 1983).

The only secure survival from this period therefore is the system of townships recorded in the Domesday Book, although even here the present boundaries may not reflect the true historical situation (Lewis 1983).

The Domesday Survey records a complex pattern of landholdings with what appears to be some freedom of tenure. Twenty four manors were recorded within the coastal vills and with the exception of North Meols the proportion of arable land appears high in relation to the topography and terrain. Interpretation of this record indicates a well-developed farming area with a population able to exploit local resources which almost certainly would have included fishing and wildfowling as well as arable and pasture. The population was possibly not more than a few score individuals within each of the coastal vills, although this should be seen in the context of a total population for Britain as a whole of 1.5 to 2 million at this time (Terret 1962).

The church represents another level of organisation in the society of the time. Although no churches or chapels were recorded in the area by the Domesday Survey, chapels were certainly in existence in North Meols and Ravenmeols by the twelfth century (Lewis

1983). The pattern of ecclesiastical parishes in the coastal zone reflects that in the north-west of England as a whole at the time. Again Lancashire was a cultural hinge point in the struggle for domination between the Celtic Church and first the English pagans and then the Gregorian Church, but there is scant record of the early Church in the area despite the suggestive Celtic name of St. Cuthberts at North Meols. After the conversion of the English, monastic houses became well established although there were no monastic lands in north-west England at the time of the Conquest. The Norman practice of endowing religious houses however saw the establishment of the Cistercian abbeys at Sawley, Merevale and Whalley, as well as the Premonstratensian order at Cockersand. Their influence spread to the coast through their granges (farmsteads staffed by lay brothers) at North Meols, Ainsdale, Ravenmeols, Altmouth and Great Altcar (Figure 1.2). The testing environment of the coast may have suited the austere principles of both orders. The Cistercians were great sheep farmers and the coast may have provided useful pastures for this purpose (Whalley Coucher 1847). The coastal marshes at Altcar, for example, were used for cattle pasture by the monastic house of Merevale, and elsewhere on the coast there is evidence from this time of horse-breeding and arable cultivation (J. Lewis pers. comm.). At Ainsdale sand was cleared, presumably to form fields. Relaxation of Cistercian principles in the thirteenth century allowed them to accept the grants of mills recorded at North Meols and Ince (Whalley Coucher 1847; Aughton 1988; Butler & Given-Wilson 1979).

The Normans also introduced a new system of 'forests' with punitive taxes and duties on all classes within forest areas. Nearly the whole of West Derby was a 'forest', including the coastal belt up to Ainsdale (Cunliffe-Shaw 1965). However the evils of forest legislation seemed to have little influence on the general progress of the farming community.

Field systems are important landscape elements in that they can give clues to land-use, social organisation and period of occupation, but modern farming and urban development has obliterated most of the evidence in the coastal belt. Fragments of medieval open field boundaries can still be identified at Ince and Little Crosby. The need to protect land from the sea or rivers would have required embankments to enclose any farming enterprise from the earliest times, and the pre-Anglo-Saxon agriculture would have been based on enclosure. Common arable would have been imposed from the early middle ages onwards for economic or administrative reasons, and in a marginal area like the coast may well have been inserted into pre-existing boundaries (Rackham 1986). Town or common fields are recorded for Formby, Crosby and Ince (Lewis 1983) but the full extent of open field is not known; the need to drain fields, or fertilise by flooding would militate against extensive open systems.

Field systems and field names have been used to identify the approximate locations of medieval settlement (Lewis 1983, see especially pp 70-87). The present villages of Churchtown, Ince and Little Crosby may be on or close to sites of later medieval settlements. The relation of medieval to modern settlement in the remaining townships is less certain (Figure 1.2). Three possible moated sites at Formby Hall, Ince Blundell Hall and Crosby Hall may indicate the increasing status of certain landowners in their local communities.

Documents and field evidence confirm the existence of settlements, or at least territories, at Ainsdale, Argarmeols, Ravenmeols and Morehouses (Hightown). Records show that Argarmeols had disappeared by 1346, Ravenmeols possibly earlier, and Ainsdale before 1555 (Lewis 1983). North Meols however seems to have gained territory during this period (Aughton 1988).

The loss of these areas indicates the continuing effect of climate and sea on the coastal belt. The high sea-level tendencies recorded in the region during the twelfth and thirteenth centuries coincided with a period of deteriorating climate which affected the whole country (Table 1.1). Floods in the upper Mersey forced the monks at Stanlaw to move their abbey to Whalley by 1296 (Butler & Given-Wilson 1979). There is however no record of inundation at the Sefton Coast, protected by the sand wave of the dunes. However as this sand wave moved across pre-existing pasture or marsh, anything emerging on the seaward side would simply be washed away. Clarification of the mechanics of this process and its timing could help to amplify the historic record.

TABLE 1.1

Climatic characteristics in Western Europe after ca. 300 AD (after Lamb 1977), from Klijn 1990.

Period (yrs AD)	Characteristics
300-400/500	Relatively warm and dry
400/500-800	Relatively cold and wet
800-950/1150	Primarily cold, later milder winters, relatively wet summers. Possibly ending around 1150 AD in Western Europe.
950/1150-1200/1300	'The Little Optimum': Higher annual temperature. Warmest period in Western Europe: 1150-1300 AD. Weaker circulation with westerly main circulation. Depression paths 3 to 4° north of current depression paths.
1200/1300-1550	Deteriorating climate in transient period. Periodically more severe winters, mostly mild and wet. Wetter summers, increased circulation and depression activity.
1500-1700*	'Little Ice Age': relatively cold winters, and wet summers, weak circulation, depression zone 3-5° south of present zone. (*the Little Ice Age is often considered to have ended around 1850).
after 1700	Improving climate, transitional period, with the exception of a shorter period around 1800. Increase in frequency and intensity of westerly winds.

In a wider context, population had increased rapidly from the time of the Conquest to a total of 4 to 5 million in the early fourteenth century (Guy 1984), a point regarded by some historians as approaching over-population; expansion of population had not been matched by improvements in agricultural production although there would have been pressures to maximise use of land which may be reflected locally in the enclosure of marshes and development of open field systems, together, perhaps, with establishment of more centralised (nucleated) settlements. This might also be the background to the woodland clearances identified in the pollen record for the area at this time (Lewis 1983). There was also a succession of wars; against the Scots, the Irish, the French, the Welsh and between Lancaster and York. The economy was strained to the limit to provide resources for these campaigns. The indirect effect on the region was such that the Black Death of 1349 was part of a continuing series of natural and human disasters (Cunliffe-Shaw 1965). The loss of territory to the sea might thus have been accelerated by lack of adequate land management arising from the economic instability and contraction during this period.

Nationally, the social and economic dislocation caused by the Plague and its subsequent recurrences reduced the population by nearly half and it remained at this level until the start of the sixteenth century. The 1450s saw an increase in the demand for wool nationally which spurred clearance and enclosure by landlords, assisted by the retracting population and weakened state of many villages (Taylor 1983). There is a record of piecemeal enclosure in Lancashire as a whole during this period and there are detailed records of such enclosures in the Sefton area although open fields did survive until quite late, and certainly until the nineteenth century in Formby for example (Lewis 1983). These enclosures probably reflected both changing agriculture and consolidation of ownership.

The fate of Church lands following the Dissolution offered many opportunities for such consolidation. The destruction of Whalley Abbey in 1537 because of the participation of the Abbot in the 'Pilgrimage of Grace' allowed Richard Molyneux to purchase Alt Grange and its associated lands thus substantially extending the Molyneux coastal landholdings (VCH III 1907, p83).

The subsequent repression of Catholicism in the Tudor period followed by the Puritan/Royalist conflict under the Stuarts led to a confusion of loyalties in predominantly Catholic Lancashire, with West Derby declaring for the King. The Civil War, which may well have started with a skirmish in Liverpool in 1642, brought Parliamentary troops through North Meols in 1644 pursuing a remnant of Prince Rupert's force after the defeat at York (Aughton 1988). Nicholas Blundell's diaries of the early eighteenth century give an insight into the problems faced by recusants and the need to maintain a degree of conformity in order to survive. Conformity allowed Robert Blundell of Ince to extend his landholdings, acquiring the manors of Ainsdale and Birkdale from Sir Cuthbert Halsall in 1633 (Harrop 1985).

The 'Glorious Revolution' of 1688 set the conditions for overseas trade through links with the Dutch, and the beginnings of a capitalist/individualist economy under a constitutional monarchy. With the spread of English influence and trade, the little port of Liverpool began to grow in response to West Indian and North American imports. Up to now the coastal belt had not been within the catchment of any significant urban centre, and the economy had remained essentially rural. The coastal marshes and dunes extended around the curve of Bootle Bay almost as far as the Pool of Liverpool itself, but as access to the port of Chester became progressively more difficult with the silting-up of the Dee, Liverpool began to assume greater importance.

The overseas extension of trade was paralleled inland by an equivalent expansion of industrial development, resource exploitation and urbanisation and Lancashire found itself at the centre of these changes. This provided the major impetus for change during the eighteenth century, with expanding agricultural markets generated by the growth of adjacent towns and cities.

Many buildings in the settlements visible in the landscape of the coastal belt can, in fact, be securely dated to the eighteenth century, and a very few to the seventeenth century. The halls at Meols, Formby, Ince and Crosby are all substantially altered or reconstructed on sites of earlier buildings. A similar process may well have happened in the villages where increasing wealth, fashion or availability of resources (e.g., brick and slate) enabled people to build more permanent structures than cruck-framed clamstaff and daub cottages, the outer form of which may still be seen in parts of Churchtown and Formby.

The overall impression of the area is one of conservatism in settlement layout and agricultural practice up to this time, perhaps enforced by the location and the economy of the area (Lewis 1983).

A particularly stormy period in the early 1700s, culminating in the inundations of 1720 (Beck 1953), together with increasingly unstable dunes as sea-levels began to recede again, forced landowners to consider new techniques of land management if the opportunities presented by expanding markets were not to be missed.

For the first time serious attempts were made to tackle the great mosses and meres. A start had been made on draining Martin Mere in 1692 by Thomas Fleetwood which was continued by Thomas Eccleston in 1781 advised by Mr Gilbert, builder of the Bridgewater Canal (Broderick undated). The year 1778 saw the progress through parliament of the Alt Drainage Act (1779), and the Alt Commissioners were established in 1779. The Alt was tidal up to Showricks Bridge near Sefton Village and flooded regularly because its outflow at periods of heavy rainfall would be frequently dammed by a high tide. Moreover, its level in relation to the surrounding lands (which were at or below normal high tide level) meant that it was virtually useless for land drainage. The works, which involved the design of flood gates by Jesse Hartley in 1833, led to the draining of the Formby and Altcar mosses and their conversion to arable agriculture (Littledale 1850). This amounted to a change in the inland landscape equivalent to the seaward changes brought about by the construction of the Docks. The establishment of Wignall's Bank (or Balling's Wharf) from 1797 onwards to prevent blowing sand reducing the depth of the Alt outflow led to serious erosion at Blundellsands in the 1930s, which required the progressive hardening of the coast in the Hall Road area (Gresswell 1953).

The creeks and channels along the coast had provided access for some shipping since at least the early thirteenth century, with reference to a 'Skypul' at Altmouth (Whalley Coucher 1847). Fairclough's Lake, a channel off the Pool in North Meols, provided convenient access for a little gentle smuggling, a form of enterprise which grew with the increasing trade entering the port of Liverpool (Aughton 1988).

From the 1750s onwards, the port began to expand rapidly, the numbers of ships and tonnage of cargo growing almost exponentially. The construction of new dock basins led to the hardening of the coast north and south of 'The Pool', the infilling of Bootle Bay and, in the twentieth century, the land claim to create the Royal Seaforth Container Dock. This, together with the construction of the training banks in the Crosby Channel, was certainly the most significant human impact on the coastal landscape throughout the period under consideration.

The final significant change of note in this period is the growth of the attraction of the seaside as a source of recreation. The development of spa and seaside towns as 'lungs' for city dwellers was well under way by the end of the century, and William Sutton built the South Port Hotel in the sand dunes south of Churchtown in 1797 (Aughton 1988).

History had finally overtaken the Sefton coast. A piece of remote coastal land which had survived at least two thousand years with remarkably little change except that imposed by the force of wind and sea, was now caught up in a process that would render the landscape almost unrecognisable to a traveller from the middle ages.

THE NINETEENTH CENTURY

The nineteenth century was perhaps the period which has most shaped the modern dune landscape. This was the era in which the owners of the large estates refined the techniques of dune stabilisation, when asparagus farming was in its hey-day and when the first experiments for large-scale afforestation were carried out. The nineteenth century also saw the rise of Southport as a resort, the building of large private houses in coastal locations (including the failed attempt to establish Formby-by-the-Sea), the advent of the railway system and the establishment of the present day coastal units such as Altcar Ranges and the several golf courses. Land was in abundant supply and the large estates of Blundell and Formby sought to 'improve' their holdings. The period is probably well-documented through archives and estate records, but a researched summary of nineteenth and twentieth century land use change has not been found. References to only the more easily obtained material are given.

The history of Formby has been documented by Bateman (1990) and Kelly (1982), and that of Ainsdale by Harrop (1985). A consequence of the coming of the Liverpool-Southport railway in 1848 was the growth of towns such as Formby and Ainsdale. Their combined population in 1851 was 1,594, whereas in 1981 the population of Formby alone was 26,795. Southport developed as a resort in the first half of the nineteenth century, and with railway links and the construction of the pier in 1860 became a fashionable Victorian seaside resort. Formby people, it is said, disliked the growing town of Southport (Jacson 1897), but some had other ideas. In 1875 the Formby Land and Building Company was incorporated. Kelly (1982) gives an account of the company which had plans to create Formby-by-the-Sea to rival Southport. The company constructed Formby Promenade, Alexandra and Albert Roads, a Lord Street and several houses in the

Figure 1.3 Formby Promenade in 1933 set within an accreting dune system. In 1992 the Promenade is completely covered although one flight of steps has been excavated and can still be seen. Photograph by R.K. Gresswell, English Nature archive, Ainsdale NNR.

9

Ravenmeols dunes before being wound up in 1902 (Figure 1.3). The developers had hoped for a second coastal railway line parallel to the present line, permission for which was not forthcoming until 1918, too late to save the company (Table 1.2).

The idea of a second railway line running in an arc round Formby Point from Hightown to Ainsdale was approved again in 1924 but without any action, presumably the growth by then of the road network deciding against it (Kelly 1982).

The landowners' attitudes to dune management changed markedly in the eighteenth and nineteenth centuries. The uncontrolled use of the dunes in medieval times had resulted in extensive sandblow and this led to the dunes being more formally managed as rabbit warrens controlled by bye-laws. Strict rules on the planting and protection of the dunes were imposed on tenants. In the latter part of the nineteenth century the Formby landscape was created through active management.

The stabilisation of the dunes was achieved only after many years and many setbacks. Perhaps the best-recorded success story is the creation of Balling's Wharf (also known as the Altcar salient) between the years 1797 and 1855. Between 1797 and 1818 the Alt Commissioners, using brushwood fencing (gorse bundles) and marram planting, reclaimed over 20 acres (8 ha). By 1855 reclamation was complete and 150 acres (61 ha) could be rented as grazing land (Cook 1989) although subsequently the tenant was pleased to

get rid of it. Turner (1984) gives more information on this project and the building out of Formby Point by the Formby and Blundell Estates between 1845 and 1906. By the end of the nineteenth century the landowners had developed consistently successful techniques for dune stabilisation and were looking to make the best use of their land.

The earliest record of tree planting on the Sefton Coast dates from the 1790s when the Reverend Richard Formby planted sycamore, ash, alder and 'fir' at what became known as Firwood (Holt 1795). The plantation was shown on the 1845 tithe map. Scotch fir is an old-fashioned name for the Scots pine (Fitter & Fitter 1967).

In 1887 Charles Weld Blundell started experimenting with pine trees after observing the success of pine plantations at Les Landes on the west coast of France. From 1893-1894 both landowners, Charles Weld-Blundell and Jonathon Formby started large scale planting using a number of species, the best and most preferred of which proved to be Corsican pine (*Pinus nigra* subsp. *laricio*) (Figure 1.4). Both Ashton (1920) and Gresswell (1953) describe the large scale planting programmes and a general history of the coastal woodlands is outlined in the Working Plan for Woodlands on the Sefton Coast (JCAS 1990). Further details are given in Wheeler *et al.*, this volume.

The pattern of coastal woodlands evident today was largely in place by 1925. Sea buckthorn (*Hippophae rhamnoides* L.) was also introduced to protect the

TABLE 1.2
Review of Proposed Developments 1875 - 1974

1875-1902	The Formby Land and Building Company had ambitious plans to establish Formby-by-the-Sea, starting with the construction of a new promenade. Had this project succeeded much of the Ravenmeols area would have now been developed.
1918	Permission was given to the Lancashire and Yorkshire Railway Company to construct extensions to the railway network at Formby. A new line was to begin at Hightown Station and to sweep round Formby Point to rejoin the main line at Ainsdale.
1947	The War Department withdrew their plans to use the Formby Point area (dunes and beach) for military training. At the time the beaches were requisitioned by the War Office and Harington barracks were still in use.
1950-1952	The closure of the Cheshire Lines railway opened up a series of development options for Southport Corporation. The railway had been a barrier to development and what was visualised was a promenade six miles long from the north of the borough to the Lido, with a dual carriageway, hotels and flower beds. Plans were also drawn up for the development of the dunes.
1966	Lancashire County Council published their Formby Area Report with proposals for a regional park at Formby. The plans included a new loop road feeding a series of five car parks, and provision for recreation.
1967	Two development proposals at Ainsdale were fought at a public enquiry. The case against Pontins was lost but Southport Corporation's plans to develop on the dune areas at Ainsdale were, at least, modified. The original development plan included 11-storey blocks of flats.
1973	Pontins wished to expand the Holiday Village at Ainsdale further into the sandhills; permission was refused but permission was given for a 70-bedroom motel on the Sands Lake site.
1973	A plan was mooted to construct an international airport (as an alternative to the Maplin site) on reclaimed land based on Taylor's Bank.
1974	The Formby Land Company, following on from Lancashire County Council's ideas, put forward development proposals for the southern part of Formby. These included a golf course, nature reserve, holiday chalets, recreation areas and a large dune lake. Some of these ideas were subsequently developed through the Coast Management Scheme.

Figure 1.4 Treeplanting at Ainsdale c. 1936. Photograph by R.K. Gresswell, English Nature archive, Ainsdale NNR.

seaward edge of the plantations (Clements & Lutley 1987). At that time there was an additional narrow coastal shelter belt of pine plantation from north of Fisherman's Path south to Formby Point, but the dunes on which they stood have since been eroded by the sea.

The nineteenth century coastal landscape was intimately linked with the more productive farmland so that a good mixed agricultural community could survive. The 1845 tithe map and schedule of Formby (Lancashire Record Office, DRL 1/27), which incidentally show a town field system probably dating back to the medieval period (Lewis 1983), show a mix of arable and pasture land from the dunes inland; while the dunes themselves were important mostly as rabbit warrens, with some sheep grazing.

Judging from manorial records now held at the Lancashire Record Office there appears to have been a long-running battle of wits between the major landowners and their own tenants as well as other local inhabitants, particularly over such issues as rabbiting and the cutting of marram for mat-making. (Manorial records held by the Lancashire Record Office, Preston). From 1710 it became the sometime manorial duty of tenants to plant marram, and in 1742 (subsequent to the great sandstorm of 1739 which destroyed Ravenmeols) an Act of Parliament was laid down "for the more effectual preventing of the cutting of Star or Bent" which made special reference to this coast.

Throughout the nineteenth century the Lords of the Manor had to cajole and threaten the population in order to enforce the restrictions of rights on the dunes

and shore. Such restricted rights included access, fishing, rabbiting, grazing, turf-cutting and the collecting of cockles, bait and driftwood; while marram-cutting was forbidden and punishable by fines, whipping, or even prison with hard labour (Figure 1.5). Manorial orders also demanded in 1829, for example, that tenants spend six days each year planting marram to the satisfaction of the Star lookers (Lancashire Record Office, DDFo 15/8-9, cited in Bateman 1990).

Harrop (1982, 1985) records how Thomas Weld-Blundell having inherited the Ince Blundell estate in the 1850s re-asserted the manorial lord's ownership of the entire shore, restricting fishing rights on the Birkdale shore to those who paid for the privilege, and resorting to intimidation and legal action to prevent others from fishing there. This seems to have been part of his strategy to assert personal ownership (sweeping aside a system of informal rights that had grown up over the previous decades), so that land could be sold off for building plots. By 1907 the remaining sandhills were strictly preserved with only a few footpaths across the forbidden ground open to the public (VCH III 1907).

Asparagus growing dates back possibly as far as the sixteenth century (Clements & Lutley 1987) and certainly both major landowners were involved from the eighteenth century. The main area centred on Formby, with some planting to the north of Freshfield (Kelly 1982). Asparagus farming was a major land use on the coast by the late nineteenth century, the field patterns being established before the tree planting programme, and the subsequent tree planting seems to have been designed to protect the fields. At its peak the Formby asparagus industry enjoyed world-wide recognition.

After 15-20 years the plants ('crowns') and beds become exhausted and are left as ley. Asparagus growing is thus a kind of shifting agriculture always requiring old beds to be left fallow and new areas to be opened or re-opened. During the early twentieth century the cultivation of asparagus occupied 101 hectares at Formby according to Rimmer (1986) and a figure of 60 hectares in 1950 is quoted by Moorhouse (1950). Despite a slight revival after the Second World War it began a steady decline locally as well as nationally in the face of foreign imports. By 1966 only 16 hectares of asparagus were grown (Coates 1966) and in recent years farming has declined to 10 hectares (Handley 1982, see also Figure 8.9, this volume). The characteristic ridge and furrow pattern of the asparagus fields is still recognisable in fields behind the dune belt at Formby (J. Lewis pers. comm.).

In 1860, Altcar Rifle Range was established on the reclaimed land west of the Alt known as Balling's Wharf for the training of Volunteer Rifle Corps. Cook (1989) gives a detailed history of Altcar Rifle Range.

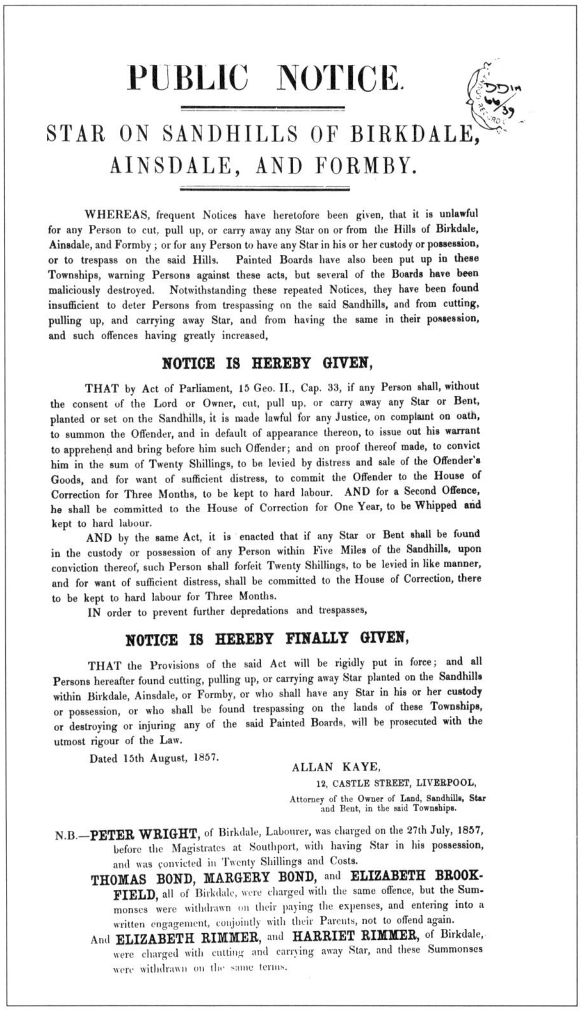

PUBLIC NOTICE.

STAR ON SANDHILLS OF BIRKDALE, AINSDALE, AND FORMBY.

WHEREAS, frequent Notices have heretofore been given, that it is unlawful for any Person to cut, pull up, or carry away any Star on or from the Hills of Birkdale, Ainsdale, and Formby; or for any Person to have any Star in his or her custody or possession, or to trespass on the said Hills. Painted Boards have also been put up in these Townships, warning Persons against these acts, but several of the Boards have been maliciously destroyed. Notwithstanding these repeated Notices, they have been found insufficient to deter Persons from trespassing on the said Sandhills, and from cutting, pulling up, and carrying away Star, and from having the same in their possession, and such offences having greatly increased,

NOTICE IS HEREBY GIVEN,

THAT by Act of Parliament, 15 Geo. II., Cap. 33, if any Person shall, without the consent of the Lord or Owner, cut, pull up, or carry away any Star or Bent, planted or set on the Sandhills, it is made lawful for any Justice, on complaint on oath, to summon the Offender, and in default of appearance thereon, to issue out his warrant to apprehend and bring before him such Offender; and on proof thereof made, to convict him in the sum of Twenty Shillings, to be levied by distress and sale of the Offender's Goods, and for want of sufficient distress, to commit the Offender to the House of Correction for Three Months, to be kept to hard labour. AND for a Second Offence, he shall be committed to the House of Correction for One Year, to be Whipped and kept to hard labour.

AND by the same Act, it is enacted that if any Star or Bent shall be found in the custody or possession of any Person within Five Miles of the Sandhills, upon conviction thereof, such Person shall forfeit Twenty Shillings, to be levied in like manner, and for want of sufficient distress, shall be committed to the House of Correction, there to be kept to hard labour for Three Months.

IN order to prevent further depredations and trespasses,

NOTICE IS HEREBY FINALLY GIVEN,

THAT the Provisions of the said Act will be rigidly put in force; and all Persons hereafter found cutting, pulling up, or carrying away Star planted on the Sandhills within Birkdale, Ainsdale, or Formby, or who shall have any Star in his or her custody or possession, or who shall be found trespassing on the lands of these Townships, or destroying or injuring any of the said Painted Boards, will be prosecuted with the utmost rigour of the Law.

Dated 15th August, 1857.

ALLAN KAYE,
12, CASTLE STREET, LIVERPOOL,
Attorney of the Owner of Land, Sandhills, Star and Bent, in the said Townships.

N.B.—PETER WRIGHT, of Birkdale, Labourer, was charged on the 27th July, 1857, before the Magistrates at Southport, with having Star in his possession, and was convicted in Twenty Shillings and Costs. THOMAS BOND, MARGERY BOND, and ELIZABETH BROOK-FIELD, all of Birkdale, were charged with the same offence, but the Summonses were withdrawn on their paying the expenses, and entering into a written engagement, conjointly with their Parents, not to offend again. And ELIZABETH RIMMER, and HARRIET RIMMER, of Birkdale, were charged with cutting and carrying away Star, and these Summonses were withdrawn on the same terms.

Figure 1.5 The cutting and collecting of marram grass (star grass) was a serious offence in the nineteenth century, punishable by fines, whipping or hard labour. The 'Star' notice is reprinted by kind permission of Col. Sir Joseph Weld OBE, TD. (LRO DD In 66/39)

Several golf courses were founded including West Lancashire (1873), Formby (1884), Hesketh (1885), Royal Birkdale (1889), Hillside (1912) and Southport and Ainsdale (1907). Until road overtook rail as the main form of transport to the coast in the twentieth century Southport remained the only mass destination. However country lovers and naturalists were already becoming aware of the natural beauty of the sandhills and sought means to protect them as nature reserves.

THE TWENTIETH CENTURY

By the beginning of the twentieth century the large estates had brought the dunes under their control through practical management and enforcement, and in so doing had transformed the 'wastelands' of the early nineteenth century into a form of productive land-use, and had created a landscape which, by and large, remains today. The estates however went into a period of decline and were unable to maintain their investment, culminating in the disposal of the Ince Blundell Settled Estate in the 1960s. The Formby Estate gave over much of their land (Lifeboat Road, Ravenmeols Local Nature Reserve) to Sefton Council in 1978 and, at the time of writing, have made little use of the remainder of their land to which the public have for many years enjoyed open access.

The precise reasons for the changes in land management are not known and would make an interesting study. The factors that might be implicated would include a general complacency about land management; the switch from accretion to erosion around much of Formby Point in the early 1900s; the late transition of Formby and Ainsdale from Manorial to Council systems from 1894 to 1917 and the subsequent priorities given to urbanisation; the impact of the First World War on labour-intensive land management; the recession in the 1920s and1930s; competition with new markets for asparagus; the requisition and use of much of the area during the First and Second World Wars; and the damage caused by uncontrolled recreation and sandwinning. Certainly by the 1950s the landowners seemed to have lost interest in estate management leading to a period of neglect and exploitation which in turn led to attempts to reverse the decline through planning proposals and land purchase by conservation organisations.

Ashton (1920) records that although between 1890 and 1895 the mere cutting of marram grass was forbidden, by the early 1900s the planting of grass had ceased to be enforced and sandblow was affecting parts of Birkdale. A high mobile dune ridge, over 50 feet high, threatened the railway, and Gresswell (1953) records that these dunes were levelled in 1923 for the construction of Waterloo Road and associated housing. Records of dune management are scarce but it is likely that unemployment relief projects in the 1930s were

Figure 1.6 Marram planting for dune stabilisation, Woodvale, June 1934. Photograph by R.K. Gresswell, English Nature archive, Ainsdale NNR. Gresswell's photographs show that not all these projects were successful but there is little information on how they were carried out or funded.

used to undertake dune restoration work and continue tree planting (Figure 1.6). No references however can be found.

The impact of military use on the Sefton Coast was considerable. Altcar Rifle Range, founded in 1860, was taken over by the War Office from 1914 to 1920 and also from 1939 to 1947, and in addition to small arms training has been used for machine gun, grenade and tank training. The ranges were extended into the Cabin Hill area for grenade training until 1979 and the area was officially cleared of explosives as recently as 1983 (Cook 1989).

Fort Crosby at Hightown was established in 1904. The fort was used to guard the Mersey during both wars although the 6" naval guns were never actually fired. The fort became disused in 1957 and was demolished in 1967. The area was finally tidied up through the use of Derelict Land Grants in 1983 but the pattern of the original minefields remains.

In the Second World War, Harington barracks were built at Formby between the village and the coast and eventually closed down in the 1960s for housing development. The barracks were probably not an important target but were nevertheless shown on Luftwaffe bombing maps. The presence of the barracks probably led to proposals by the War Office in 1945 for

2000 acres (809 ha) at Formby (750 acres (304 ha) above high water) to be used for training, i.e. the whole of Formby Point including Lifeboat Road and Victoria Road. In 1947 the War Office withdrew their plans in the face of local opposition and the involvement of Formby's prospective MP, then Harold Wilson (Table 1.2). Military use of the foreshore between Ainsdale and Crosby continued despite protests until 1958 (the beach was officially requisitioned from 1944 to 1957). The military use of the coast from 1939 to 1958 is not well documented but it probably had a bearing on attitudes towards land management since landowners were unlikely to invest time or money in land which had been effectively taken over for military use. Since a major effect of the long-standing foreshore requisition and other War Office proposals was to remove control and create uncertainty over the future of the land, military use on the Sefton Coast has probably had a greater impact than is widely recognised.

Another twentieth century activity which has left a lasting impression on the landscape is sandwinning, an industry which continues in Sefton with foreshore sandwinning from the Horse Bank in the Ribble estuary. There is probably no record of the first sand-extraction but by the 1950s it was an important industry. Turner (1984) gives a summary of the history of sandwinning at Southport but not details of the extent of the work at Formby. Prior to 1940 and for

13

some time after the war Southport Corporation sold sand from any area where it was causing nuisance. The type of wind-blown sand found between Southport and Crosby is known in the foundry trade as 'Southport Sea Sand' and the Institute of British Foundrymen stated in 1964 that the "sand is superior to many other silica sands obtainable in this country" (Coates 1966). From 1952 to 1963 the sale of sand from the dunes was let to tender. Two areas were worked, north and south of Shore Road in the frontal dunes at Ainsdale, and over the 12 year period 816,467 tons were extracted. The present-day slack system in the Birkdale and Ainsdale frontal dunes probably dates from this period. In 1966, after a break of three years to assess the scheme (Gresswell 1966) sandwinning switched to the foreshore north of Shore Road where from 1966 to 1973, 570,135 tons were removed. A washing plant was set up in the sandhills but the industry was seen to be incompatible with the recreational use of the beach and was closed down. Another large sand-removal project in the Ainsdale area was the removal of Little Balls Hill (SD 302115) on the National Nature Reserve/Local Nature Reserve boundary in 1974. Big Balls Hill (SD 305115) on the other side of the coastal road almost suffered a similar fate but was stabilised in 1983 and continues to support a colony of sand lizards (*Lacerta agilis* L.). Sand winning on the Horse Bank by William Rainfords Limited began in 1972.

At Formby the picture is less clear. The Joint Countryside Advisory Service have records of seven applications for sand extraction between 1949 and 1959 but these do not include some of the largest quarries at Lifeboat Road and Ravenmeols. Sandwinning has shaped much of the Formby landscape, particularly at Cabin Hill, Ravenmeols Local Nature Reserve and Lifeboat Road where slack habitats have developed in worked out areas. There is no evidence of any sand extraction on the Blundell lands. In 1958 Formby Urban District Council, concerned about the risk of widespread flooding due to uncontrolled sandwinning, enacted a Coast Protection Order under Section 18 of the Coast Protection Act 1949. Coates (1966) states that all applications for sand winning from 1958 onwards were refused, thus effectively bringing the industry to a close in Formby.

Two developing land uses have run in parallel, namely the growing interest in and desire to protect nature in its broadest sense, and the growth in the recreational use of the dunes and beaches. The two interests often clash and much of the work of the Coast Management Scheme is to do with resolving this conflict. In Victorian times recreational pressure was concentrated in the resort, leaving much of the wilderness dune area for the enjoyment of pioneer naturalists. The scientific importance of the dunes was recognised by these early

Figure 1.7 Ainsdale-on-sea 1926. The photograph shows Ainsdale-on-sea station, the Sands hotel and boating lake (Bulrush slack), the promenade buildings and surrounding dunes. The fate of the large stone gateposts leading to the shore is unknown. Photograph supplied by Aerofilms Ltd.

14

Figure 1.8 Ainsdale beach, August bank holiday 1938. The Lido was in its hey-day as a bathing centre. Photograph by R.K. Gresswell, English Nature archive, Ainsdale NNR.

naturalists. Both Ainsdale and Freshfield dunes were included in the first ever reserves list, the 1915 survey of "areas worthy of protection" carried out by the Society for the Promotion of Nature Reserves - and Ainsdale, in particular, appeared in a number of national surveys from that time on. Ainsdale was one of the top twenty-two sites listed by the Nature Reserves Investigation Committee in 1944 and was eventually purchased by the Nature Conservancy in 1965 (Houston & Jones 1987). The coast, despite development, is listed as the largest dune system in the U.K. (Doody 1991).

There is no clear reference to why and when the main dune area became an important recreation site. Shore Road, Ainsdale was probably the first development following the construction of the Cheshire Lines Railway along the coast just inland of the high water mark in the mid 1890s. In the early 1900s Shore Road, Ainsdale Beach station, some seaside buildings and a boating lake (Bulrush Slack (SD 301129) now known as Sands Lake) were developed (Figure 1.7). The Lido was constructed in 1933 as a bathing centre and along with the earlier buildings remained the only substantial developments until Pontins Holiday Village in 1968. Ainsdale beach had all the makings of a pleasure beach with good access by road and rail, plenty of room on a safe bathing beach and backed by sandhills for shelter and play (Figure 1.8). It has, by and large, retained its character.

Liverpool people were probably responsible for making Formby a popular destination and it has retained its image as a Merseyside resource (74% of all visitors, Fairhurst 1976) compared to a wider catchment area at Ainsdale and Southport. By the early 1960s Formby Point was becoming so popular that the uncontrolled parking and access was leading to environmental degradation. The first comprehensive visitor survey

was carried out by Lancashire County Council on 25 July 1965 (summarised in Coates 1966). The weather was ideal and approximately 10,000 people visited the area (this figure compares well to a count of 11,000 in 1988 on a similarly good day). These figures were used by Lancashire County Council to support proposals for a regional coastal park to be developed at Formby. The plans suggested a new road network at the rear of the dunes feeding five new car parks, an improved access network, restoration work and tree planting. The County's plans marked a change in direction towards active management of the dune system as an amenity and in a sense were a forerunner of the Coast Management Scheme. Nothing came of Lancashire County Council's 1966 proposals due, in part, to the County's inability to acquire the necessary land and the purchase of the northern part of the site by the National Trust in 1967. The concept of a Formby Coastal Park was taken up by the Mountrule Land Development Company (the Formby estate) in 1974 and after protracted discussions the plans were shelved and part of the land leased to Sefton Council.

The battle to win greater protection for wildlife and habitats on the coast has at times led to acrimonious exchanges between the interests of building development and nature conservation. In particular the ambitious development plans of Southport Borough Council in the 1960s were being opposed by the Nature Conservancy and other conservation organisations. Jackson (1979) documents the spread of development into the dune area and the loss of sand lizard habitat (Figure 1.9). In an effort to safeguard the dunes the Nature Conservancy designated SSSIs at Formby (1963), Ainsdale (1965) and Southport (1966) so allowing for consultation over any proposals. In 1966 Southport Borough Council published development proposals for Ainsdale and western Birkdale.

Figure 1.9 The development of Pontin's Holiday Village in 1968.

Compare to Figure 1.7. The photograph pre-dates the development of Southbeach Park estate to the east of the coast road in the early 1970s. Little Balls Hill is the large blowout near the pinewoods. Photograph (AWE 41) by J.K. St. Joseph. © British Crown copyright/MOD reproduced with the permission of the Controller of Her Britannic Majesty's Stationery Office.

A study of the coast in the early 1970s (McNaught 1973) makes reference to the tensions which existed and gives the following example of a typical Southport response to the Conservancy's proposed extension of the SSSI in 1971 which put an end to long term plans for development:

> "I would rate the housing of people and their families as far more important than the fate of a few newts and toads. They are of academic interest to professors who live in a dream world. Unfortunately many of us have to live in a world which requires four walls and a roof". Alderman H Barner, deputy leader of Southport Borough Council, quoted in Liverpool Evening Post, 16 April 1971. Quoted in McNaught (1973).

This illustrates the gulf that existed between the two interests and is a classic example of the type of conflict that the Countryside Commission sought to address through their pioneering new approach to countryside management in the early 1970s which established the framework on which the Coast Management Scheme was based.

THE SEFTON COAST MANAGEMENT SCHEME

The background, development and operation of the Sefton Coast Management Scheme is documented by Houston & Jones (1987). Local Government reorganisation in 1974 allowed the newly created Merseyside County Council to appraise the problems of the Sefton coast and place them in the wider context of the developing Structure Plan (Wood 1980). The mid 1970s were critical years during which the concepts of the present approach to planning and management on the coast were developed.

In the early 1970s the loss of duneland to residential development continued (especially at Hightown). The Formby estate were proposing the development of a regional coastal park at Formby Point, taking up Lancashire County Council's original 1966 proposals, and now including a golf course (Edmund Kirby & Sons 1974). Conservation organisations such as the British Herpetological Society and the then Lancashire Naturalists' Trust were expressing increasing concern about the fragmentation and damage to dune habitats (Beebee 1978a; Smith 1975) and surveys undertaken by Merseyside County Council (Fairhurst 1976) confirmed the intensity and impact of recreation pressure.

The need for intervention through restoration schemes was apparent and in discussions, the County Council, Sefton Borough Council and the Countryside Commission agreed that such schemes could only be successful if linked to long term management. The Sefton Coast Management Scheme was developed (Merseyside County Council 1977a) and formally established in 1978 with the appointment of a Project Officer a year later.

In the meantime Merseyside County Council had started work on two large-scale restoration projects at Formby Point on behalf of Sefton Borough Council (Lifeboat Road) and the National Trust (Victoria Road). For each project the County Council prepared detailed surveys and proposals (Merseyside County Council 1977b, 1978) with advice on restoration techniques (University of Liverpool 1976) and hydrology (Edmondson 1976; University of Liverpool 1978) provided by specialists.

In the eight year period between December 1977 and November 1985 the County Council's work concentrated on the stabilisation of the frontal dunes, the improvement of car parking and access, the provision of informal recreation facilities and the management of woodlands. The majority of the work was carried out by temporary staff employed under successive programmes funded by the Manpower Services Commission. The work of the County Council was summarised in a final report (Wood 1985).

The Sefton Coast Management Scheme is a countryside management project and closely follows the Heritage Coast style of management pioneered by the Countryside Commission in the early 1970s. The principle of this style of countryside management involves the employment of a Project Officer (syn. Coast Management Officer) to encourage a corporate approach between landowners and agencies. In 1978 the main landholding interests on the coast were the Nature Conservancy Council, the National Trust, Sefton Borough Council, the Territorial Army and several large golf courses and private estates. The management scheme and the management plans that followed (SMBC 1983, 1989) are based on a voluntary agreement between these various landowners to pursue common policies for the overall benefit of the coast.

The role of the Project Officer and the scheme's structure and achievements are also described in Houston & Jones (1987) and Houston (1989). The Sefton Coast Management Scheme was extended in 1983 to include the dune area to the south of the Alt and further extended in 1991 to cover the whole of the Sefton Coast (with the exception of the Liverpool Freeport and the Southport seafront). The same approach to management which has proved successful on the dune coast since 1978 will be extended to include the Crosby Marine Park, the northern marshes and the entire beach area.

ACKNOWLEDGEMENTS

Several people have helped with this review. In particular the authors acknowledge assistance from Barbara Yorke for information on early tree planting, Jennifer Lewis for reviewing the text and providing additional material and Tony Smith for help with the chronology. Their support is greatly appreciated.

Ceri Jones (Review co-ordinator)

Sefton Metropolitan Borough Council
Planning Department
Vermont House
375 Stanley Road
Bootle
Merseyside L20 3RY

A full list of contributors is given in Appendix 2

APPENDIX TO CHAPTER 1: CHRONOLOGY OF THE SEFTON COAST

1423   Record from the Netherlands of artificial establishment of marram grass by planting, so principles of dune stabilisation were probably well known in the 15th Century.

1630s   'Hawslookers' appointed for the first time by the Manors of Ainsdale and Birkdale. In 1637 three local inhabitants were fined for gathering marram grass.

1667   Record of Henry Blundell and Robert Formby establishing rabbit warrens at Formby and setting their boundary at Wicks Lane. Agreement for division of 'Hawes, Sandie Hilles and Coney Warrans of Formbie' LRO DDFo/34/1

1671   Henry Blundell given 300 year lease of wreck of the sea in manors of Formby, Birkdale and Ainsdale.

1689   Greenville Collins' map of the Mersey area. First useful map.

1710   From this date it was a sometime manorial duty to plant marram and from 1711 landowners began to insert clauses in leases compelling tenants to plant marram.

1715   Customs officials describe the coast as "a place of the greatest smuggling in the country". The Isle of Man had declared itself independent in 1523 and became a major route for smuggling goods into Britain.

1719   Formby landmark (lighthouse) built.

1720   A great inundation of the coast on 18-19 December. The sea flooded over 660 acres (267 ha) of land and demolished many houses.

1727   First record in Court Leet of a fine for marram cutting

1729   List of Court officals for Formby includes for the first time "lookers that no person get Star and set where need requireth"

1730   First record of a fine for not planting marram.

1739   Sandstorm buries village of Ravenmeols.

1742   Act passed "for the more effectual preventing of the cutting of Star or Bent"

1753   Thomas Radcliffe of Ormskirk, attorney, draws up an agreement by the lessees of commons, Coney-Warrens and waste grounds of Formby to prosecute stealers of rabbits. Obviously the warreners were fed up with poachers. LRO DDln / 49 / 31

1757   'Starr Setters' appointed by the manors of Ainsdale and Birkdale to oversee the planting of marram. From the mid 1760s all new leases included a requirement to plant marram grass.

1765   Act of Parliament passed in an attempt to give protection to rabbit warrens from poaching.

1776   Britain's first lifeboat station established at Formby.

1779   Alt Commissioners appointed under 1778 Alt Drainage Act. New floodgates built on Alt.

1797   Alt Commissioners start reclamation work (first 20 acres (8 ha)completed by 1818)

1828   Formby Point erosion recorded (E. Eyes).

1829   Formby General Court Order reinforces the 1729 order and asks Star-lookers to work extra days. Other activities are forbidden, including sod-cutting, collecting driftwood, cockling and bait digging.

1833   "Highest Tide of the 19th Century" 31st December 1833. 7.18m above O.D. at Hesketh Arms. (Bland/Barrow)

1840   Training of the River Ribble started at The Naze.

1841   First National Census shows Ainsdale and Birkdale as agricultural communities.

1845   Tithe map and schedule for Formby.

1846   Southport Improvement Commissioners (the first 'Council') nominated by Act of Parliament.

1847   Thomas Weld-Blundell wins seven year legal battle to gain the Ince Blundell estate.

1848   Completion of Liverpool-Southport railway.

1848   First Ordnance Survey map of Formby.

1855   St. Lukes Church (the little church in the sandhills) built.

1855   Reclamation of Balling's Wharf (Altcar Rifle Range) complete and rented for grazing.

1857   Public notices created at Birkdale, Ainsdale and Formby reminding readers of the punishment for cutting marram. (Figure 1.5)

1860   Construction of Southport pier.

1860   Establishment of Altcar Rifle Range. Range opened by Lord Sefton on 28th July.

1867   Southport receives its charter.

1870 - 1900   Reclamation of Massams slack.

1873   West Lancashire Golf Club founded.

1875   Establishment of Formby Land and Building Company (wound up in 1902)

1880   Dumping of refuse in Liverpool Bay started.

1884   Formby Golf Club founded.

1885   Southport Corporation purchase the town foreshore.

1885	Hesketh Golf Club established.
1887	First conifer planting experiments by Charles Weld-Blundell.
1889	(Royal) Birkdale Golf Club founded.
1890	First dredging in River Mersey, at Bar.
1893/94	Large scale afforestation projects started by Charles Weld-Blundell and Jonathon Formby.
1894	Southport and District Wildfowlers' Association formed.
1895	Southport petitions Parliament against proposed extension of River Ribble training walls (Petition unsuccessful).
1896	Dumping of Sewage Sludge in Liverpool Bay commenced.
1904	Construction of Fort Crosby at Hightown
1905	Ainsdale becomes part of Birkdale.
1907	Southport and Ainsdale Golf Club established.
1909	Work begins on the training banks of the outer Mersey. (Taylor's Bank)
1910	Early flying experiments at Freshfield. Five hangars set up near Victoria Road.
1911	Mr C.S. Weld-Blundell and Jonathon Formby give evidence to the Royal Commission on Coast Erosion and Afforestation.
1912	Hillside Golf Club established.
1912	Ainsdale and Birkdale amalgamated with Southport.
1913	West Lancashire Territorial Association purchase 500 acres (202 ha) of foreshore at Altcar from Mr F.N. Blundell.
1914	Southport sea bathing lake opened.
1915	Ainsdale and Freshfield dunes listed in survey of "areas worthy of protection" by the Society for the Promotion of Nature Reserves.
1916	Final closure of Formby Lifeboat Station
1919	Coast erosion on Lancashire and Cheshire coasts causing local press comment.
1919-1920	Coast erosion causes concern at Blundellsands due to migration of River Alt.
1921	Efforts to control rabbits started at Altcar Rifle Range.
1924	Dredging of the River Mersey reaches its peak at 25 million hopper tons/yr 1924-1925.
1927	Storm surge on the night of 28th to 29th November at 6.1 metres above O.D. causes serious damage.

1928	Remainder of Birkdale and Ainsdale foreshore purchased by Southport Corporation. Subsequently the sandhills were also bought.
1933	Construction of Ainsdale Lido.
1936	River Alt diverted by training wall north of Hall Road.
1937	Training of the River Ribble completed (South Salters Spit).
1938	Tank training started at Altcar (a new area was provided in 1948).
1939	Southport Corporation purchase remainder of northern foreshore from the Hesketh Estate.
1941	R.A.F. Woodvale established on the site of the former Freshfield Golf Club.
1942	Tipping of rubble along Crosby-Hightown shore started.
1945	War Office propose that Formby Point be used for military training.
1945	First accurate aerial photography carried out by RAF.
1946	Southport-Ainsdale shore bus service introduced.
1950s	Dumping of refuse in Liverpool Bay by Liverpool and Salford stopped after campaign by Southport.
1952	Southport and Cheshire Lines extension railway closed. Closure opens possibilities for development south of Southport, because shore will be accessible.
1953	Publication of *Sandy Shores in South Lancashire* by R.K. Gresswell.
1955	Newspaper reports mercy killings of myxomatosis rabbits (2000 in 3 months), implying that the disease was widespread by 1954. Evening Express 1.2.1955.
1956	British Nicotine Company begin tipping in dunes south of Victoria Road.
1956	Formby Point caravan site established at Lifeboat Road.
1956	Southport Sanctuary designated. (the second such site to be designated in the UK under Protection of Birds Act 1954)
1957	Fort Crosby becomes redundant.
1957	Completion of River Mersey Training Banks.
1958	Formby Coast Protection Order under Coast Protection Act (1949).
1959	Pinetrees caravan site relocated at Victoria Road due to marine erosion. This site was abandoned and relocated in 1981.

1960 - 1965	Major extension of Hillside Golf Course.
1961	Pine Tree Cafe collapses into the sea after storm erosion on 24 October
1963	Permission given for housing development at Hightown. MOD sell Fort Crosby Coast Defence Battery to Crosby Borough, including 417 acres (170 ha) of foreshore.
1963	Declaration of Formby Sand Dunes SSSI.
1965	Lifeboat Station, now used as a cafe, demolished.
1965	National Trust launch Enterprise Neptune.
1965	Declaration of Ainsdale Sand Dunes NNR and SSSI.
1965	First Formby Point visitor survey carried out by Lancashire County Council.
1966	Declaration of Southport Sand Dunes and Foreshore SSS1
1966	Lancashire County Council publish the Formby Area Report with plans for a coastal regional park.
1966	First sand extraction from Horsebank by W. Rainford Ltd, (the idea was first mooted in 1961).
1966	Mersey Channels deepened by dredging from 24ft to 28ft: new ruling depth.
1967	Demolition of Fort Crosby, Hightown
1967	National Trust purchase Freshfield Dune area
1967-1968	Numerous storm surges cause increased rate of erosion around Formby coastline.
1968	Pontin's Holiday Village opened at Ainsdale
1970	First efforts at Altcar Range to conserve natterjack toads.
1971/72	First artificial scrapes dug on Birkdale Hills by Lancashire Naturalists' Trust.
1971	Flood protection bank completed at Cabin Hill by Mersey and Weaver River Authority.
1972	Alt pumping station opened.
1973	Hovercraft service launched at Southport.
1973	Little Balls Hill (Ainsdale) removed and dunes stabilised.
1974	Local Government Reorganisation.
1974	Proposals by Mountrule Land Development Company for country park at Formby Point.
1974	Tobacco waste tipping ceased at Formby.
1975	Mersey channels allowed to revert to 24ft ruling depth.

1975	Merseyside County Council Formby Point Visitor Survey.
1977	Storm Surge 11 November. 6.11 metres above O.D.
1977	Merseyside County Council start dune restoration projects at Formby Point.
1978	Formby Land Company agree to lease Lifeboat Road and Ravenmeols Dunes to Sefton Council.
1978	Formal agreement to establish Sefton Coast Management Scheme. Partners were Merseyside County Council, Sefton Borough Council and Countryside Commission
1979	Project Officer for Sefton Coast Management Scheme appointed.
1979	Military use of Cabin Hill area for grenade training ceases. Area officially declared safe in 1983.
1979	Altcar Sand Dunes and Foreshore SSSI designated.
1980	Closure of the Port of Preston - No further maintenance or dredging in the River Ribble.
1980	Designation of Ainsdale and Birkdale Hills Local Nature Reserve.
1980	Formby Point Visitor Survey by Sefton Council.
1981	Pinetree Caravan site (Victoria Road) moved inland due to coast erosion.
1983	Storm Surge, January 31. 6.0 metres above O.D.
1983	Sefton Coast Management Scheme extended to south of River Alt.
1983	Coast Management Plan published by Sefton Council.
1984	Cabin Hill National Nature Reserve leased from the Formby Trust.
1990	Storm surge. February 26th - 28th. 6.3 metres above O.D.
1991	Designation of Cabin Hill National Nature Reserve.
1991	Coast Management Scheme extended to include all the undeveloped coastal zone and beaches within Sefton..

SECTION 2

GEOMORPHOLOGY

CHAPTER TWO

Coastal and Sea-level Changes

A.J. Plater, D. Huddart, J. B. Innes, K. Pye, A.J. Smith, and M.J. Tooley.

INTRODUCTION

In this chapter, a review of past and current research on the geomorphological evolution of the Sefton Coast is presented. Thus whilst Table 2.1 summarises and generalises the main features of the geological sequences in the area, this chapter focuses on the coastal processes of the quaternary period (during which unconsolidated materials were deposited). Coastal development during the last 10,000 years (The Holocene) has involved lateral displacements of the coastline and, hence, the lowlands which lie behind the Sefton dune system and contain the evidence for these displacements are also included in this review. Similarly, an investigation of the dunes also requires a clear understanding of the contiguous nearshore system from which the dune sediment is derived. Consequently, the scope of this chapter is much broader than an analysis of the dune system for which the Sefton Coast is internationally famous.

In response to major fluctuations in a number of factors, primarily climate and sea-level, the Sefton Coast has evolved into the sand-dominated dune system we see today between the Mersey and Ribble estuaries. This dynamic coastline fronts an extensive 'mossland' environment which has recorded changes in coastal geomorphology during the last 9,000 years or so. Consequently, our knowledge of the Sefton Coast not only covers the period of historical and archaeological records, but extends back, with a reasonable degree of certainty, to the end of the last major glacial event which affected the U.K. Understanding how this coastline has responded to past changes in climate and sea-level provides the context for current and future research activities.

EARLY RESEARCH: OBSERVATIONS AND OPINIONS

The vulnerability of the Lancashire lowlands to inundation by the sea and, therefore, the importance of sea-level changes in their evolution, was first noted by the Reverend Richard James (1636) from direct comparison of ground surface altitude with that of the spring tides. Commenting "on the origin of the beds of silty clay and peat..." in the coastal lowlands of south-west Lancashire, Binney and Talbot (1843) suggested that the different sedimentary units were deposited in response to the periodic breaching of coastal barriers, progressive sedimentation, and the blocking of channels by sand banks. In contrast, Reade (1871) identified a series of intercalated biogenic and minerogenic stratigraphic units (layers of peat and silt) which, he suggested, were the consequence of rhythmic land uplift and subsidence. Indeed, historical variations in relative sea-level on the west coast of England had previously been examined by Picton (1849). The dichotomy represented by these early works still exists to some extent today; i.e. to what extent are the sedimentary sequences observed in the Lancashire mosslands the result of sea-level change or the product of changes in coastal morphology resulting from variations in storm activity, sediment supply and/or sediment processing (erosion, transport and deposition)?

Further evidence concerning the origin of the unconsolidated deposits of the region was provided by the work of C.E. de Rance (1869, 1872, 1877 and 1878) and the continuing research of Reade (1872, 1881a, b, 1902 and 1908b). Environmental and

TABLE 2.1
The Geological Sequence for South West Lancashire

(Adapted from Hall & Folland 1967)

			Typical thickness (m)
Recent and Post Glacial		Blown Sand	
		Freshwater, Estuarine	
	D	& Marine Alluvium	Highly
	R	Peat	Variable
	I	Downholland Silt	0-60
	F	Shirdley Hill Sand	(not all
	T		necessarily present)
Glacial		Upper Boulder Clay	
		Middle Sands	
		Lower Boulder Clay	
Triassic (Keuper)		Keuper Marls	
		Keuper Waterstones	340
		Keuper Sandstones	
Triassic (Bunter)	S	Upper Mottled Sandstone	
	O	Pebble Beds	610
	L	Lower Mottled Sandstone	
	I		
	D		
Permian		Manchester Marl	
		Collyhurst Sandstone	800
Carboniferous		Millstone Grit	380+

chronological data were later obtained through a detailed analysis of the macro- and micro-fossils contained within the biogenic sediments (Travis 1908, 1922a; Travis 1926, 1929; Erdtman 1928; and Blackburn, in Cope 1939), whilst the stratigraphic record was elucidated further by the work of Cope (1939), Wray and Cope (1948) and the Soil Survey (Hall 1954-5).

The work of Gresswell (1937, 1953, 1957 and 1964) includes a model of coastal evolution in which sea-level was assumed to be initially low at the culmination of the last glaciation (approximately 18,000 years BP).

With the retreat of the ice and the release of water into the oceans as climate warmed, sea-level rose relatively rapidly (Figure 2.1) and spread eastward onto the low-lying parts of the Lancashire coast.

Following the lead of Wright (1914), Gresswell mapped what he interpreted as a series of coastal landforms and geomorphic features at an altitude of approximately +5.2m O.D.†[1] which he termed the "Hillhouse Coastline" and assigned an age of approximately 5000 years BP (later adjusted to 6000 years BP) from direct analogy with an extensive raised beach feature in Scotland. As the shoreline then

retreated westwards from this mid-Holocene maximum due to continued glacio-isostatic uplift, Gresswell (1953) believed that sand accumulated as a regressive wedge; replacing blue-grey estuarine-marine silts and freshwater peats with wind-blown sand. Although Gresswell's model has formed the basis for many works on the coastal evolution of the north-west region, subsequent detailed palaeobotanical, stratigraphic and altitudinal investigations have proved it to be significantly flawed (Tooley 1976, 1978a).

The supply of sediment to the coastal dune system and the sediment dynamics (erosion, transport and deposition) and bedforms of the Sefton shore were also the subject of investigation by Gresswell (1937, 1953). The coastal dunes were thought to have formed in response to the onshore movement of sand during the later Holocene. Indeed, Reade (1881a) measured the rate of sand accumulation in selected sites in south-west Lancashire and, from an assumed sand thickness, calculated the age of the dunes to 2580 years. Information regarding the average rate of coastal progradation (seaward extension) and dune advance near Ainsdale was also obtained by Salisbury (1920) from map and tree ring evidence. However, Ashton (1909) had previously used map and documentary records to illustrate that high dunes did not exist in the

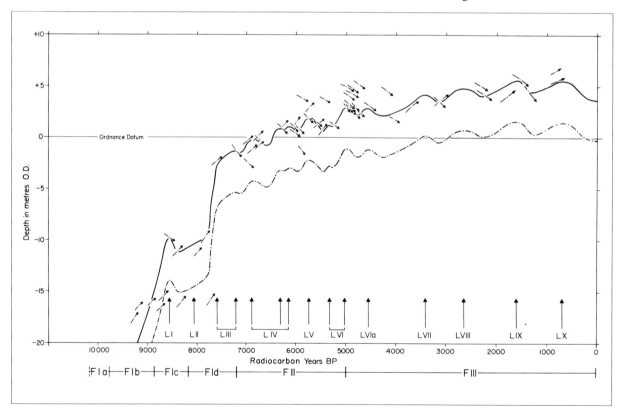

Figure 2.1 Relative sea-level changes in north-west England (after Tooley 1978a). A point and an arrow pointing upwards is the age and altitude of a sea-level index point from a transgressive overlap (Tooley 1982): a point and an arrow pointing downwards is from a regressive overlap. Both overlaps contain evidence of marine or near marine conditions and are interpreted as palaeo - high water marks. The continuous line traces the palaeo - high water mark from 9200 BP to the present, whereas the dot-dash line traces the palaeo - mean tide level, assuming no variations in tidal range. LI to LX are the marine transgressions recorded at Lytham, and FIa to FIII are Flandrian Chronozones established at Red Moss, Lancashire (Hibbert, Switsnur and West 1971). O.D. is Ordnance Datum.

†[1] O.D. refers to Ordnance Datum, the standard sea level of the Ordnance Survey, now mean sea-level at Newlyn, Cornwall. Mean sea-level at Liverpool is 0.27m above O.D.

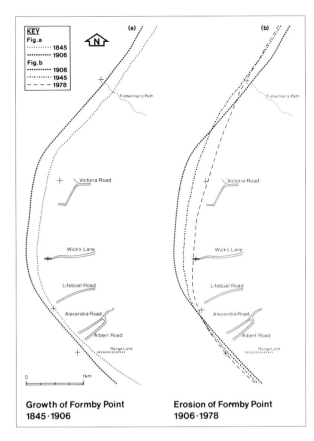

Figure 2.2 Growth of Formby Point showing accretion under active management (a) and subsequent erosion (b). (from Turner 1984)

Formby area prior to 1700 AD. The source of the arenaceous sediment was the subject of an early study by Barron (1938), who found that the Mersey and the Ribble supplied only minor amounts of sand to the coast during the Holocene. However, Cashin (1949) considered that the supply of sand from the Mersey estuary may have been enhanced during the early 20th century by the construction of training walls between 1909 and 1939. With these recent changes in mind, it is interesting to note that successive Ordnance Survey maps show a seaward development of Formby Point between 1845 and 1906, (Figure 2.2) but after approximately 1900 erosion seems to have taken place (Gresswell 1937, 1953).

These early investigations laid the foundations for the more specific research which has been carried out on the Lancashire mosslands and the Sefton dune system. Indeed, it is clear from the above review that research since the 1950s has merely put the 'meat on the bones' in terms of the evolution of the Sefton Coast.

THE MOSSLANDS: SEFTON'S FOSSIL COASTLINE

The extensive and detailed research of Michael Tooley on past environments in north-west England (1969, 1970, 1971, 1973, 1974, 1976, 1977a, 1977b, 1978a, 1978b, 1979, 1980, 1982, 1985a, 1985b; Tooley & Kear

1977; Huddart *et al.* 1977; Innes *et al.* 1989) represents probably the most comprehensive palaeogeographic reconstruction exercise to have been carried out in the UK. A thorough analysis of the sediments and landforms identified at sites between the present coastline and the A59 trunk road is provided in Tooley (1978a), together with an interpretation of the Holocene evolution of the Sefton Coast in the context of sea-level trends in north-west Europe. (see Figure 1.1)

INUNDATIONS BY THE SEA

Tooley (1978a) suggested that four, perhaps five, marine transgressions (long-term inundations by the sea) can be identified in the sediments of the Sefton mosslands.

The earliest transgression is recorded at Formby where peat deposition ceased as estuarine silts began to accumulate at an altitude of approximately -10m O.D. around 8000 years BP. This first transgression (DM-I) is recorded further eastward in the sediments of Downholland Moss by a blue clay deposited between 6980 and 6760 years BP, culminating at approximately 6750 years BP. At Downholland Moss, the mean altitude of this transgressive contact[2] is -0.72m O.D. and that of the succeeding regressive event, where there is a return to peat deposition, is -0.19m O.D. This phase of deposition represents almost 10m of relative sea-level rise over a period of approximately 1200 years, at an average rate of more than 8mm per year.

The second transgression is shown as a single unit in the Downholland Moss stratigraphy, culminating at 6050+/-65 years BP where the regressive contact is recorded at an altitude of approximately +1.0m O.D. The onset of this transgression is placed at approximately 6500 years BP. The second transgression (DM-II) has also been identified in the sediments immediately east of Southport where the mean altitudes of the transgressive and regressive contacts are +0.33m O.D. and +1.07m O.D. respectively.

The third transgressive event (DM-III) is represented in the Downholland Moss stratigraphy by a layer of silty clay. The onset of this transgression is tentatively placed at 5565+/-205 years BP, although the succeeding regression has been dated at 5615+/-45 years BP. Tooley (1978a), suggests that the third transgression was initiated at approximately 5900 years BP. Thus, this transgressive event appears to have been rather short-lived, depositing a thin minerogenic unit between +1.27m O.D. and +1.59m O.D. in the Sefton lowlands. The third transgression is also recorded at Crossens where the mean altitudes of the transgressive and regressive contacts are +0.86m O.D. and +1.80m O.D. respectively.

---

[2] A transgressive contact is the term given to a change in sedimentation where terrestrial (land-based) sediments are overlain by marine or estuarine sediments. A regressive contact is one where marine or estuarine sediments pass upward into terrestrial deposits

Transgression four (IV) is recorded at the Alt Mouth, Formby and Birkdale in a series of sands, silts and clays between transgressive and regressive boundaries at altitudes of +2.90m O.D. and +3.37m O.D. respectively. Tooley (1978a) proposes that this fourth transgressive phase occurred between 4800 and 4545 years BP.

The final transgression affecting the Sefton Coast can be inferred from the evidence from Formby Foreshore where a radiocarbon date of 2335+/-120 years BP was derived from a woody peat from a fossil dune slack at +5.08m O.D. The evidence for a marine transgression at this time is rather conjectural and relies upon the work of Jelgersma et al. (1970a) in which the formation of the dune slacks in the Netherlands is considered to be closely related to periods of marine transgression.

RECENT CRUSTAL MOVEMENTS

The inferred sea-level trends were considered in great detail by Tooley (1978a) but, equally importantly, he proposed that the differences in timing and altitude of the recorded marine transgression surfaces in north-west England, Wales and south-west Scotland would provide a measure of the amount of rebound of the land following removal of the ice load (isostatic recovery) for different parts of the UK crust since deglaciation. However, one must bear in mind that these spatial and temporal variations in the sea-level record may also have been due to other factors, such as storm activity, changes in coastal morphology or variations in sedimentation rate (Tooley 1978b, 1979, 1985b). Indeed, Binney and Talbot (1843) had previously interpreted changes in coastal lowland sedimentation with respect to the successive formation and breaching of a coastal barrier feature. In terms of global (eustatic) sea-level change and glacio-isostatic crustal movements (rebound), the coast of north-west England proved to be critical to a consideration of isostatic recovery (Tooley 1978a). The Lancashire coast occupied a position marginal to the area of maximum ice loading and, therefore, suffered both positive and negative crustal movements during the late Devensian (the last glaciation) and the Holocene. Indeed, Tooley (1978a) showed that the "time transgressive" pivot between the "uplifting" north and the "subsiding" south passed across Morecambe Bay. More recent work by Shennan (1989) has shown that there has been no uplift in south-west Lancashire during the past 6000 years, and that the pivot of glacio-isostatic recovery in the UK lies slightly further south, running from the estuary of the River Tees to the mouth of the River Mersey.

THE SHIRDLEY HILL SAND

The glacial basement of the mossland region is overlain by up to 5m of sand, known as the Shirdley Hill Sand. The yellow or white fine to medium sands are made up of a wind-blown and a water-lain facies (Wilson 1985)

and are subdivided into distinct units by intercalated beds of peat or organic sand and, west of Haskayne, the sands form parabolic dunes of modest relief. To the west of the +7.0m contour, the sands pass under a suite of silts, clays and peats such as those found at Downholland Moss. The origin of the Shirdley Hill Sand has been the subject of considerable debate since Gresswell's work on the Hillhouse Coastline (1937, 1953, 1957, 1964). Gresswell (1953, 1957) proposed that the Shirdley Hill Sands are coastal in origin and began to accumulate during the late Atlantic and the early Sub-Boreal periods (approx. 5000 years BP). However, Godwin (1959) proposed that the Shirdley Hill Sands are analogous to the cover-sands of Europe and demonstrated a late-Devensian age, in contradiction to the mid-post-glacial age and coastal origin assigned to them by Gresswell (1953), Wray and Cope (1948) and Evans and Arthurton (1973). Botanical investigations and absolute dating of the intercalated biogenic deposits and grain-size analyses of the sands (Tooley & Kear 1977; Tooley 1978a; Wilson et al. 1981; Wilson 1985; Innes 1986; Kear & Wilson 1986; Innes et al. 1989) support a late Devensian age, and corroborate the findings of Godwin (1959). Thus, rather than being the product of a stable to regressing sea, the Shirdley Hill Sand is the result of cold phase activity during a climatic deterioration (arctic desert conditions) after 10455+/-110 years BP and later reworking by water and wind (Tooley 1978a, 1985b).

ARCHAEOLOGICAL INVESTIGATIONS

It is not the aim of this review to describe studies of archaeology, but one must not overlook the value of archaeological investigations in the palaeogeographic reconstruction of the Sefton coast and the impact of anthropogenic activity on coastal evolution (Innes & Tomlinson 1991). The chapter by Jones et al. (this volume) records examples where several settlements were overwhelmed by blown sand in the Middle Ages. This period of active sand movement follows the final phase of widespread dune stability in the UK dated to approximately 800 years BP (Tooley 1990). Documentary work on the burial of old havens and inlets at Old Formby and Argarmeols by blowing sand, and the tidal inundation of other settlements (Lewis 1983) has been of considerable relevance to the evolution of the Sefton coast on the local scale.

CURRENT STUDIES

Detailed research into past environments is continuing on the Lancashire mosslands, providing further information regarding the response of the Sefton Coast to past changes in sea-level. However, with an established stratigraphic record, researchers must now look to other techniques to extend our understanding of coastal evolution. The study of pollen and algae (diatoms) in the Holocene sediments of the mosslands has long been

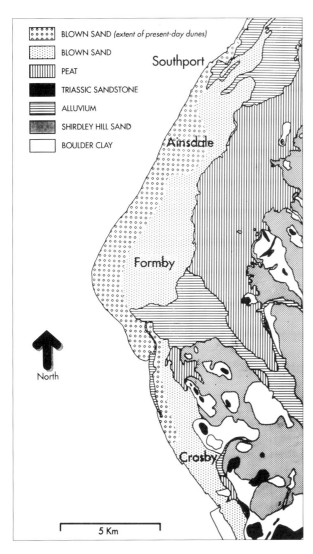

Figure 2.3 The extent of blown sand deposits along the Sefton Coast. Source: Geological Survey of England and Wales (Surveyed 1936).

the University of Durham, Michael Tooley has been investigating the luminescence properties of Holocene marine sediments in south-west Lancashire with the aim of extending the knowledge of Holocene sea-level changes in north-west England.

THE DUNES: SEFTON'S DYNAMIC COASTLINE

SEDIMENT SUPPLY

The Sefton dune system is located between Crosby and Southport and is part of the dune complex extending from Blundellsands to the Ribble estuary (Figure 2.3). Hence, the coastline is influenced by the estuaries of the Mersey and the Ribble as well as the processes which operate in the eastern Irish Sea (Pye 1990).

In Liverpool Bay there is a net shoreward drift of sediment near the bed due to the flood-ebb asymmetry (Figure 2.4). The flood tidal currents move in an eastward direction and part immediately offshore from Formby Point to flow towards the Ribble and the Mersey estuaries. Bedform patterns on the floor of the eastern Irish sea and the results of sea bed drifter investigations confirm that net sediment movement is in an easterly direction (Sly 1966; Belderson & Stride

employed to provide information on sea-level trends, vegetational succession and environmental salinity. Several examples of these micropalaeontological investigations are cited in Tooley (1978a). Whilst Michael Tooley and Jim Innes at the University of Durham have continued to apply these techniques to new sites in the region, David Huddart at Liverpool Polytechnic has studied sea-level changes in south-west Lancashire using the presence of Foraminifera (shelled single-celled aquatic animals) in sediments as indicators of depositional environments. Past work has been carried out in association with Michael Tooley on Downholland Moss and Altcar Moss, and future work will concentrate on the line of the new A565 - M57 link. Tooley and Huddart have also been investigating the biostratigraphy of the Holocene sediments in south-west Lancashire with reference to sea-level changes.

The study of sediment luminescence has considerable potential in the field of sea-level research. Following deposition, sediment particles acquire luminescence with time and, thus, it is possible to obtain information regarding the age of a particular sediment and clues to its mode of origin. In collaboration with Ian Bailiff at

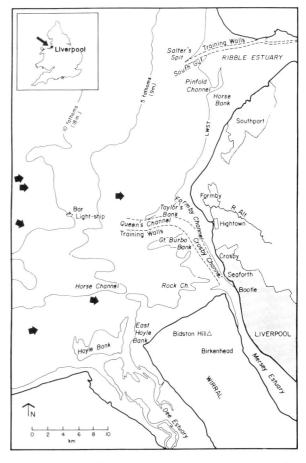

Figure 2.4 Location of the Sefton coast showing the net shoreward drift of sediment. The arrows indicate the direction of sand wave movement on the floor of the Irish Sea (after Sly 1966).

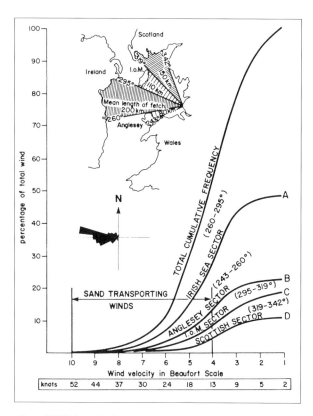

Figure 2.5 Wind velocity frequency distribution for different Irish Sea sectors (modified after Gresswell 1953, Sly 1966). Also shown are the maximum lengths of wave fetch in each sector and the wind rose for sand-moving winds (>20 km hr⁻¹) recorded at Southport (extracted from Meteorological Office Monthly Weather Reports)

1969; Best 1972; Best *et al.* 1973; Halliwell 1973; Pye 1990). Consequently, the main source of sand appears to be the fluvio-glacial (glacial outwash) sediments found on the floor of the Irish Sea (Wright *et al.* 1971). The dominant winds and waves approach the Sefton coastline from the west and west-north-west (Gresswell 1953; Sly 1966; Hydraulics Research Station 1969; Bell *et al.* 1975), corresponding with the region of maximum fetch over the Irish Sea (approx. 200km) (Figure 2.5). Incident wave spectra have been the subject of considerable analysis (Darbyshire 1958; Murthy & Cook 1962; Draper & Blakey 1969; Hydraulics Research Station 1969, 1977). Parker (1975) notes that the most common wave conditions are those of moderate energy possessing a significant wave height of between 0.6m and 1.0m with a period of between 4.0 and 4.5 seconds, and the highest measured waves have been recorded at 9.4m with a period of 8.7 seconds (Tucker 1963; Draper 1966).

The general conditions cited above agree well with the results of the Hydraulics Research Station (1969), although Pye (1990) suggests that severe storm waves in the eastern Irish Sea only reach a height of 5.7m with a period of 8.7 seconds.

It is interesting to note that, because of the shallow depth of the eastern Irish Sea, the incident waves are refracted as they pass over the offshore sand banks and become focused on Formby Point. Consequently, wave crests are normal to the shore at Formby, but subsequent divergence leads to some longshore drift to the north and south (Gresswell 1953; Hydraulics Research Station 1969; Pye 1990). Further research on the hydrodynamics of the Sefton Coast was carried out between 1980 and 1986 by Tony Smith of the Engineer's department of Sefton Borough Council. Whilst seconded to Liverpool University, Smith compiled the 'Sefton Coast Database', which contains the existing research, literature, plans and records relevant to sediment processing at the coastline in a readily accessible form, and includes an area by area description of several coastal zones in Sefton. In association with staff at Liverpool University, Imperial College London, and British Maritime Technology, Sefton Borough Council also sponsored the development of a numerical model of waves, tides and currents for the Sefton coastline. The model has enabled more detailed investigation of the evolution of this dynamic coastal system.

Considerable nearshore accretion has been taking place in Liverpool Bay during the 19th and 20th centuries (Hydraulics Research Station 1958), possibly due to dredge spoil reworking (McDowell & O'Connor 1987; O'Connor 1987) or to training wall construction (Cashin 1949; Hydraulic Research Station 1958; Price & Kendrick 1963; O'Connor 1987). Significant accretion has also been taking place within the Ribble estuary following training wall construction works between 1840 and 1938 (Barron 1938; Hydraulic Research Station 1965, 1968, 1977, 1980). The sediment transport dynamics and bedforms on the Sefton shore have been the subject of investigation by several workers (Gresswell 1937, 1957; Parker 1971, 1974, 1975; Wright 1976).

The nearshore zone is characterised by a series of symmetrical sand ridges which are between 0.5m and 1.0m high with a wavelength of between 300m and 500m, which are aligned sub-parallel to the intertidal zone. The lower foreshore comprises a muddy sandflat which attenuates in width to the north, whilst the upper

Figure 2.6 Ridge and runnel features on Formby Foreshore (1990). Three distinct ridges and three runnels with interconnecting channels can be seen on this photograph.

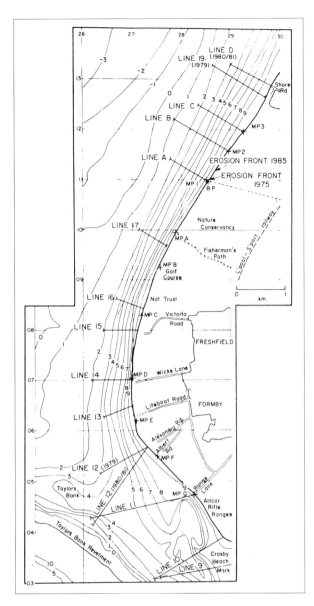

Figure 2.7 Map showing the location of marker posts (MP) and survey lines where measurements of dune erosion/accretion and changes in the beach profile are made by the Sefton Borough Engineer's Department. The contours indicate height in metres relative to Chart Datum (-4.42 m O.D), surveyed in 1979.

beach sediment budget and an attenuation of the backshore. Consequently, the frontal dune system has become much more vulnerable to wave attack during storms. The 220m of accretion near Victoria Road between 1845 and 1906 (Figure 2.2) has been countered by approximately 400m of erosion at Formby Point since the turn of the century. Hence, the average beach gradient is relatively steep near the centre of Formby Point, but becomes much more shallow towards the north and south.

DUNE CHRONOLOGY AND MORPHOLOGY

The Sefton dune system covers an area of approximately 30km², attaining a maximum width of 4km at Formby Point. The dunes are well developed at the seaward margin of the system and grade eastward into a sand sheet with little relief. Radio-carbon dates from where the aeolian (wind-blown) sediments leaven a sequence of intercalated peats and estuarine silts indicate that the main phase of dune development appears to have been between 4500 and 2500 years BP (Tooley 1977, 1982, 1990; Innes 1982; Pye 1990; Innes & Tooley, this volume).

The cause of this dune development is uncertain, although Gresswell (1953) has suggested emplacement during a mid-Holocene regression and Pye (1990) has considered the effects of a significant time lag between the initial post-glacial inundation and the consequent liberation of sand from marine reworking of the fluvioglacial source areas. Tooley (1990) recently suggested that sand dunes systems, such as that on the Sefton coast, have undergone widespread phases of active development and stabilisation. From an analysis of published radiocarbon dates, Tooley proposes that there was a period of dune building in north-west England, north-west Scotland and Northern Ireland at approximately 5000 years BP, with a more widespread phase of dune stability between 2500 and 2000 years BP. This phase of dune stability is manifest in the Sefton dunes at Formby where a dune slack soil and woody detritus has been dated to 2335+/-120 years BP (Tooley 1978a). A comparable date of 2510+/-120 years BP was reported from an *in situ* oak stump in the same dune slack peat horizon by Pye (1990). The observed temporal patterns of dune development on the Sefton coast can be correlated with a more coherent chronology from the Netherlands (Jelgersma *et al.* 1970b), indicating some larger scale climatic forcing of dune system evolution.

The morphology of the dunes along the Sefton coast has been significantly influenced by human activities. Early studies illustrated that extensive marram grass planting at the turn of the eighteenth century probably led to the growth of high frontal dunes at Formby (Ashton 1909; Travis 1915). Other human activities which have affected the dune system include sand-winning, waste-dumping and the landscaping of

foreshore comprises a series of intertidal ridges and runnels (Figure 2.6). The ridge and runnel features lie obliquely to the curve of the high water mark such that, to the north and south of Formby Point, they trend away from the shoreline.

The Engineer's department of Sefton Council has maintained a record of accretion and erosion along its sand dune coastline since the mid 1950s (Figures 2.7 and 2.8), and possesses records of beach cross-sections and shore surveys dating back to the 1880s. To supplement the data on shoreline and dune system evolution, comprehensive aerial photographs are also kept by the Engineer's department. This wealth of research material allowed Pye and Smith (1988) to extend the work on the sediment dynamics of Formby Point.

The erosional trend since approximately 1900 is considered to be associated with the onset of a negative

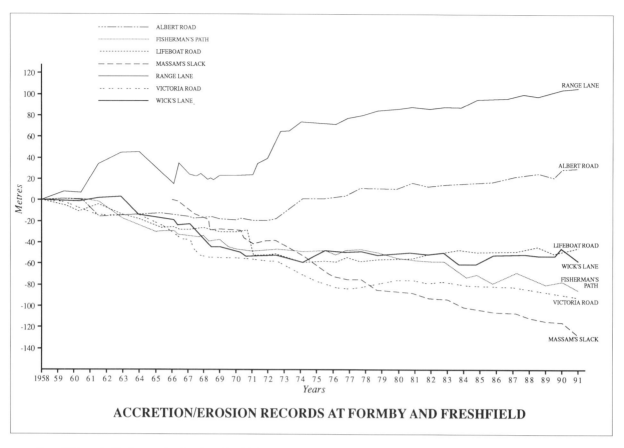

Figure 2.8 Accretion/Erosion records at Formby and Freshfield, 1958-1991. Data from measurements taken by Sefton Borough Engineer's Department.

selected areas for agriculture, access roads, caravan parks, car parks and other recreational uses. The planting of conifers and dune grasses, and the setting out of brushwood fences during the late nineteenth and the early twentieth centuries led to notable stabilisation and foredune development (Pye 1990; Jones *et al.*, this volume). The dunes formed during the nineteenth century form roughly parallel ridges separated by

slacks which become water-logged during periods when the water table is high (Figure 2.9). This belt of parallel ridges is up to 200m wide in places, but erosion at Formby Point since 1906 has removed a significant proportion of the central area.

Landward of this parallel dune and slack system is a more irregular zone of low hummocky dunes which formed during the period before 1880 (Pye 1990). The irregular nature is probably due to marram planting in the absence of brushwood fencing, resulting in more irregular sand accumulation. Several slacks within this system represent natural blowouts, although true parabolic dunes are poorly developed. Pye (1990) suggested that the nature of these transgressive sand sheets at Formby reflects three major factors:

i) The natural dune vegetation offers relatively little resistance to blowout development and sand encroachment on a broad front;

ii) The directional variability of the wind is relatively large; and

iii) The development and maintenance of well-defined dune forms is hindered at Formby by the high pedestrian pressure.

Figure 2.9 Massam's slack and parallel dune ridges, Ainsdale Sand Dunes NNR. Aerial photograph (UT 19, undated ca.1964) by J.K. St. Joseph. Crown Copyright. © British Crown Copyright / MOD reproduced with the permission of the Controller of Her Majesty's Stationery Office

Figure 2.10 Extent of dune erosion at Formby Point following the storm surge of 26th February 1990. The high tide exceeded 6.3 m OD at Liverpool and 6.4 m OD at Southport. Structural damage was caused at Southport and Crosby and the dune frontage suffered severe erosion, amounting to 6.0 m at Albert Road, 8.3 m at Lifeboat Road, 11.1 m at Wicks Lane, 13.6 m at Victoria Road, 7.5 m at Fisherman's Path and 6.0 m between Ainsdale and Southport. Near Fisherman's Path erosion formed cliffs 8-10 m high. At Massam's slack where previous erosion had truncated the ends of dune ridges created artificially in the 1920s, waves overtopped the frontal ridge and flooded the slack behind. (Pye 1991).

In addition, periodic wave erosion of the foredunes and localised high wind energy may have affected the formation of the Sefton dune system. An evolutionary model of dune systems, based on evidence from the Sefton coast, was recently proposed by Pye (1990).

Figure 2.11 Destruction of foredunes by public pressure, Victoria Road, Formby (SD 273083), mid-1970s.

CURRENT STUDIES

Kenneth Pye at the Postgraduate Research Institute for Sedimentology of Reading University, currently has a NERC-funded postgraduate research student, Adrian Neal, working on the Holocene evolution of the coast (see Pye & Neal, this volume). The aims of the project include obtaining a clear understanding of the stratigraphic and morphological development of the coast during the Holocene, obtaining a better understanding of the present-day coastal sediment transport dynamics, especially beach-dune-nearshore interaction, and to model the effects of changes in wind and wave climate, sea-level and nearshore topography over time scales of 10 - 1000 years. This latter aim will be developed further through research on the effects of changes in sea-level and wind/wave climate on coastal dune systems in north-west England, sponsored by the Nuffield Foundation, in which Pye has focused on the effects of large storms on the sediment budget of the Sefton Coast. The nature of dune erosion caused by the storm surge of 26th February 1990 (Figure 2.10), and subsequent backshore recovery, was analysed by Pye (1991). The entire dune frontage between Hightown and Southport suffered erosion during this storm, reaching a maximum of 13.6m near Victoria Road. The effect of storms on the Sefton Coast was also considered in recent work by Andrew Plater at the University of

Figure 2.12 Dune restoration in progress at Victoria Road. Dune ridges were rebuilt on sand-trapping (brushwood) fences, the accumulated sand re-planted with marram grass and access controlled along boardwalk paths.

Liverpool. Using detailed data supplied by Tony Smith of the Engineer's department of Sefton Council, together with that supplied by other engineers in north-west England and north Wales, Plater has examined the impact of the storm surges of February 1990 on coastal systems. A wider ranging discussion of the role of storms in the sediment transport dynamics of the Sefton Coast is presented in Pye (1992). Palaeoenvironmental investigations on the dune system have also been continued by Innes, Huddart and Tooley, with the aim of bridging the gap between the Holocene and the historical data on coastal evolution.

COASTAL MANAGEMENT

Increasing pressure in the twentieth century led to severe dune degradation in several areas where the public gained access to the beach (Figure 2.11). The Sefton Coast Management Scheme was established in 1978 partly in response to this problem, to mitigate this dune degradation and to reduce the threat of marine inundation. This initiative has brought together a number of land-owners and managers to overcome the developmental problems which arise from multiple ownership, both private and corporate, and uncoordinated utilisation of the coast. The Coast Management Scheme Steering Group (SMBC 1983) identified eight management objectives which included dune conservation, landscape maintenance and

renewal, woodland management, nature conservation, foreshore management, visitor management, interpretation, and monitoring. These objectives were later 'fine tuned' in the 1989 Coast Management Plan Review (SMBC 1989). The dune conservation and landscape maintenance objectives have been addressed through a programme of brushwood fence construction, marram planting, and boardwalk emplacement (Figure 2.12). Sand accumulation has been encouraged on the frontal dunes via innovative brushwood fence construction, whilst selected areas of rapidly eroding dune front have been allowed to continue to erode.

The research and management objectives of the Sefton Coast Management Scheme represent one of the most co-ordinated approaches to coastal utilisation in the UK. The present research interest of the Engineer's department of Sefton Council is to gain a better understanding of the sources of beach material and localised processes of sediment transport, with the aim of determining the optimum strategies for Sefton's dune coast management. Tooley also has an active research interest in the traditional methods of sand dune conservation in south-west Lancashire.

THE FUTURE: RESEARCH PRIORITIES

In order to identify a series of research priorities for the Sefton Coast, one must consider future climatic and sea-level trends. Unfortunately, the prediction of future climate relies to a considerable degree on a number of simplifying assumptions and the input of accurate data on a large scale. Whilst the simplification procedure reduces the resolution of any model, the paucity of available climatic data further increases the degree of uncertainty in the final result. Hence, the 'informed' predictions are often in the form of 'best estimate' scenarios. In this review, the climatic and sea-level predictions cited in a recent publication by the Department of the Environment (1991) will be considered. Hence, by 2030AD, the mean global surface air temperature is estimated to be 0.7°C - 2.0°C higher than present, with a best estimate of 1.4°C. Precipitation in the UK will be, on average, 5% higher in 2030AD than at present, and sea-level will rise by approximately 200mm. It is interesting to note that the majority of this sea-level rise will come from the melting of alpine glaciers and the thermal expansion of the oceans (Warrick & Farmer 1990). The addition of water to the oceans from the melting of the Greenland ice sheet during this period is more than compensated for by the removal of water from the oceans by increased precipitation around the Antarctic ice sheet. However, beyond the year 2030AD it is difficult to model the response of the Antarctic system and, consequently, a catastrophic rise of sea-level cannot be ruled out during the latter part of the 21st century. Even without a large magnitude rise in sea-level, the predicted rise between now and 2030AD represents a three-fold acceleration in the present rate of sea-level rise. Statistical analyses show that the predicted 200mm rise in sea-level will increase the frequency of abnormal tidal levels and storm surges along the coast. This is of considerable significance for coastal systems as the frequency of the 1 in 100 year extreme level will be increased by approximately one order of magnitude.

The predicted changes in climate, sea-level and storm activity will have far-reaching consequences for the Sefton Coast. Detailed research has shown that the form of the coastline is governed to a great extent by changes in sea-level and sediment processing patterns. There is considerable information regarding coastal change as a consequence of sea-level rise and fall, but how will the supply of sediment to the coast change as we enter the next century? Will the dynamic dune system which fronts the Sefton Coast be able to keep pace with the rising sea, or will there be a large-scale destruction of the dunes as more frequent storms create weaknesses which gradual sea-level rise will be able to exploit? The research interests of Kenneth Pye and Tony Smith are addressing these questions, but should more support be given to studying the dynamics of the coastal system during the next forty years? It appears from the recent literature that the main impact of climatic change in the immediate future will be the increased frequency of abnormal tidal levels and storm surges. If this is the case, further research is required concerning the susceptibility of coastal systems to infrequent high-magnitude storm events. The Sefton Coast Management Scheme has an important role to play in this phase of research as utilisation of the coast will be greatly affected by sea-level rise and increased storm activity. The emphasis will clearly have to switch from balancing the different uses of the Sefton Coast to establishing whether the dune system can sustain any form of activity as time progresses.

From a coastal utilisation point of view, there is a need for a clearer understanding of how mankind has influenced the evolution of the Sefton Coast in recent years. This review has listed several works in which coastal engineering, dredging and dune management are considered to have affected erosion and accretion rates in the past. Continued offshore aggregate extraction is likely to influence the supply of sediment from the Irish Sea, but there are other less obvious factors to consider. The closure of the Port of Preston, the end of training wall maintenance and the recent by-passing works may cut off any sediment supply to the south-west Lancashire dunes. Similar 'down-drift' effects will probably arise if stabilisation of Formby Point is made a priority (Figure 2.13). Coastal managers must bear in mind that the coast is a dynamic system in which an output from one storage forms the input to another. An important issue here is that natural systems do not respect administrative boundaries and, hence, the scale of coastal management schemes must be attuned to the operation of sediment processing cells.

The impact of climatic change on coastal management and engineering must not be underestimated. The 19th and 20th centuries witnessed the implementation of many coastal protection works through which mankind appeared to be able to modify the behaviour of the waves and tides to their advantage. However, the period from the 18th to the early 20th centuries was rather quiescent in terms of severe storm events (Lamb 1982). Consequently, our management and defence schemes may yet have to withstand the 'normal' operation of the sea. The predicted increase in the frequency of storm surges and abnormal tidal levels will be extremely important in terms of future coastal management and geomorphologists must identify how the processing of sediment will respond to these changes.

With the aim of improving our understanding of sediment processing at the coastal interface, there are a number of other problems which can be addressed. Effective sediment tracing would provide useful information regarding the fate of sewage and pollutant inputs which find their way to the Sefton Coast.

Figure 2.13. The greatest rate of coastal erosion in recent years is recorded at Massams slack to the north of Victoria Road (see Figure 2.8). Gypsy Wood, photographed here in 1967, with Massams slack behind, has now been lost to erosion. Photograph by R.K. Gresswell, English Nature archive, Ainsdale NNR.

Similarly, the impact of offshore aggregate extraction on the supply of sediment to the Sefton dune system may be assessed through the application of radio-isotopic, mineral magnetic or luminescence tracing techniques. As well as being a useful method of input tracing, sediment borne radio-isotopes also represent a major environmental hazard in coastal systems. Areas of fine sediment accretion, such as the saltmarshes and mudflats of the Ribble estuary, may have entrapped significantly radioactive sediments from the Irish Sea. The sedimentary environments of the Sefton Coast must be investigated to assess this potential hazard.

In the context of the predicted environmental changes, is there still a place for the study of past environments? From an academic point of view, the Lancashire mosslands and the fossil dune slacks provide a well-understood system in which new techniques can be tested and established. Indeed, the establishing of new techniques may highlight many deficiencies in our present knowledge of coastal evolution and provide further information regarding the response of coastal systems to changes in sea-level, storm activity and sediment supply. The development of sediment luminescence techniques is an excellent example of this type of palaeoenvironmental research. In terms of the predicted changes in storm activity, has this phenomenon been fully considered in the Holocene evolution of the Lancashire mosslands? The work of Binney and Talbot (1843) represents this alternative approach to coastal evolution, with less emphasis being placed on sea-level rise. Clearly, this puts a very different perspective on the future evolution of the Sefton Coast and highlights the importance of further palaeoenvironmental research.

A. J. Plater (Review co-ordinator)

Department of Geography
University of Liverpool
Roxby Building
PO Box 147
Liverpool
L69 3BX

A full list of contributors is given in Appendix 2.

CHAPTER THREE

The Age and Vegetational History of the Sefton Coast Dunes.

J.B.Innes and M.J.Tooley

INTRODUCTION

Holocene blown sand deposits, forming a complex system of dunes and sand sheets, are the distinctive morphological feature of Sefton's coastal scenery, even though greatly modified and diminished in area due to the impact of human settlement, agriculture and recreation (Gresswell 1937, 1953; Pye 1990; Pye & Smith 1988). The blown sand areas, and in particular the sandhills which still stretch from Southport to Waterloo but formerly extended south beyond Bootle, have long been acknowledged as adding an invaluable element of environmental diversity to Sefton's landscape. As Reade (1908a) remarked, while some observers have considered the dune and drained mossland scenery of the Sefton shoreline to be "dreary beyond conception", in reality the dunes form a dynamic system which has strongly influenced, and been influenced by, the relationship between land and sea on this coast over a very long period of time. Throughout their history the coastal blown sand areas will have represented a specialised ecosystem with microclimate, soil, drainage and vegetation patterns particularly distinct from those developed in the adjacent mosslands (Gagen 1982), but also different from the other landscape units of the south Sefton area (Innes & Tomlinson 1983, 1991) such as sandstone outcrops, glacial till, fluvio-glacial outwash sands, late glacial coversands (Shirdley Hill Sand), marine silts and clays (Downholland Silt) and riverine alluvium. Human occupation and exploitation of the blown sand areas, from prehistoric times onwards, is therefore likely to have been a significant factor in their history, especially during phases of relatively stable dunes with low sand mobility and developing soil profiles (Tooley 1980). Natural factors of climate and sea-level change would, however, have remained the dominant influences in overall dune system development (Tooley 1978a, 1982, 1985a, 1985b).

RECORD OF INVESTIGATIONS

Although the blown sand formations along the coast had been a source of interest for some centuries (e.g. James 1636; Blundell 1702-11; Harrop 1985) it was not until the latter half of the nineteenth century that their systematic scientific investigation and description was undertaken, with a view to establishing their stratigraphic relationships with the complex suite of unconsolidated Holocene sediments present in the region (de Rance 1869, 1877; Reade 1871, 1881b, 1908b). As the sand formations are almost everywhere stratigraphically superimposed upon the Holocene peats, clays, silts and sands of the coastal fringe, they were clearly (with the marshes of the Alt and Ribble) the most recently deposited of Sefton's major sedimentary units. Their true age, mode of origin and associated palaeoenvironments remained conjectural. However, Reade (1881b) measured the amount of sand accumulation at two sites over a number of years, calculated an annual accumulation rate, and from an estimated sand thickness was able to arrive at an age for the Sefton dune system of about 2580 years. The stratigraphic research of these early workers did, however, establish that the dune system was a composite feature which had evolved through a number of phases of sand movement and was not the result of a unitary depositional event. At least two major separate blown sand units could be distinguished, the sandhills of the coastal margin and a

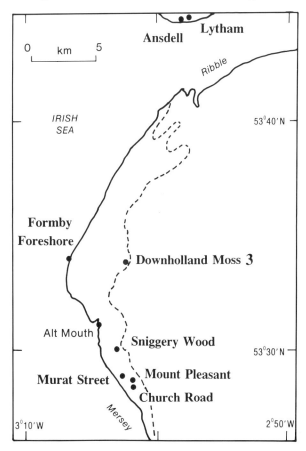

Figure 3.1 Location of sites of radiocarbon dated stratigraphic contacts between peat and blown sand on the Sefton coast. The dashed line represents the distribution of dune sand in the area.

level sand sheet which extends landward of the coastline (Wray & Cope 1948), and these have subsequently been termed the Dune Sand and the Formby Series (Hall & Folland 1967). Intercalations of sand and peat in the area of the landward sand-sheet apron showed that sand transport had been intermittent and suggested periodic episodes of erosion and redeposition, between which stable conditions prevailed. Similarly, organic lenses and soil horizons within the coastal fringe sandhills around Liverpool Bay (Travis 1922a) showed that the sand barrier had on occasion become sufficiently stabilised for dune slack environments to form and perhaps to persist for a considerable length of time. Salisbury (1920) counted the annual rings of creeping willow (*Salix repens* L.) recovered from the oldest dune slacks and calculated the average rate of dune advance along a lateral transect through the dunes near Ainsdale. He also made use of early maps, such as John Speed's of AD 1610, and these and other documentary sources have enabled authors to posit that the present high dunes around Formby are of relatively recent formation during the last few centuries, and that from medieval times onwards lands and settlements along the Sefton coast have been overwhelmed by blowing sand during periodic episodes of dune instability (Ashton 1909; Lewis 1983).

AGE AND VEGETATIONAL HISTORY OF THE DUNES

Founded upon the lithostratigraphic evidence, the modern research techniques of radiocarbon dating supported by pollen and diatom analysis have clarified the age and palaeoenvironmental context of the Sefton coastal blown sand. Organic slack deposits from the dunes and peat/sand contacts from the sand-sheet zone have been dated and serve as index points for the construction of a dune chronology (Tooley 1978a, 1990). The location of these sites is shown in Figure 3.1. The earliest site of relevance is that of Altmouth (Travis 1926; Tooley 1977a, 1982) near Hightown, where a peat bed overlying marine clay is exposed on the foreshore and runs beneath the adjacent dune sand. The base of the peat forms a regressive overlap contact in which marine conditions give way to freshwater and terrestrial conditions and is dated to 4545 ± 90BP (Hv-2679)†[1]. It marks the start of a well attested early Flandrian III relative fall in sea-level on this coast and pre-dates the later overblowing of the peat bed by dune sand (see Figure 1.1). Evidence from the southern Sefton area suggests that burial of the local mossland by blowing sand was not long delayed after this date, for at Sniggery Wood near Little Crosby (Innes 1982) peat immediately beneath blown sand yielded a date of 4510 ± 50BP (SRR-2698). These dates may be

contrasted with the later date of 4090 ± 170BP (Hv-4705) for the burial of peat by blown sand at Downholland Moss 3, situated in the region of the sand-sheet deposits which cover the western part of the mosslands inland of Formby and which form the eastward limit of the dune system (Tooley 1978a). Stratigraphic and pollen analytical research by Stoney (1988) on Formby Moss has recorded a number of discrete sand intercalations within peat of early post-Elm decline age (a little after 5000 BP), prior to its final burial by blown sand. She found little evidence that human activity had been responsible for sand destabilisation and the complex sand blowing at Formby Moss was probably part of the general early Flandrian III sand migration which buried the mossland surface in this area.

Also on Formby Moss, there is evidence of eighteenth century AD peat cuttings overblown by sand, attesting to a similar period of sand instability during the Little Ice Age. The surface sand sheet at Downholland Moss 3 is about a metre thick, but the upper peat layers at the site also include a little blown sand, while further east on Downholland Moss a significant proportion of blown sand has also been incorporated into the surface peat layers, up to 25% of the sediment in places, although without the supervening sand sheet. At the latter site sand must have been blowing into lagoonal limnic sediments while further seawards a thick layer of blown sand was being deposited. The presence of sand within the upper layers of the peat at Downholland Moss 3, as well as above it, suggests that no hiatus exists between the peat and the blown sand and that the sand blowing was the process which truncated peat formation. The radiocarbon date can therefore be accepted as a reliable indicator of the age of sand deposition.

Considerable sand also occurs in the upper peat layers at Sniggery Wood, and the pollen diagram (Figure 3.2) shows the vegetational changes which were associated with the approach of the blowing sand and its final overwhelming of the mossland environments. The lower two-thirds of the diagram show the existence of freshwater aquatic environments laying down reedswamp and fen peats. *Quercus* (oak) and *Alnus* (alder) dominated the fenwood but were gradually replaced by *Betula* (birch) as the site dried and became more acidic. At about 50cm there is a marked increase in aquatic herbs and *Sphagnum* (bog moss), shortly before the arrival of sand grains in the peat and the sharp increase in pollen frequency of *Calluna* (heather). This heather abundance, and a lesser rise in *Pinus* (pine), suggests open conditions and unstable , sandy, acidic soils, presumably resulting from the invading blown sand prior to its actual burial of the site. The rise in aquatic conditions before the heather peak may

---

†[1] The Codes which follow each radiocarbon date refer to its radiocarbon laboratory code number, which is specific to each date. Hv=Hanover, GU=Glasgow University, SRR=Scottish Research Reactor, East Kilbride

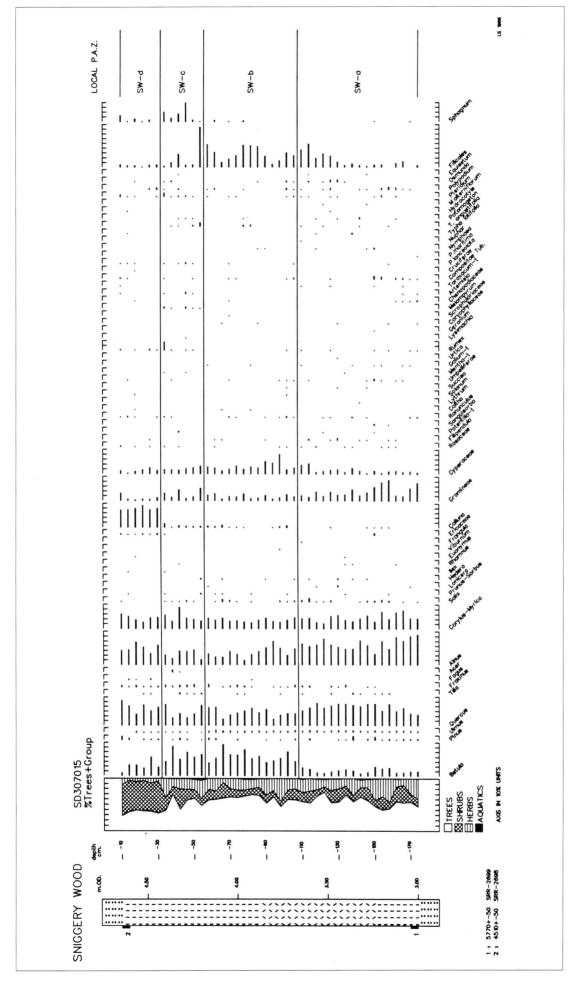

Figure 3.2 Pollen diagram from Sniggery Wood, Little Crosby. The histogram bars in this and the other pollen diagrams represent the relative percentages of each pollen type recorded at each analysed level. The stratigraphic column on the left shows the following succession: 1. Shirdley Hill Sand 2. Reedswamp peat 3. Woody detrital peat 4. Herbaceous peat 5. Blown sand. The diagram is divided into four local pollen assemblage zones (SW-a to d), defined by major changes in the pollen record. One of the most significant features of the diagram is the great increase in *Calluna* (heather) pollen which defines zone SW-d, prior to burial of the peat by blown sand.

37

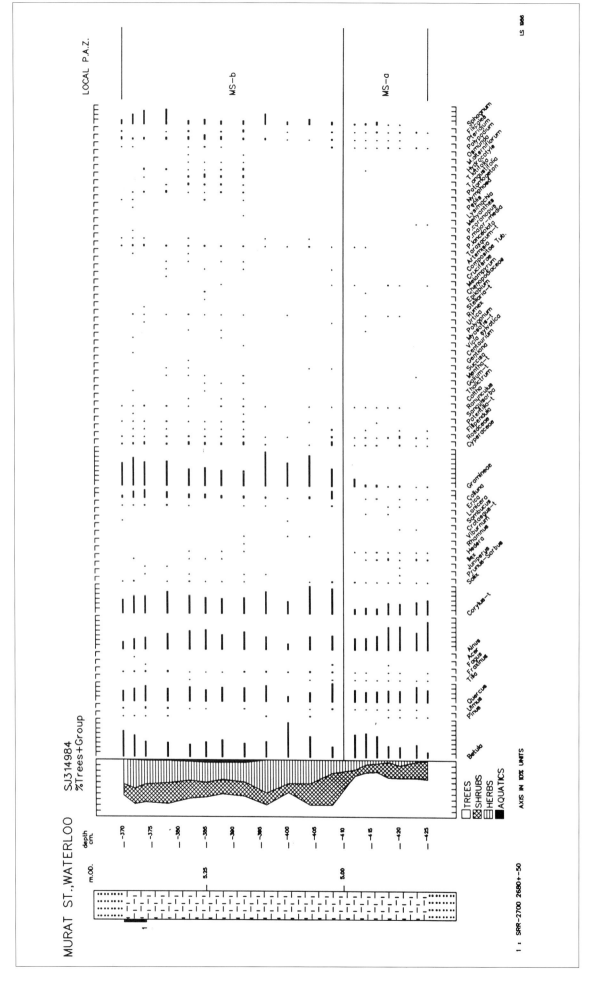

Figure 3.3 Pollen diagram from Murat Street, Waterloo, Crosby. The stratigraphic column on the left shows the following succession from the base: 1. Shirdley Hill Sand 2. Humified herbaceous peat 3. Blown sand. The diagram is divided into two local pollen assemblage zones (MS-a to b) defined by major changes in the pollen record, particularly the rise of *Corylus/Myrica* (hazel type) and Gramineae (grass) pollen.

reflect the impedance of drainage and the ponding of water in the mire system by the approaching sand dunes and sheet. The early post-Elm decline (Flandrian III) pollen flora of zone SW-d agrees well with the radiocarbon date for the upper peat contact. The vegetation successions recorded in the upper Sniggery Wood profile may well be representative of environmental change in much of the Sefton coastal area where sand overblew mossland habitats. However, at the nearby site of Mount Pleasant, Waterloo where sand buried peat after 3910 ± 50BP (SRR-2931), there is no abundant heather but there is clear evidence of agriculture, including *Plantago lanceolata* (ribwort plantain) and cereal-type pollen, showing the presence of human influence to have been an important factor in the vegetation history of the blown sand fringes.

In summary, therefore, the initial period of sand migration and dune building occurred on the Sefton coast between about 4600BP and 4000BP, broadly equivalent in date to the formation of the Older Dunes in the Netherlands (Jelgersma *et al.* 1970b). It corresponds with the extended period of relatively lowered sea-level (see Figure 1.1), and thus also of water-tables in the coastal fringes, recorded in early Flandrian III at Altmouth and elsewhere (Tooley 1978a). It was probably also a period of increased storminess and an enhanced wind climate. Sea-level fall provided a reservoir of intertidal sandy deposits which became destabilised upon drying, blew inland and accumulated as a barrier system, perhaps upon sand or shingle banks (Tooley 1985a). The dune system became stabilised in the early centuries after 4000BP due to a renewed higher sea-level.

This dune stability has been interrupted by more recent phases of sand movement during the later prehistoric and historic periods. Higher sea-level persisted from about 3800BP for several centuries and was associated with stable dunes and peat growth, although it is

possible that localised sand destabilisation did occur. Falling sea-levels around 3000BP, however, led to renewed overblowing of the mossland margins by sand. At Church Road, Waterloo a thin peat bed resting on boulder clay was buried after 3200 ± 60BP (SRR-2930) and is covered by over 4m of blown sand. It contains some limited pollen evidence of woodland disturbance and the creation of open habitat conditions, due either to human activity or the natural soil instability associated with sand encroachment. Much clearer is the pollen evidence of forest clearance in the upper layers of the peat at Murat Street, Waterloo (Figure 3.3), suggesting quite intensive agricultural activity in the back dune area. Although no cereal-type pollen occurs, ribwort plantain (*Plantago lanceolata* L.) and a range of other open habitat weeds are recorded as well as a rising heather (*Calluna*) curve and peak bracken (*Pteridium*) values. The peat/sand boundary is dated to 2680 ± 50BP (SRR-2700) and lies beneath over 5m of blown sand. Major forest clearance may have been at least partly responsible for sand destabilisation. As at Sniggery Wood a big increase in aquatic pollen in the upper profile points to local drainage and vegetation changes at Murat Street caused by the migrating blown sand.

A well marked phase of dune stability occurred after about 2500BP, when soils developed and peats accumulated in the dune slacks. Tooley (1978a, 1990) has recorded a dune slack soil with woody detritus dated to 2335 ± 120BP (Hv-4709), now located in the upper intertidal zone at Formby Foreshore. The pollen diagram (Figure 3.4) contains herbs typical of dune slack associations (O'Garra 1976) and is dominated by oak and alder. Hoof prints of domestic oxen in this deposit first recorded in 1974 illustrate continued human activity in the stable dune system (Tooley 1990). The recovery of part of a sample from a tree trunk dated to 2510 ± 120BP (Pye 1990) from this peat supports the age of this stable dune phase.

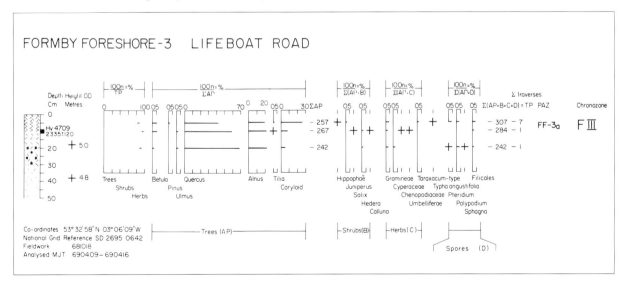

Figure 3.4 Pollen diagram from Formby Foreshore 3 - Lifeboat Road. The stratigraphic column on the left shows the following succession from the base: 1. Blown sand 2. Iron stained blown sand 3. Organic sand 4 Detrital peat. A single pollen assemblage zone is recognised, FF3-a. Crosses represent less than 1% of total pollen counted.

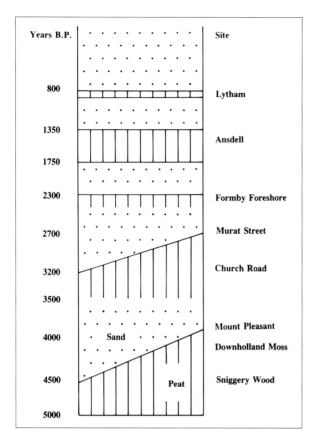

Figure 3.5 A summary of the chronology of sand dune history in the Sefton area. All radiocarbon dates for dune history are more recent than 5000BP, and fall within the Flandrian III chronozone. The ¹⁴C dates are radiocarbon years and have not been calibrated to calendar years. Dots represent blown sand, vertical lines represent peat. Five periods of organic accumulation and dune stability are recorded. Angled lines represent diachronous period boundaries. Open boundaries are shown when their date is not known.

Two later periods of sand stability are recorded in areas close to Liverpool Bay. Although evidence for them is not yet forthcoming from the Sefton coast, similar data are likely to be recovered in Sefton in due course and they complete our knowledge of the cyclical dune chronology. At Ansdell on the north shore of the Ribble organic horizons and peat intercalating sand have been dated to between 1795 ± 240BP (Hv-5214) and 1370 ± 85BP (Hv-4708), and have yielded pollen evidence of nearby mixed oak woodland, extensive forest clearance for agriculture including cereals and local aquatic dune slack communities (Tooley 1978a). A final stable period is dated to between 830 ± 50BP (Hv-3846) and 805 ± 70BP (Hv-4417) north of the Ribble at Lytham (Tooley 1978a), and is broadly confirmed by dates on a number of 'soil bed' horizons and peaty bands in the dune system of north Wirral (Kenna 1986) ranging from 925 ± 50BP (GU-1311) to 540 ± 40BP (SRR-1403), all of which include a typical dune slack pollen flora. Averaging about 800BP (Tooley 1985a, 1985b) this stable phase corresponds with the age of the Younger Dunes period in the Netherlands. Each of these later dune stability periods in Sefton and adjacent areas was followed by renewed sand blowing and peat burial.

CONCLUSIONS

Chronostratigraphic and biostratigraphic research on peat/sand contacts has established a broad dune chronology and environmental history for Sefton, and this is summarised in Figure 3.5. The coastal dune system was in place by 4000BP after several centuries of sand migration, and from this time onwards the adjacent mosslands were repeatedly overblown. Palaeosols and peat beds within the dune sand bear witness to a cyclicity of dune formation. Four main interruptions in sand accumulation may be recognised; c. 3500, 2335, 1795-1370 and 800 radiocarbon years ago. Naturally unstable sandy, acid soils and the activities of man have combined to create plant communities on the dune system which have increased the diversity of Sefton's vegetation history. Finally, although we have a sound research methodology and a framework of information upon which to base future work, much more detailed data are needed before the history of Sefton's dune coast and its relationship to the mosslands may be securely understood.

ACKNOWLEDGEMENTS

We are most grateful to Dr. Ian Shennan, Department of Geography, University of Durham for providing his computer programme NEWPLOT 10# to draw the pollen diagrams.

J. B. Innes   M. J. Tooley

Environmental Research Centre
University of Durham
Durham
DH1 3LE

Stratigraphy and Age Structure of the Sefton Dune Complex: Preliminary Results of Field Drilling Investigations

K. Pye and A. Neal

INTRODUCTION

The present day Sefton coast is transitional between open coast and estuarine regimes, being influenced by processes both in the eastern Irish Sea and in the Ribble and Mersey estuaries. Sediment transport and depositional processes in the eastern Irish Sea are dominated by strong tidal currents and moderate wave energy conditions (Pye 1990). Thus most of the coast is backed by sandy beaches and coastal dunes. Mud deposition is restricted mainly to the relatively sheltered margins of the Ribble estuary, the Alt estuary and the middle reaches of the Mersey estuary.

On the landward side of the coastal dunes is an extensive area of estuarine and freshwater alluvium with interbedded peat beds. Much of this area lies below the level of extreme high water spring tides, and

land levels are falling locally due to recent drainage schemes. Previous drilling investigations have demonstrated that the estuarine alluvium and peat overlies Shirdley Hill Sand, an aeolian coversand of Loch Lomond Stadial age (Wilson *et al.* 1981; Kear & Wilson 1986), and glacial till of late Devensian age (Evans & Arthurton 1973). These deposits in turn overlie an eroded bedrock surface composed largely of Triassic sandstones and marls.

Wind-blown sands associated with the modern coastal dune complex overlie peat and estuarine muds along the western margin of Downholland Moss and in the Hightown - Little Crosby area, and on the basis of radiocarbon evidence the onset of aeolian sedimentation has been inferred to have begun 4000 - 4500 conventional radiocarbon years ago†[1] (Tooley 1978a; Innes 1983). Radiocarbon dates from the

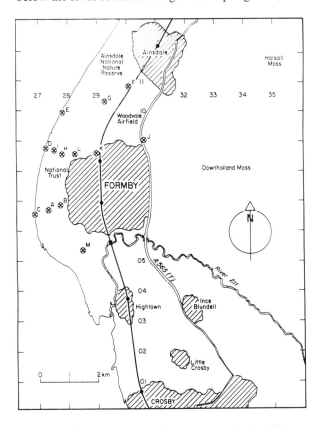

Figure 4.1 Map showing location of boreholes in Phase 1 of the drilling investigation.

Figure 4.2 Shell and auger rig used in the field.

---

†[1] Conventional radiocarbon ages are not calibrated for temporal variation in the ^{14}C content of the atmosphere. Combined radiocarbon and tree ring dating studies have shown that ages in radiocarbon years differ from actual ages in sidereal years (363 days, 6 hours, 9 minutes, 9.6 seconds) by up to several hundred years during the Holocene; calibration curves have been published by Pearson and Stuiver (1986) and Stuiver *et al.* (1986). A computer calibration program has been published by Stuiver and Reimer (1986).

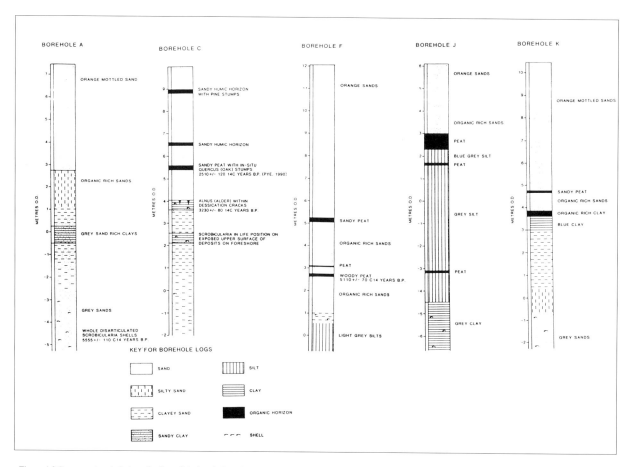

Figure 4.3 Summary borehole logs for five of the boreholes whose positions are shown in Figure 4.1. The log for borehole C is a composite log which also includes information obtained from neighbouring forehsore exposures.

estuarine mud and peat sequence indicate that these deposits were substantially formed between 8000 and 4000 radiocarbon years ago. On this basis it has been inferred that there was a transition from mud-dominated sedimentation to sand-dominated sedimentation along this coast soon after sea-level attained its present position in the mid-Holocene. However, the stratigraphy and age structure of the coastal dune deposits have not previously been investigated in detail, and this interpretation of the sedimentary history of the coast is based on limited data.

CURRENT RESEARCH

A recent drilling investigation undertaken by the authors has provided new evidence which provides support for an alternative interpretation of the Holocene history of the coast. Fourteen shell and auger holes were drilled to a maximum depth of 14 m along three transects between Ainsdale and the south side of Formby Point (Figure 4.1 and Figure 4.2). Samples were collected for sedimentological and palaeoecological analysis, and for radiocarbon and optical luminescence dating. The analyses are not yet complete, but a preliminary interpretation can be made based on the data so far available (Figure 4.3).

The boreholes drilled close to the present day shoreline between Lifeboat Road and Fisherman's Path showed that beach and nearshore sands extend to more than 12 m below the level of mean high water spring tides (4.88m O.D.). Intact but disarticulated *Scrobicularia* and *Cardium* shells recovered from sands at a depth of -4.5m O.D. in Borehole A, located to the north of the Lifeboat Road car park, gave an age of 5555 ± 110 ^{14}C years BP. (Beta 47679 - age corrected for local 'old carbon' reservoir effect). A dune slack peat encountered at 2.8m O.D. in Borehole F, on the eastern margin of the Ainsdale NNR, gave an age of 5110 ± 70 ^{14}C years BP (Beta 47680). Near the eastern edge of Formby Golf Club and Freshfield station the dune sands are underlain at approximately 3 - 4m O.D. by an estuarine mud unit which overlies at least 5 metres of muddy sands which become less muddy with depth. The silt and mud unit becomes thicker towards the east, attaining a thickness of more than 6m near the A565 by-pass (Figure 4.3). These results suggest that the estuarine mud (Downholland Silt) and peat deposits represent a back-barrier sequence which accumulated in the lee of an extensive sand barrier which must have been in existence by about 5500 ^{14}C years BP. The uppermost backbarrier deposits were subsequently buried by transgressive sheets of wind-blown sand along their western margin. Examination of air photographs suggests that the northern back-barrier area, between Ainsdale and Southport, was drained by tidal creeks which flowed towards the Ribble estuary,

Figure 4.4 Exposure of sandy silts on the foreshore at Formby Point, 1985.

while the southern backbarrier area was drained by creeks flowing towards the River Alt (Pye & Neal, 1992).

Muddy sediments are also periodically exposed on the present day foreshore between Lifeboat Road and Massam's Slack (Figure 4.4). Near Lifeboat Road the upper surface of the silts is characterised by the development of large desiccation polygons which contain the remains of a large number of woody stems and roots which have been identified as *Alnus* (Alder) (Figure 4.5). One such *in situ* Alder stem produced a radiocarbon date of 3230 ± 80 ^{14}C years BP (Beta 47682). These sediments in turn are overlain by a deeply podzolized dune or dune slack sand unit which outcrops at the foot of the dunes just to the north of the Lifeboat Road beach access road (see composite log C in Figure 4.3). The soil profile developed on this dune sand unit contains a thick organic-rich Ao horizon and the remains of a number of *in situ* tree stumps and roots. Part of one such stump, identified as *Quercus* (oak), gave a conventional radiocarbon age of 2510 ± 120 ^{14}C years BP (Pye 1990). A similar date of 2333 ± 120 ^{14}C years was reported by Tooley (1970), who also demonstrated that the pollen spectra of the soil is dominated by oak and alder (see Figure 3.3, Innes & Tooley, this volume).

The muddy deposits exposed on the foreshore generally show well-preserved lamination and contain varying amounts of fine sand. Shells of the bivalve *Scrobicularia*, many in life position, are abundant, particularly towards the northern end of the exposure. However, the lateral and vertical distribution of the *Scrobicularia* suggests that they burrowed down into the silt through an overlying layer of sandy sediment, and are younger than the silt bed. This is confirmed by a radiocarbon date of 310 ± 70 ^{14}C years BP (Beta 47681) obtained from *Scrobicularia* shells collected near Dale Slack gutter (Pye & Neal, 1992). When allowance is made for the local 'old carbon' reservoir effect applicable to North Atlantic ocean water the corrected age is essentially 'modern'. The silts also contain numerous hoofprint impressions, believed to represent more than one species of deer and ox, at several levels in the sequence.

Drilling showed that the muds are relatively thin (less than 0.5 m) and wedge out in a landwards direction. The possibility that they are part of the Downholland Silt backbarrier sequence can therefore be ruled out. The surface of the deposits dips slightly seaward, from approximately 3.1m O.D. near the landward margin to approximately 1.5m O.D. at the present seaward limit, although the maximum thickness of the deposits in this direction may formerly have been as much as a metre. The remaining mud beds have a maximum width of approximately 100 m, but at least a further 100 m has been eroded since their existence was first documented in the 1960s. The mud unit overlies a reddish brown

43

Figure 4.5 Alder stems growing within desiccation polygons on the surface of a former mudflat, exposure located on the upper beach just north of Lifeboat Road, September 1990.

beach sand unit containing the remains of broken shells and in turn is now overlain by modern yellowish brown beach sands. On stratigraphic grounds the mud unit must be older than 3000 years, and is probably younger than 5000 years. At present it is uncertain whether the mud was deposited in the lee of a small barrier which has since been eroded or at the landward extremity of a very wide belt of intertidal flats and sandbanks, similar to the area of modern-day mud accumulation north of Southport pier. It is also not presently possible to rule out the possibility that wave energy in the eastern Irish Sea was lower at the time the muds were deposited, allowing mud accumulation to take place on relatively unprotected shores.

SUMMARY

Our preliminary results suggest that as sea level reached its approximate present position around 5500 years ago the coast began to prograde seawards in response to continued abundant sediment supply to the nearshore and intertidal zones. Progradation appears to have begun from a former shoreline located approximately 200m inland of the present beach at Formby Point and 1km inland of the present beach near Fisherman's Path. Initial fieldwork in the eroding foredune areas around Formby Point indicates that progradation was marked by at least four episodes of dune instability and three periods of dune stability. However, parallel studies of the present day shoreline and dune dynamics suggest that there have been major longshore variations in erosion/accretion and dune mobility at any one time, reflecting local variations in beach sediment budget and wave exposure (Pye & Neal 1992).

Significant coastal progradation took place all along the coast between the Alt mouth and Southport in the nineteenth century, but there was a change to erosion around Formby Point after 1900 (Pye & Smith 1988; Plater et al., this volume). The reasons for this change are discussed in detail elsewhere (Pye 1992), but the most important direct cause appears to be a change in the pattern of nearshore sediment transport induced by changes in the morphology of offshore banks and channels. Caution must therefore be exercised in interpreting earlier phases of dune instability and stability as coast-wide events, and in drawing inferences about changes in sea level and regional wind/wave climate. It will only be possible to make reliable palaeoclimatic interpretations when a more detailed picture of the age structure of the deposits is available. With this end in mind, the authors, in collaboration with S. Stokes of Oxford University, are currently attempting to date the dune deposits directly using optically stimulated luminescence (OSL) techniques. Studies are also in hand to define more precisely the relationship between present day dune building activity and beach sediment budget, and to quantify the role of storm events in determining medium and long-term beach morphodynamics (Pye 1991).

Kenneth Pye   Adrian Neal

Postgraduate Research Institute for Sedimentology
Reading University
PO Box 227
Whiteknights
Reading RG6 2AB

SECTION 3

SOILS,

NUTRIENT CYCLING

AND HYDROLOGY

CHAPTER FIVE

Soils and Nutrient Cycling

P.A. James

INTRODUCTION

The dunes of the Southport - Formby area were chosen by E.J. Salisbury for one of the earliest, possibly the first, detailed analysis of soil chemical change across a succession of land surfaces of increasing age (Salisbury 1925). Though it may now be judged as imprecise in certain important respects, the study was remarkable because of its conceptual approach. Soil-orientated research of more recent decades has been less seminal but generally more precise and of much greater detail. Research themes have covered the classification and development of soil in all environments of the duneland, soil nutrient levels in relation to a number of ecological aspects, the microflora of pinewood soils and chemical fluxes through dune soils and through the whole dune system. This review covers published papers and Soil Survey monographs and unpublished reports, higher degree theses and a selection of undergraduate theses which merit inclusion. Of the last, there are likely to have been many completed which are not known to the author: thus there may be worthwhile studies which are not reviewed below.

The research has been disparate and a comprehensive sampling and analysis of soil profiles is still required throughout open and afforested dune and slack areas of the whole dune system. From the point of view of duneland ecological management, the soil aspects of chief importance are the following. First, the nature and extent of soil development in the several dune environments: these are major determinants of the content and availability of nutrients and water and of the activities of soil organisms. The physical and chemical character of the soil profile indicates and therefore provides a key to the understanding of the combined influence of the character and landform morphology of the parent sand; climate; microclimate and hydrology; vegetation; fauna and people; and of the factor of time through which the dune system has formed and evolved.

A second soil aspect of management importance is that of soil processes, particularly those which govern source, flux and resultant concentration of nutrients available to plants. Finally, there is the aspect of dune erosion in which geomorphological change sets the timescales of soil development and in which soil erodibility, always very high in young dune systems and determined largely by amount of organic matter incorporation, is a factor.

The chief soil-forming and related processes are listed in Table 5.1. The eighth item, atmospheric deposition, listed under 'dune ridges' in the table, is a factor of the soil-forming environment rather than a soil-forming process, but is included because of the relatively high input of marine-derived aerosols and solutes to the land on this exposed coast.

TABLE 5.1.
Chief soil-forming processes in the Sefton duneland.

Dune ridges
1. Deposition and erosion of sand.
2. Organic matter incorporation and mineralisation.
3. Cation adsorption on humus.
4. Decalcification.
5. Acidification.
6. Mineral weathering.
7. Leaching.
8. Atmospheric deposition of solutes and solids.

Pinewoods
1. Pine needle litter accumulation.
2. Acid humus formation.
3. Acidification.
4. Weak podzolization.

Dune slacks
1. Accumulation of peaty organic matter.
2. Gleying: chemical reduction of oxides (e.g. of iron) in oxygen-deficient, wet mineral soil.

SOIL CLASSIFICATION

The soils of the dune system have been classified in at least five published works. Hall and Folland (1967) mapped the area as 'Dune Sand' in the 1:63,360 Soil Survey map of the South-West Lancashire Coastal Plain and described the soil groups present as *skeletal soils* on mobile dunes, *pararendzinas* on dunes stabilized by vegetation, *ground-water gleys* in slacks and *micropodzols* beneath deep pine litter. Two of these groups were later classified by the Soil Survey as *series*, typical sand pararendzinas as the Sandwich Series and the gleys as the Greatstone Series (Jarvis *et al.* 1984; Beard *et al.* 1987) but the complexity of the soil pattern prevented separate mapping of these groups at the scale of the published maps. James and Wharfe (1989) present a more detailed classification together with a soil map of the Ainsdale Sand Dunes National Nature Reserve (Ainsdale NNR) which was based upon air photo interpretation: soil groups recognised are raw sand, sand pararendzina, gley and peaty gley of the

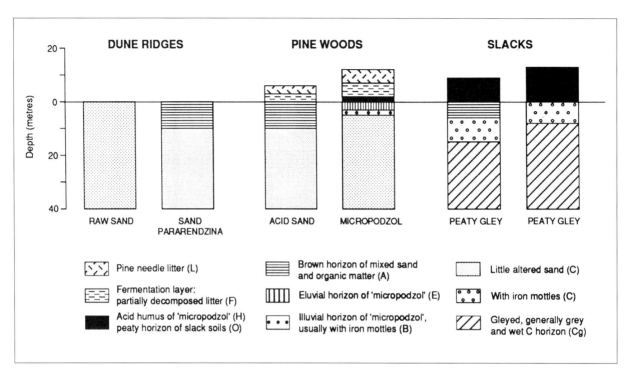

Figure 5.1. Soil classification and profile morphology of representative soils.

slacks and, beneath pine litter, sand with strongly acid A horizon and micropodzol. In the last paper referred to above, data are presented to quantify the chemical conditions typical across the age range of each of these soil groups. Figure 5.1 summarizes the classification used in the present review and depicts diagrammatically the profile morphology of each soil.

PEDOGENETIC TRENDS

The selected analytical data graphed in Figure 5.2 represent gradients of pedogenesis and the fullest extent of development reached by soils in the several duneland environments of the present day. The timescale of the gradient for the non-afforested dunes and for the intervening slacks, according to the dating reported by Salisbury (1925), is of the order of 300 years; that for acidification and related processes beneath pinewoods is the maximum age of tree cover: the oldest pine stands in the Ainsdale NNR were planted in 1887 (Edmondson *et al.*, this volume). Salisbury's estimates of the age range of dune surfaces appears not to accord with other evidence of the history of development of the dune system, which shows that dunes existed in the area between 2000 and 2500 years ago, and possibly some 5000 years ago (Plater *et al.*, this volume). However, because of natural and anthropogenic erosion and other disturbance, the age of the duneland surfaces we see at present may well fall mostly within the timescale accepted by Salisbury. It is

certain that nowhere in the dune system can soils be considered to have reached anything near maximum potential development and steady state.

RAW SANDS AND SAND PARARENDZINAS

Freshly deposited sand, as well as that exposed by erosion of the shallow surface layer of chemically altered sand, is alkaline (the high pH values of near 9 reflecting the abundance of sodium as well as of calcium and other bases), calcareous (% calcium carbonate commonly between 4 and 8), and low in organic matter (1% or less). Of the exchangeable basic cations†[1], calcium occurs in greatest abundance, sodium, potassium and magnesium tending to be of similar concentration and generally less than 2 mg 100g^{-1} (see Figure 5.2).

For a seaward foredune slope at Ainsdale with sand couch grass (*Elytrigia juncea* (L.) Nevski) Johnson (1979) gives figures of 1.09 µg g^{-1} available nitrate-N, 0.87 µg g^{-1} ammonium-N and 1.7 µg g^{-1} available phosphorus. Minton (1985) analysed the mineralogy of a foredune raw sand profile at Ainsdale, the following being mean percent values of each mineral for eight samples in the profile: quartz (45.6), feldspar (21.7), calcite(4.3), hornblende (5.3), augite (6.3), and chromite (0.92). Others present were opaque minerals (6.7), clasts (5.7), andalusite, riebeckite, staurolite, apatite and kyanite. Profile 2 in Figure 5.2 represents a sand pararendzina developed at 800m from the seaward limit of the dunes. Acidification and humus incorporation

---

† [1] A cation is an atom which carries a positive electrical charge. It may become attached to fine particles in the soil (clay and humus) where it may be detached by (exchanged for) a cation of another element. The cations of calcium, magnesium, potassium and sodium are the chief basic exchangeable cations in the soil. Hydrogen is also a cation, but is an acid rather than a base. The process of acidification is the replacement of basic cations attached to particle surfaces by hydrogen cations from the soil solution.

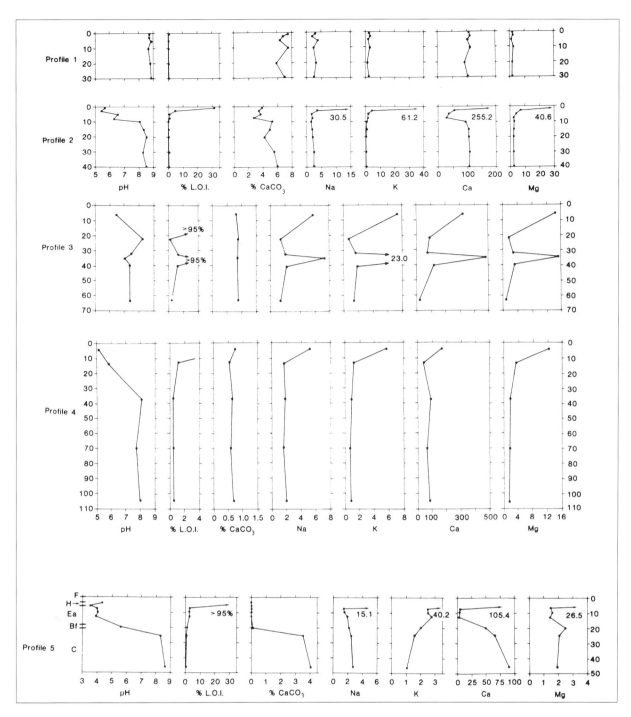

Figure 5.2. Selected data for raw sand (profile 1), sand pararendzina (profile 2), slack soils (profiles 3 and 4) and 'micropodzol' (profile 5). Modified from James and Wharfe (1989), p.291.

control the curves depicted, with pH falling to 5.5 at lowest and organic matter rising to 30% within the uppermost 1cm. Exchangeable cation levels are greatly enhanced by the increase in cation exchange capacity†² associated with the humus. However, the distinct A horizon of the pararendzina is very shallow, being only about 10cm in thickness. At this depth, values for all properties determined rise to levels very similar to those of little altered sand of foredune raw soils.

The graphs of profile 2, Figure 5.2, emphasize the weak expression of soil development and the extreme

vulnerability of the dune soil to erosion. From the curves it is clear that sampling of the dune soils for chemical analysis must be done with precision if the details of chemical change with depth are to quantified.

The maximum extent of decalcification and acidification in soils of non-afforested dune ridges, and possibly an incipient podzolization, would occur beneath vegetation which contains heather (*Calluna vulgaris* L.) though the author has not analysed such soils on the Sefton duneland and knows of no data derived by other workers. Heather now grows on dunes

---

†² The potential store, or space, in a soil for holding exchangeable cations. It is determined by the amount of clay and humus in the soil.

in the Southport and Ainsdale golf course (Edmondson *et al.* 1988/99), and upon the low-lying Formby Series (Beard *et al.* 1987) which occurs inland and beyond the limit of the dune system.

Minton (1985) analyzed the mineralogy of a pararendzina near to the site of that of profile 2, Figure 5.2, this being at 800m inland from the front of the dune system. Mean percentages of four samples from the A horizon are as follows: quartz (57), feldspar (20), calcite (1.5), hornblende (3.4), augite (3.8), chromite (1.7), opaque minerals (8.4) and clasts (1.5). Thus although minerals such as calcite and augite survive in the older pararendzina, they are much reduced in quantity whereas the resistant quartz, for example, increases markedly. Minton reports that in thin section the appearance of all minerals from the pararendzina reflects weathering, and that down-profile trends clearly show less intense alteration with depth in the soil.

SOILS OF THE PINEWOODS

The microclimate and ecology of the pinewoods form a distinctly different soil-forming environment from that of the open dunes; though the chief factor determining the nature of soil development is the deposition of acid needle litter in places to a depth of 20cm. The pH falls to a minimum of 3.5 at the base of the narrow humus horizon and remains very low (4.0 in the most acid soils) in the underlying E horizon. Normally within 20cm, or less, of the mineral soil surface the soil is alkaline. Profile 5 in Figure 5.2 lay beneath a 46 year-old stand of Corsican pine (*Pinus nigra* ssp. *laricio* Maire) and shows the features of the *micropodzol* common to most of the pinewood soils: narrow bleached E and weakly developed rusty-mottled B horizons which are caused by the mobilization and leaching of iron and of other constituents by the process of podzolization. The threshold for this process in the dune soils is clearly pH 5.0 or less; the youngest pine stand where podzolization has been reported was 21 years (Moriarty 1978). The marked shallowness of the podzol may reflect the ineffectiveness of leaching in the shelter of the pine canopy and its litter rather than the timescale of the process. If heather had colonized any site before the pinewoods were planted, podzolization would have occurred in association with it. Moriarty (1978) found that, despite the acidification of the soil in the natural succession prior to planting, the pH of the uppermost mineral horizon decreases significantly with increasing age of pine stand ($r = -0.68$; $p = .01$).

In his research into the ecological effects of pinewood removal, Sturgess (1991) has examined a number of soil profiles beneath pinewoods and where woodland has been removed at different dates in the Ainsdale NNR and at Formby. A selection of his data are given in Table 5.2. There is little incorporation of organic matter in the mineral horizons. Organic horizons have a lower

pH, higher concentrations of total and ammonium-nitrogen and higher concentrations of available phosphate than the mineral horizons. The concentration of nitrate-nitrogen is low in the acid organic horizons and reaches a maximum in the less acid mineral soil at 3 to 5cm. In sites felled 50 years ago, surface organic matter and nitrogen content is similar to values for pararendzinas, although levels of ammonium-nitrogen and phosphate are as high as in woodland soils. After 10 years, the amount of organic matter shows a reduction, and the concentrations of nitrate-nitrogen a slight increase in the litter layer. The carbon/nitrogen (C/N) ratio decreases with time after felling.

TABLE 5.2.
A selection of data from Sturgess (1991).
Representative values for nitrogen and phosphate are given for a sand pararendzina and a pinewood soil.

	Total N $mg\ g^{-1}$	NH$_4$ $mg\ 100g^{-1}$	NO$_3$ $mg\ 100g^{-1}$	PO$_4$ $mg\ 100g^{-1}$
Pararendzina:				
1cm depth:	4	0.5	0.002	0.6
5cm depth:	<1	0.02	0.003	<0.1
Pinewood soil:				
1cm depth:	6	1.5	0.02	3.0
5cm depth:	<1	0.02	0.1	0.02

A number of studies on the distribution and activities of soil micro-organisms in organic and mineral horizons of dune pinewood soils (all beneath Corsican pine) at Freshfield were undertaken in the 1960s. Soil fungi were examined by Indraratne (1964), Parkinson and Balasooriya (1967, 1969), Balasooriya and Parkinson (1967) and Parkinson and Crouch (1969). The soils were chosen for mycological analyses partly because of the close juxtaposition of acid and alkaline conditions in the soil profile.

Seasonal variation in fungal activity was found to be related particularly to moisture conditions within the soil. The dune pinewood habitat for mycoflora in the organic horizons was found to be very similar to that of Scots pine (*Pinus sylvestris* L.) woodland on a different substrate in Delamere Forest. Hodkinson (1966) isolated fungi responsible for the decomposition of pine roots in A and C horizons. The colonization of living roots differed little between A and C horizons, but dead roots in the A were colonized by greater number and diversity of fungi than those in the C.

Physiological activity in the pinewood soil was determined by Kibble (1966) by measuring oxygen uptake and carbon dioxide output in L and F horizons. The former was found to correlate with needle fall in autumn and with low moisture contents in the summer. No seasonal fluctuations were found to take place in the mineral horizons. The bacteria of an incipient podzol beneath pinewood at Freshfield were analysed by Goodfellow (1966) and Goodfellow *et al.* (1968). Davies (1967) and Davies and Williams (1970), studying actinomycetes, found that these organisms were present in greatest number at the boundary of the A and C horizons, though the greatest diversity of species were isolated from the C horizon. Baxby (1967) and Gray and Baxby (1968) isolated the micro-organisms responsible for the decomposition of chitin in the same soil. The chitin is derived from arthropods and fungi. The fungi are the most important group of organisms involved in the decomposition, followed by bacteria and actinomycetes, the first being particularly dominant in the H and A1 horizons, the second and third being more important in the C horizon. Chitin decomposed more rapidly in the A1 horizon than in the H, and most slowly in the C. The species of fungi colonizing chitin were similar in the H and A horizons, but differed from those in the C. Sturgess (1991 and this volume) has analysed the pinewood soil seed bank at Ainsdale NNR. Weed seeds which have accumulated since afforestation were found to occur in the organic horizons, whereas surviving seeds of dune species lie within the mineral soil. With increasing age of pine plantation, the number of viable dune species seeds decreases. Sturgess (1991) has also analyzed fungal infection (V.A. mycorrhiza) of the roots of four vascular plant species. Incidence of infection was highest in unplanted dune soil and lowest in pinewood soil. Ectomycorrhizal species were most abundant in the organic soil horizon of a 10 year-old firebreak soil, which Sturgess believes may reflect the nitrogen immobilisation phase in this soil.

SLACK SOILS

The slacks comprise a distinct pedogenetic subsystem of the duneland but are related to the dune ridges by transport along two pathways: wind deposition of sand in the slacks, and percolation to the ground-water table which carries solutes from dune ridges and concentrates them where they may influence the chemistry of slack soils. The chief control of slack soil development is the fluctuating ground-water table. Thus redox conditions†[3] determine the morphology of the mineral soil and moisture and eutrophication†[4] account for the quantity of organic matter production and accumulation as peaty topsoil. Previous work on slack soil profile morphology suggests that there is a dichotomy of profiles, with an oxidised mineral horizon occurring immediately below the organic surface horizon in the drier soils where water table is relatively deep, and an absence of such an horizon where water table lies nearer to the surface (the two types of profile are illustrated in Figure 5.1).

The spatial pattern of slack soils in the Ainsdale NNR has been analysed by Evans (1980) and James and Wharfe (1989). Edmondson (1991) has analysed slack soil properties in relation to the spatial distribution of vegetation and ground water table depth. Important factors in the pattern of slack soils are depth to ground-water table and relief of the slack surface (which is related to past sand deposition). A third factor is that of relative age of the slack, or its distance from the sea: there is a soil succession in the slacks which is as clear as that across the dune ridges. Thus, for example, pH, depth and exchangeable sodium content of the organic topsoil decrease significantly with distance from the sea. However, depth to ground-water table increases significantly inland, producing its own gradient of influence. James and Wharfe (1989) isolated and demonstrated the particular importance of ground-water table depth on the spatial pattern of the slack soil profile morphology and chemistry.

The ecologically favourable nutrient and moisture status of the slack soils are of prime importance in duneland management. Johnson (1979), however, found lower levels of available nitrate-N in the top 10cm of two slack soils toward the seaward edge of the Ainsdale NNR than on some foredune and near-front dune ridges: $0.7\mu g\ g^{-1}$ in a slack with red fescue (*Festuca rubra* L.) and sea buckthorn (*Hippophae rhamnoides* L.) and $0.75\mu g\ g^{-1}$ in a slack with restharrow (*Ononis repens* L.). Ammonium-N, on the other hand, was higher in the slack soils ($1.45\mu g\ g^{-1}$ compared with $0.95\mu g\ g^{-1}$). The concentration of phosphorus available to plants in the slacks was appreciably higher than on neighbouring dune ridges ($3.35\mu g\ g^{-1}$ compared with $1.95\mu g\ g^{-1}$).

NUTRIENT FLUX

NITROGEN

From determinations at Formby Point and on dune sand in the Ainsdale NNR, Johnson (1979) estimated annual rates of nitrogen input in rainwater, in airstream aerosols and by biological fixation by dune vegetation; annual mineralisation†[5] of nitrogen was also estimated. The results are summarized in Table 5.3. Rates of deposition from aerosols (Table 5.3B) were attributed particularly to the marine source. Fixation†[6] rates associated with marram grass (*Ammophila arenaria* (L.) Link) were relatively low (Table 5.3C) but very significant considering the low levels of organic nitrogen in fresh dune sand (0.01 to 0.04%).

---

†[3] The degree of chemical reduction (in wet, oxygen-deficient conditions) or oxidation (in well-aerated, drier conditions).

†[4] Enrichment with plant nutrients.

†[5] The biochemical transformation of nitrogen in organic matter to inorganic, soluble form.

†[6] Fixation is the incorporation of nitrogen into organic tissue by micro-organisms. One group of these organisms lives in nodules on the roots of certain plant species. The fixed nitrogen thus is added to the pool of soil organic nitrogen which may be released by decomposition as soluble nitrogen available to other plants.

Nitrogen mineralisation rates (Table 5.3D) were found to be high (4 to 11% *per annum* compared to 2 to 3% in most mineral soils). High rates of cycling and uptake of nitrogen were attributed to favourable conditions of aeration, temperature, moisture, base status†[7] and C/N ratio.

CALCIUM, MAGNESIUM, SODIUM AND POTASSIUM

Flux of four basic cations of pedological importance, calcium, magnesium, sodium and potassium, has been analysed for non-afforested dune ridges in a transect across the dune succession in the northern part of the Ainsdale NNR (James & Wharfe 1984, 1989; Wharfe 1984; James *et al.* 1986). The pH of rainwater collected in this area over a period of 44 months has been analysed in relation to both atmospheric sulphur dioxide levels recorded for the period at Formby and to wind direction and speed (Wharfe & James 1985).

Atmospheric inputs of cations were determined for bulk precipitation and for impacted aerosols. Rates of leaching through raw sand and pararendzina soils were measured in 30cm-deep soil cores in the field, and rates of cation output from the open dune system as a whole were estimated from concentrations in ground water. Rate of movement of ground water toward the sea was estimated using the data of Clarke (1980). Flux rates derived were compared with stores of several cation fractions in soil and biomass.

Selected data on cation inputs and losses are shown in Table 5.4. Atmospheric deposition rates reflect the strong marine influence on a coast lying nearly perpendicular to the prevailing wind and Ainsdale ranks high amongst British coastal sites for which comparable data are available (James & Wharfe 1984). When deposition in airstream aerosol impaction is added to that in rainfall very high values of total deposition are derived, particularly for sodium. Deposition is high across the whole non-afforested duneland and comprises an ecological and soil factor of considerable importance.

Cation balances for the two types of soil, raw sand and sand pararendzina, are given in Table 5.4. High and positive balances for sodium reflect the dominance of the high input rates. The higher negative calcium balance for both soils is controlled by continued high weathering release and leaching of this element from the calcareous soil; similarly magnesium is lost, but the soil mineral source is much smaller. Total atmospheric input of potassium is lower than for the other three elements and leaching exceeds input by a factor of two in the raw sand; in the pararendzina, however, leaching loss is much lower and reflects the importance of the cation holding capacity of the humus which has become incorporated into the A horizon of the soil. In general, the wide input/output ratios, particularly for calcium, reflect disequilibrium typical of soils in early stages of development.

Soil chemical change may be estimated for the timescale of soil development in the dune system by extrapolating the rates of change given by the annual balances derived for the four chemical elements in Table 5.4. The result may be compared with the amount of change as inferred from the difference in soil chemistry between youngest and oldest soils in the present-day dune succession. For example, the

---

TABLE 5.3.

Selected results of research by Johnson (1979) into inputs and transformations of nitrogen.

Atmospheric inputs were measured at Formby coastguard station; other determinations were on dune sand near the seaward edge of the dune system at Ainsdale. All figures in kg ha^{-1} a^{-1} (where not %)

3A. Estimated annual rainwater input:
NH$_4$-N = 1.66
NO$_3$-N = 3.58
Total soluble N = 5.24

3B. Estimated input by airstream aerosol impact:
NH$_4$-N = 3.38
NO$_3$-N = 1.63
Total soluble N = 5.01

3C. Biological N fixation for 100% cover values, estimated from work of Waughman (1972):

Ammophila arenaria:	4.9
Lotus corniculatus:	47.8
young *Hippophae rhamnoides*:	231.2

3D. Estimated N mineralised *per annum*:

	pH	% organic N	% N mineralised	N mineralised in top 15 cm Kg ha^{-1} a^{-1}
dry slack	7.7	0.036	11.2	90.0
top 2nd ridge	8.2	0.014	3.9	12.5
dry slack	7.7	0.024	6.5	35.0

---

†[7] The quantity of exchangeable basic cations in the soil.

TABLE 5.4.

Selected results of research by James and Wharfe (1989) into flux of basic cations in a raw sand (R) and sand pararendzina (P) each of 30cm depth. Figures in kg ha⁻¹ a⁻¹.

	Na		K		Ca		Mg	
	R	P	R	P	R	P	R	P
Atmospheric input:								
1 Bulk precipitation	128	143	8	9	32	27	14	15
2 Aerosol impaction	126	38	6	2	11	4	4	4
3 total 1 + 2	254	181	14	11	43	31	18	19
4 leaching loss	147	71	30	8	371	361	33	31
Balance (3-4)	**+107**	**+110**	**-16**	**+3**	**-328**	**-330**	**-15**	**-12**

difference in total potassium content (including that occurring in vegetation) between raw dune soils and the most fully developed pararendzinas is 1600 kg ha⁻¹ (James & Wharfe 1989). The gain in potassium predicted for a 200-year period, by extrapolating the mean annual rate of accumulation determined at a number of sites across the dune succession (two of which are included in Table 5.4) is 1300 kg ha⁻¹ a⁻¹. Such an approach assumes constancy of soil process rates over time and there are several sources of possible error. One possible reason for the discrepancy between the values derived from the two approaches of modelling change in potassium content is that the actual timescale of soil development has been greater than the 200 years used in the extrapolation of the current process rate.

SOIL RESEARCH, MANAGEMENT AND THE FUTURE

The ability to predict change in terrestrial ecosystems is essential to sound management of those ecosystems. Such prediction, always fraught with problems, is possible only with a sound knowledge of the abiotic (namely edaphic, hydrologic and atmospheric) parameters of the systems. The likely forcing factors of future change in the environment of the Sefton duneland are fourfold: 1. anthropogenic influences (especially recreation and management, including conservation measures); 2. marine erosion; 3. sea-level rise and 4. climatic change. Because of the vulnerability of unconsolidated dune deposits to erosion, dune

systems respond more rapidly to both natural and human-induced environmental change than most other terrestrial ecosystems. The prerequisite to sound modelling of the soil response to any of these possible influences is mentioned in the introduction to this section and is viewed by the author as a first research priority: the production of a comprehensive soil data base. This would involve chemical and physical analysis of soil profiles in a sampling framework preferably compatible with that of the National Sand Dune Vegetation Survey - Sefton Coast (Edmondson *et al.* 1988/89). Equal in importance to, though much more costly than the detailed characterisation of soils, would be the monitoring of the dynamics of the soil processes which are of particular ecological significance, these being the flux of nutrients and the movement of water. Of the nutrients, much more is required to be known about nitrogen and phosphorus which are especially limiting in dune sand.

The implications for coastal areas of predicted relatively rapid and imminent change in sea level and climate are now attracting much attention.

Possible effects on coastal dune systems are being analysed in the LICC Project (Landscape Ecological Impact of Climatic Change on Coastal Dunes in Europe) initiated by The Netherlands Ministry of Physical Planning and the Environment (Van der Meulen *et al.* 1989). A review of likely impacts on U.K. coastal lands is given by Doornkamp (1990). The response of the soil to such environmental forcing is a challenging research field, involving complex modelling of soil chemical, physical and biological processes. Although discussion of such modelling lies outside the scope of the present review a general outline of responses to possible environmental change is given in Table 5.5, though it has to be emphasized that prediction of that change itself is very problematic.

Best estimates of climatic and sea-level changes used for Table 5.5 are those accepted by Plater *et al.* (this volume). Apart from marine erosion, the most significant direct influence upon pedological change is hydrological, in terms of both ground water and soil moisture. One can envisage increasing dryness and instability of near-surface sand, reduced leaching and,

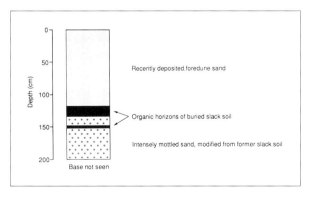

Figure 5.3. Section exposed by marine erosion at Formby Point in 1972.

TABLE 5.5.
One possible scenario of climatic and sea level change and associated soil response within a 40-year timescale.

CLIMATE AND SEA-LEVEL CONDITIONS
Mean temperature increase of 1.4°C.
5% increase in precipitation.
Higher wind strength and increased storm activity.
Greater deposition on dune system of marine derived aerosols and solutes.
Sea-level rise of 20cm with increased frequency of abnormal tides.

HYDROLOGICAL AND GEOMORPHOLOGICAL RESPONSES
Higher summer evapotranspiration, therefore lower effective rainfall.
Lower soil moisture content. Drop in water table level.
Greater inland intrusion of brackish ground water: this would form a wedge beneath a thinner layer of fresh ground water.
Marine erosion of dune front.
Greater dune erosion: transgressive sand deposition across former stable dunes near seaward edge of dune system; erosion of dune ridges further inland; deposition of sand in slacks.

IMPLICATIONS FOR SOILS
1. **Raw sands:** these would increase in extent. Reduced rates of stabilisation and evolution of soil to pararendzina.

2. **Sand pararendzinas:** burial by sand; lower soil moisture content: slower rates of production and incorporation of organic matter; reduction in concentration of N, P, and exchangeable basic cations associated with soil humus; reduced leaching: reduced rates of decalcification and acidification; reduced rates of mineral weathering.
The gross effect could be reduced rate of soil formation.

3. **Slack soils:** periodic marine inundation of some slacks at seaward edge of dune system; increased accumulation of sand on soil surface; reduced soil moisture content: reduced production and accumulation of organic matter; increased humification and mineralisation of peat; reduced rate of acidification; reduced influence of ground water in terms of chemical reduction and eutrophication. Therefore slack soils less rich in organic matter and nutrients, though initially peat mineralisation would release significant amounts of nutrients.

4. **Pinewood soils:** reduced soil moisture content; a likely stabilisation of 'micropodzol' profiles in drier conditions.

as a consequence of greater wind strengths, increased deposition of marine-derived aerosols and solutes upon the duneland. One general effect is likely to be higher concentration of bases in the dune soils, particularly the pararendzinas. Thus the balances derived for all four bases shown in Table 5.4 are likely to shift in a positive direction, though the outcome for potassium is less certain as this element appears to be more dependent than the other three upon organic matter incorporation. Soil organic matter concentrations are likely to be lower than at present with less favourable moisture and nutrient levels resulting in lower biomass production.

Rapid and very considerable, at least local, change in the geomorphology, pedology and ecology of the duneland has occurred in the recent past in response to only local environmental change caused by coastal erosion in the area of Formby Point. The response to this influence is shown in Figure 5.3, a profile exposed in the eroding dune cliff in 1972. The details of the section represent a major change in the dune environment at this site from a dune slack condition with associated typical peaty gleyed soil to a foredune condition, with a depth of rapidly deposited sand carrying a sparse growth of marram grass.

The depth of pronounced iron oxide mottling in the buried slack soil suggests that the water table has dropped some tens of centimetres as a result of the sea

erosion of the dunes. Thus it is clear that environmental change at the global scale does not have to be invoked as a cause of local major transformation of a dune landscape. In addition to the local action of the sea, the other potent force which commonly transforms heavily used dune systems is erosion related to trampling and other human disturbance. The importance of this impact is clearly reflected in the distribution of bare sand and sparsely-vegetated surfaces on the Sefton duneland.

P A James

Department of Geography
University of Liverpool
Roxby Building
PO Box 147
Liverpool L69 3BX

CHAPTER SIX

Hydrological Investigations in the Ainsdale Sand Dunes National Nature Reserve

D. Clarke and R. K. Pegg

INTRODUCTION

When the Ainsdale Sand Dunes National Nature Reserve (Ainsdale NNR) was established in 1965 water table levels were relatively high and many of the slack floors were flooded for much of the year. The wettest areas were on the seaward margin and in the open dunes in the northern part of the reserve. Standing water up to 40 cm deep (that is above ground level) was recorded at a number of sites in the winter of 1969.

However in 1970 a distinct lowering of the water table was observed. Again in 1971 the water levels failed to rise above ground level and all slacks were dry. At this stage the Nature Conservancy Council wardens became concerned about the impact of falling water levels on the fauna and flora of the area. In particular the future of the rare natterjack toad (*Bufo calamita* L.) was thought to be at risk.

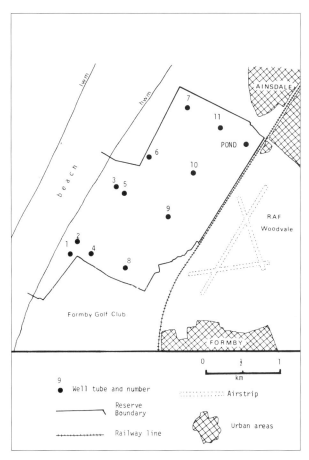

Figure 6.1 The Well Tube Network at Ainsdale NNR

In February 1972 a network of 11 groundwater observation wells came into operation (Figure 6.1). They were installed by the NCC wardens and monitored on a monthly basis. The Department of Geography at Liverpool University became involved and a number of studies have been made of the hydrological system. Initially the vegetational and hydrological aspects were examined and since 1975 more detailed hydrological investigations have been undertaken.

This chapter presents a summary of some of the data collected during the twenty years of hydrological studies and discusses some of the problems encountered.

THE SIMPLE WATERBALANCE

The basis of the initial studies was an attempt to evaluate the groundwater balance of the system. Therefore the inputs and outputs have been evaluated and compared with the seasonal fluctuations in storage.

The most simple approach is to evaluate the basic waterbalance equation:

Inflow = Outflow ± Change in Storage (1)

However such an approach is normally applied to enclosed drainage basins. When applied to an open dune system with virtually no overland outflow components the equation becomes rather less simple. However, when the median water level contour map, for the period 1972-1982, is examined (Figure 6.2) the Ainsdale NNR system appears to be probably separated from external influences on the inland side. Since ground water flow occurs normal (i.e. at right angles) to the contours there is no gradient to north or south thus allowing ground water changes in the reserve to be viewed in isolation. Lateral seepage of groundwater from the north or south cannot take place under these conditions. The amount of vertical percolation of water was formerly considered negligible (Clarke 1980), and in this chapter this assumption is retained. However, recent borehole data indicates that not all of the dune area is underlain by an impermeable substrate (K. Pye pers. comm.) and so a future hydrological model may have to incorporate vertical percolation of water. The main outflows are thus thought to be evaporation and

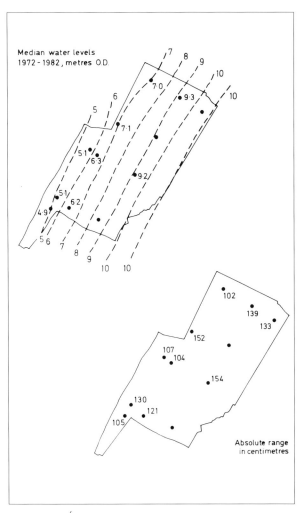

Figure 6.2 Ainsdale NNR Groundwater Levels

transpiration and to a lesser extent lateral seepage to the coast in the west and inland to the east, while the main input is precipitation.

Finally, changes in storage in equation (1) complete the system. As far as this chapter is concerned only groundwater storage changes will be considered. This is because in the many low-lying wet slacks the watertable is only rarely more than 1 m below the surface. However, below dune ridges very dry conditions can develop but the problems of estimating storage in these areas without expensive equipment or destroying the sites have yet to be overcome.

EVALUATING THE WATERBALANCE PARAMETERS

Since 1968 the NCC wardens have collected on-site rainfall data. Unfortunately the original site was poor, being very close to trees. A long term study of rainfall trends requires a consistent, correctly expressed network of gauges. With this in mind the Meteorological Office sites at Southport, Formby, Hightown, Bidston and Blackpool have been examined. The average rainfall for various periods for these stations is shown in Table 6.1.

The general trends of the groundwater levels measured in the Ainsdale NNR 1972-1990 are very much dependent upon the annual rainfall (Figure 6.3).It is evident that the seasonal fluctuations in evapotranspiration have a considerable influence in such a low-lying, shallow watertable. Estimates of potential evapotranspiration have been calculated for the area using the Penman method (1948). However, since a large area of the reserve is pine plantation the approach proposed by Calder and Newson (1979) has also been used.

TABLE 6.1
Selection of Mean Annual Rainfall Data

Station	Period	Mean
Southport	1964-76	831.4
Formby	1964-76	836.2
Hightown	1964-76	826.6
Bidston	1876-1990	727.7
Blackpool	1916-1950	850.0

Having evaluated the inputs (rainfall) and the major output (evapotranspiration) the groundwater flow component of the system has been quantified. In order to estimate the rate of flow, information on the depth of sand (aquifer), its hydraulic conductivity and the water table slope were needed.

An approximate geological section through the Ainsdale NNR constructed using data from several sources (Wray & Cope 1948; Gresswell 1953) is shown in Figure 6.4. The model described in this chapter assumes that the vertical deep percolation component is negligible (Todd 1959; Hall & Folland 1967) and makes the simplifying assumption that the strata underlying the sand can be considered impermeable. The hydraulic conductivity was measured in the field and laboratory (Clarke 1980) and values between 10-15 m/day with an average of 12.5 m/day derived. (At 10°C groundwater temperature). Since a long run of measurements of groundwater level is available the saturated thickness of the aquifer can be easily determined by superimposing these data on the geological cross-section. For example, two water levels have been chosen to represent a very dry summer (August 1976) and a very wet winter (February 1977). By using Darcy's Law the rate of groundwater flow from the system can be calculated. A full discussion of the approach is to be found elsewhere (Clarke 1980).

Darcy's Law states: $Q = - K.A. (dh/dL)$ (2)

Where Q is the outflow per unit time
K is the hydraulic conductivity of the aquifer
A is the cross-sectional area of the aquifer
dh/dL is the hydraulic gradient

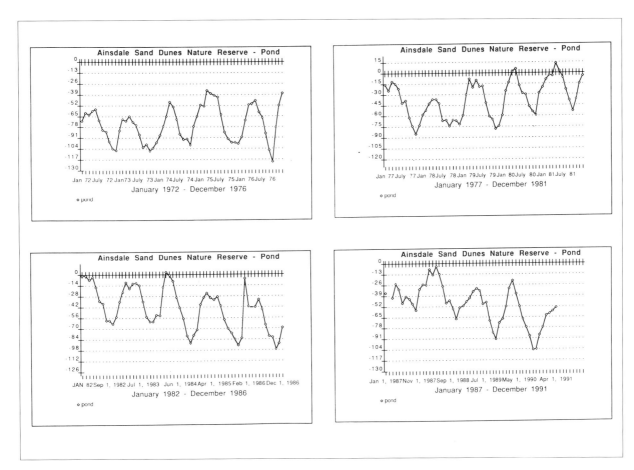

6.3 Ainsdale NNR Groundwater Levels 1972-1990 (Pond)

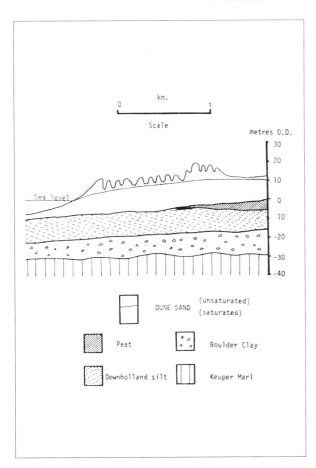

Figure 6.4 Geological Section adopted for Ainsdale NNR

Considering a 'slice' through the Ainsdale NNR of unit width the outflow per unit width can be calculated by substituting the saturated thickness of the aquifer for the area term A in (2).

Then for a very dry summer

$$Q = -12.5 \times 11.5 \times (-9.25/1950)$$

$$Q = 0.68 \text{m}^3 \text{ day}^{-1} \text{m}^{-1}$$

Likewise for a very wet winter

$$Q = 0.82 \text{ m}^3 \text{ day}^{-1} \text{ m}^{-1}$$

By assuming that this slice is representative of the whole of Ainsdale NNR the rates of groundwater flow can be expressed in rainfall and evapotranspiration units. The outflows for dry and wet periods become 127 mm/year and 158mm/year respectively. Obviously using this approach it is possible to calculate the assumed outflow on a monthly basis throughout the long data-run. Computer simulation models are being developed to do this.

The average components of the system are shown in Table 6.2 for the period 1972-1982. These data mask the large variation in a decade which includes the build up to the 1976 drought and the very wet conditions experienced in the early 1980s. It also shows how

Figure 6.5. Dune slack, Ainsdale and Birkdale Hills Local Nature Reserve, February 1993 (Slack 170). Extremely low water levels of August 1992 were followed by very high levels in February 1993. The average rise in the dune water-table measured at twelve wells on Ainsdale NNR was 75cm over six months. This is similar to the rapid rise in levels between August 1976 and February 1977.

potential evapotranspiration over-estimates the evaporative losses during dry periods. More detailed analysis is in hand and a close study of the response of the groundwater system to the extreme conditions experienced during the study to date will be undertaken.

TABLE 6.2
Average values of the Waterbalance variable 1972-1982

Rainfall	832 mm/yr
Potential Evapotranspiration (40% pine forest cover)	640 mm/yr
Ground water flow	140 mm/yr
Channel flow	20 mm/yr
*Change in groundwater and Soil moisture storage	+32 mm/yr

*1972 to 1982 saw a substantial increase in water levels over the area

CONCLUSIONS

The delicate balance between the components of the groundwater system in Ainsdale NNR can be shown to be very dependent upon the controlling climate parameters. The levels of standing water are almost totally dependent upon the effective rainfall in the preceding months. Very rapid changes in state occur. For example the record low water levels of August 1976 were immediately followed by very high levels in February 1977 (see also Figure 6.5). The transformation from dry to wet occurred in a few days in September 1976. The value of these studies is considerable. Much work remains to be done on the complex relationships in the system. It is essential that good quality data collection is maintained. Indeed there is a very real need for a high quality meteorological station with accurate rainfall and potential evapotranspiration data relevant to the system.

Roy Pegg

Enterprise and Enrichment
14 Oxford Street
PO Box 147
The University
Liverpool L69 3BX

Derek Clarke

Institute of Irrigation Studies
Department of Civil Engineering
University of Southampton
Highfield
Southampton SO9 5NH

CHAPTER SEVEN

The Importance of Hydrological Processes in Sand Dune Ecosystems

P.S. Jones

INTRODUCTION

Studies in north-western Europe have demonstrated that hydrological and successional factors are the two most important determinants of the structure and species composition of dune slack vegetation (Westhoff 1947; Ranwell 1960; Willis *et al*. 1959). The duration and seasonality of flooding, together with the amplitude of yearly fluctuations in groundwater level, are of prime importance in firstly determining the range of primary coloniser species, and secondly the whole successional sequence of vegetation types. In addition within a given dune system many soil chemical processes are influenced by the groundwater regime of individual slacks. The availability of divalent iron (Fe^{2+}) and manganese (Mn^{2+}) (both can be highly toxic to plants) is strongly influenced by the duration and seasonality of flooding, (Jones 1967; Jones & Etherington 1971) and the availability of inorganic nitrogen is closely related to soil redox processes. In addition groundwater factors (especially groundwater outflow and the seasonal flushing of soil profiles) are of some importance with respect to nutrient cycling, (James *et al*. 1986).

The monitoring of hydrological processes may thus give some insight into the nature of soil chemical conditions, but more importantly may yield information concerning, i) the groundwater balance and dynamics of the whole dune system aquifer, ii) long term trends in groundwater behaviour, and iii) the effect of turf stripping and sand re-mobilisation upon the future composition of vegetation.

THE RELATIONSHIP BETWEEN HYDROLOGY AND VEGETATION COMPOSITION

Numerous studies have demonstrated the importance of hydrological factors with respect to the species composition and structure of dune slack vegetation (e.g. Blanchard 1952; Ranwell 1960; Willis *et al*. 1959; Crawford & Wishart 1966; Van der Laan 1979, 1985). Some of these studies give the impression that for a given set of hydrological conditions it is possible to predict broadly the type of vegetation which will develop after a certain period. This information is potentially of great use to the dune manager concerned with the artificial creation of new slack habitats through sand and turf excavation.

The formation of new dune slacks by natural processes is now a comparatively rare event at many of the British west coast sites. Accordingly many managers are turning to the artificial creation of wet bare sand areas to provide emergency refugia for plant communities associated with the first thirty years of succession in slacks.

Prior to either the creation of a new dune slack or turf stripping, the following hydrological factors should be considered.

i) The depth of flooding in a slack is principally dependent on two factors. Firstly if there is a route by which surface water can flow out of the slack the depth of winter flooding will be maintained at a certain maximum level, and will only rise above this if the outward flow is impeded, either by deliberate blockage or by especially deep flooding 'downstream'. Secondly in a slack where there is no surface water outflow the depth of flooding will depend upon the position of the ground surface of the slack relative to the elevation of the water table in the immediately surrounding area. Slacks which may have been formed during dry periods may be considered here, with deflation of sand continuing to a depth considerably below the average position of the winter water table level.

ii) Slacks at the seaward edge (Jones 1992) and centre (Willis *et al*. 1959) of a dune system aquifer typically exhibit a large annual groundwater range , whilst slacks adjacent to permanent water bodies or areas at the centre of large parabolic slacks show a much reduced range which may amount to less than 50% of the maximum recorded on a given system.

Where there is a risk of creating areas of bare sand at locations especially prone to erosion (e.g. frontal dunes or visitor honey-pots) it may be advisable to first short-list a series of locations apparently suitable for excavation followed by a minimum of twelve months observation of water levels at dipwells specifically installed for this purpose.

Turf stripping operations are different in that the slack is already formed and much smaller volumes of material are removed. Grootjans *et al*. (1988) suggest that this may be the best management option for some overgrown slack communities, especially where leaching has occurred. This technique has the advantage that provided a reasonably shallow depth of material is removed the hydrological regime will largely be preserved.

The sequence of vegetation types which develop on freshly bared wet sand varies considerably both from site to site and within a site. The random arrival of propagules is obviously a factor contributing to the considerable point to point variation in species composition observed by many workers (Blanchard 1952; Martin 1959; Ranwell 1960; Londo 1971; Jones & Etherington 1989) on what is a fairly homogeneous medium. The species composition of vegetation within the first thirty years may show a strong component of ruderal species (e.g. greater plantain *Plantago major* L.). Many of the rarer uncompetitive dune slack species are prominent at this stage including small-fruited yellow sedge (*Carex viridula* ssp. *viridula* Michx.), bog pimpernel (*Anagallis tenella* (L.) L.), few-flowered spike-rush (*Eleocharis quinqueflora* (Hartmann) O.Schwarz) and (in South Wales) fen orchid (*Liparis loeselii* (L.) Rich.). In addition in wet slacks a species rich thalloid liverwort component may develop once sand movement has all but ceased.

Once a continuous vegetation canopy is established certain broad generalisations may be made concerning species composition. Ranwell (1972a) produced a useful summary which broadly applies to most of the English and Welsh calcareous west coast hindshore systems, and is reproduced here in modified form.

SEMI-AQUATIC HABITAT

This habitat has no clear National Vegetation Classification (NVC) equivalent (see Edmondson *et al.,* p 66 this volume for an explanation of the NVC).

Water table is very rarely more than 0.5 m below the soil surface, with surface flooding throughout the year or from autumn to late spring - early summer. Winter water levels invariably exceed 0.5 m in depth. Rooting zone is water-logged throughout most of the growing season with sand heavily gleyed and strongly negative redox potentials (an increase in negative electrical charge, here associated with low oxygen levels) during spring and summer. Divalent iron and manganese are present throughout growing season, especially once some organic matter is present, and precipitates of ferrous sulphide may be visible.

Amphibious plants with perennating parts under the water surface, such as shoreweed (*Littorella uniflora* (L.) Asch.) and amphibious bistort (*Persicaria amphibia* (L.) Gray) are typical components of the flora which may be dominated by tall emergent species such as water horsetail (*Equisetum fluviatale* L.) and reedmace (*Typha latifolia* L.). Creeping willow (*Salix repens* L.) is not usually a dominant species in these situations, and typically has a rather depauperate

Figure 7.1 Winter flooding of a wind-formed wet slack, Ainsdale Hills, March 1980.

appearance with a sparse canopy subtended by relatively few leaf-bearing branches. The lower limit of the distribution of creeping willow in slacks is probably conditioned jointly by both the depth and seasonality of flooding, (Blanchard 1952; Edmondson *et al.* this volume).

WET SLACK HABITAT A

NVC equivalents: SD1 *Salix repens - Calliergon cuspidatum* dune slack community; SD17 *Potentilla anserina - Carex nigra* dune slack community.

Water table rarely falls more than 1.2 m below soil surface with surface winter flooding from 10 to 50 cm in depth. Rooting zone is only rarely out of contact with the capillary fringe of the water table, and moderately low redox potentials may develop during the early summer months. Creeping willow is invariably the dominant species, but common sedge (*Carex nigra* (L.) Reichard), glaucous sedge (*Carex flacca* Schreb.) and marsh pennywort (*Hydrocotyle vulgaris* L.) are also often present at high cover values. These slacks are usually sufficiently wet to preclude domination by grasses, although creeping bent grass (*Agrostis stolonifera* L.) is frequent, and exceptionally purple moor-grass (*Molinia caerulea* (L.) Moench) may form dense stands. Variegated horsetail (*Equisetum variegatum* Schleicher) may occur as a local dominant, and in slacks with deep winter flooding often develops a tufted growth form.

Pleurocarpous mosses usually form a dense carpet up to several decimetres thick, and in south Wales at least there is a clear successional trend from *Campylium stellatum* (Hedw.) J. Lange & C. Jens. and *Drepanocladus sendtneri* (H.Mull.) Warnst through to eventual domination by *Calliergon cuspidatum* (Hedw.) Kindb.

Figure 7.2 Wet slack, Ainsdale Hills, March 1985. The boundary between slack vegetation and dry dune vegetation is clearly marked by a 'tide-line'.

WET SLACK HABITAT B

NVC equivalent: SD14. *Salix repens - Campylium stellatum* dune slack community.

These ecosystems tend to have a similar flooding regime to those described above, but the depth of winter flooding is strictly limited to less than 10 cm or so by the surface flow of water out of the slack. Ranwell (1959), Clarke (1980), Edmondson *et al.* (this volume) and Jones (1992) have all described slacks which fall into this category, and species diversity is usually high (up to 43 flowering plant and bryophyte species per square metre in S. Wales). The shallow winter flooding seems to be just enough to prevent domination by grasses, although red fescue (*Festuca rubra* L.), spreading meadow-grass (*Poa humilis* Ehrh. ex Hoffm.) and heath grass (*Danthonia decumbens* (L.) DC.) may all occur as local dominants, and creeping willow rarely forms a continuous canopy. White clover (*Trifolium repens* L.), strawberry clover (*Trifolium fragiferum* L.) and birdsfoot trefoil (*Lotus corniculatus* L.) may all occur as local dominants.

DRY SLACK HABITAT

NVC equivalent: SD16 *Salix repens - Holcus lanatus* dune slack community.

Water table may range between 0.5 and 2.0 m below ground surface during the summer months, and soil profiles usually remain out of capillary contact with the water table throughout the growing season. Winter flooding only occurs exceptionally, and is usually of short duration. Soils in these dry slacks almost never become chemically reducing, and even flooding of the root zone is rare. Creeping willow may be dominant, but more usually grasses compose a significant proportion of the above ground biomass, with red fescue, Yorkshire fog (*Holcus lanatus* L.) and

spreading meadow-grass all abundant. Both rough hawkbit (*Leontodon hispidus* L.) and restharrow (*Ononis repens* L.) may also be dominant. Associated species which are usually rare in dune slacks may include bugle (*Ajuga reptans* L.) and ragwort (*Senecio jacobaea* L.).

Provided that information relating to the maximum and minimum level of the water table is available for sites chosen for excavation the dune manager is thus provided with some degree of control over the species composition and structure of vegetation in artificially created slacks. The importance of creating a habitat which is physiographically similar to naturally formed slacks is clear (Van der Maarel 1979). The creation of deep ponds with steeply inclined margins not only introduces an alien element to the dune landscape, but also fails to effect the re-establishment of dune slack communities of a form similar to those which evolve naturally (Londo 1971).

DETECTION OF LONG TERM CHANGES IN GROUNDWATER STATUS

Both Ainsdale NNR (see Clarke & Pegg, this volume) and Braunton Burrows NNR (North Devon) have hydrological records extending back over twenty years. Such information may show a long term trend towards becoming either drier or wetter.

With a shift to drier conditions, scrub may encroach (Doody 1985b; Leach & Kinnear 1985), thereby affecting site management. Indeed the distribution of many species is critically related to the mean water table level (Van der Laan 1979) Many examples exist in the Dutch literature concerning the loss of species from dune slacks following the disturbance resulting from groundwater extraction to both the average level of the water table and its yearly fluctuation (Van Zadelhoff 1981; Mennema *et al.* 1985; Grootjans *et al.* 1988; Londo 1971).

The effects of an increase in the average water table level are difficult to predict. In many of the Dutch studies reporting the effects of dune system aquifer recharge with nutrient rich river water[1] it is not possible to separate the ecological effects of an increased nutrient load from the increase in mean groundwater level (Van Dijk 1989). In addition in infiltrated dune areas massive variations in water level may occur quite out of sequence with the normal seasonal fluctuations, and this in itself tends to lead to the development of species-poor vegetation types.

Many dune slack species are adapted to changes in the duration and depth of flooding and average

---

[1] Several large dune areas in the Netherlands are employed as water catchments where abstracted river water is filtered through the sand before entering the public water supply system. For an explanation see Van Dijk (1989).

groundwater position. Grootjans *et al.* (1988) have noted that several species are able to migrate up and down a height gradient in dune slacks in response to wet and dry periods; and Van der Laan (1979) has noted similar effects. In addition, many species (especially perennials) have dormant meristematic tissues which facilitate the survival of individuals through unfavourable periods.

Human interference of the natural groundwater regime of British coastal dunes occurs on a very small scale at a handful of sites. For the most part this relates to low volume pumping of water for immediate local needs (notably golf course irrigation).

The use on an intensive scale of sand dunes for water extraction and storage has never been a problem in the British Isles as water resource needs are met by upland catchments, deep groundwater abstraction and reservoirs. The partial afforestation of a number of nationally important sites (e.g. Ainsdale, Tentsmuir in Scotland, Newborough Warren on Anglesey and Pembrey in South Wales) has however been implicated as a possible factor contributing to lowered water levels, although there is almost no quantitative information to support this.

Baseline hydrological data may be utilised, with other data, to argue for the structural integrity of duneland ecosystems, and is likely to be of critical importance in a number of future planning debates.

For example, groundwater budget analyses at Kenfig NNR, (Jones 1992) have served to provide some 'assessment of risk' to the duneland aquifer with respect to alterations to both the groundwater regime and groundwater chemistry of neighbouring sites.

THE USE OF HYDROLOGICAL DATA IN PREDICTIVE STUDIES

Clarke (1980) was able to predict groundwater levels at Ainsdale NNR from meteorological data with some success. The close relationship which exists between groundwater fluctuations and the balance between rainfall and evapotranspiration should permit the development of a predictive model to qualitatively assess longer term trends in relation to climatic change (see below). This illustrates how a detailed hydrological data base may serve a function for which it was not originally designed.

RESEARCH PRIORITIES

i)   The effect of a global rise in sea level upon natural hydrological processes in dune systems has received scant attention in the literature. Van Huis (1989) suggests that rising sea level, plus increased precipitation will result in a rise in coastal groundwater levels, but to what extent this will be balanced by the effects of increased summer evaporation and a decrease in the moisture content of the soil is unclear. The resolution of this question is clearly of great importance, not just because of the effects on dune slack and phreatophytic (water table-utilising) vegetation in general, but also because of the more widespread consequences for whole dune system stability. It is to be hoped that Pan-European monitoring projects, preferably using standardised methods, will enable some preliminary assessments of change to be made within the next five to ten years (Van der Meulen 1990).

ii)   Effects of occasional sea water flooding and the re-adjustment of foredune systems upon the physical and chemical dynamics of the groundwater system could be investigated using transects of dipwells running from seaward slacks right through to the embryo dune zone.

iii)   There is still enormous scope for detailed investigations of the relationship between hydrology and species distribution in dune slacks. Very few studies, for example, have examined the distribution of invertebrate groups in relation to groundwater regime, and longer term studies to assess species population changes in slacks over a range of groundwater regimes will be necessary if useful predictive models are to be developed for the future.

iv)   Techniques for incorporating hydrological data onto geographic information systems (GIS) must be considered, in particular the transfer of interpolated water levels into a digital form which is both ultimately useful to managers and true to the original data.

v)   Comparisons of groundwater data collected at other sites, both in Great Britain and other parts of Europe is essential as a prelude to predictive modelling. The fundamental geohydrological similarity of many west coast hindshore systems offers valid comparisons between sites with: i) different climatic settings ii) varying landuse characteristics (e.g. un-afforested versus afforested) iii) erosive versus accretive coasts and iv) natural versus modified neighbouring aquifers.

P.S. Jones

Kenfig NNR
Ton-Kenfig
Pyle
Mid Glamorgan CF33 4PT.

SECTION 4

VEGETATION STUDIES

CHAPTER EIGHT

Plant Communities and Succession

S.E. Edmondson, P.S. Gateley, P. Rooney, and P.W. Sturgess.

INTRODUCTION

The present-day area of sand dune vegetation on the Sefton coast stretches in a shallow crescent, from the north of Seaforth Dock (the northernmost of the Liverpool docks) to the sand-winning plant north of Southport. At both the southern and northern ends of this area, building development and alteration of the natural landscape has confined the surviving sand dune vegetation to a very narrow strip at the top of the beach.

Examination of the drift geology map (see Figure 2.3) clearly indicates the former extent of dune landscape to have been much larger, both extending southwards into the city of Liverpool and eastwards on land now developed for a range of land uses including golf courses, housing, military, agricultural, the resort of Southport and others. These developments, which largely result from the proximity of the area to large centres of population such as Liverpool, have therefore considerably reduced the area of what Ratcliffe (1977) describes as the fourth largest dune system in Britain, and nowhere has the complete successional series of plant communities been allowed to persist across the full width of the blown sand area.

In 1952 Salisbury observed that the dunes at Formby, Ainsdale and Southport "still retained large unspoilt areas and exhibit in a striking manner the formation of parallel dune ridges ... (which) clearly show the development of dune soils and their changing flora". Today the Sefton coast dunes still boast the most natural landscapes of Merseyside with nationally important plant communities, but the natural ecological processes have been continually hindered and altered by peoples' activities since the time of Salisbury's observation (when already much natural dunescape had been lost).

It is essential to take stock of the current status of plant communities and processes operating on the dunes so as to minimise future loss of natural resources.

EXISTING VEGETATION SURVEY AND ANALYSIS

Malloch (1989) outlines an "often described" sand dune vegetation zonation for Britain (see Figure 8.1) but notes that there is surprisingly little specific detail of the vegetation to be found in the literature.

Blanchard (1952) noted the lack of detailed accounts of the ecology of the Sefton coast dunes and described the communities of a small section of what is now the southern end of Ainsdale Sand Dunes National Nature Reserve (Ainsdale NNR). The general model of succession proposed by Gordon and Savidge (1963) excludes several important developmental details. Also, a number of factors influencing the pathways of dune succession have altered since these models were proposed.

Payne (1983a) provided a detailed analysis of succession for both dune and slack vegetation at Ainsdale based on observation of the dominant plant species, although clear descriptions of associated plant species are given. He describes a "typical" early dune successional series from embryo sand couch grass (*Elytrigia juncea* (L.) Nevski) dunes, to marram (*Ammophila arenaria* (L.) Link) mobile dunes, to marram - red fescue (*Festuca rubra* L.) dunes, then a sequence which varies from previously described series and is typical of this area of the coast. He describes the subsequent development of red fescue - dewberry (*Rubus caesius* L.) dune which is followed by an extensive band of creeping willow (*Salix repens* L.) - dewberry dwarf shrub dune with grasses being an important element, especially on the north facing slopes. This is followed by development towards communities of more acidic conditions characterised by lichens, mosses and liverworts (bryophytes) and the appearance of common bent (*Agrostis capillaris* L.) and sheep's fescue (*Festuca ovina* L.). Payne also suggests a model for dune slack succession based largely on the trend towards increasingly dry conditions and the development of acidity and/or scrub.

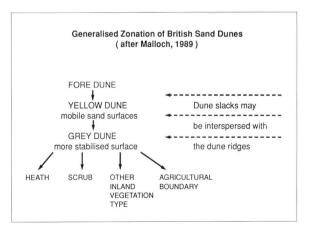

Figure 8.1 Generalised Zonation of British Sand Dunes (after Malloch 1989)

TABLE 8.1
N.V.C Shingle, Strandline and Sand Dunes.
Preliminary Conspectus used in the 1988 survey of the Sefton Coast Dunes

SD1 Crambe maritima - Glaucium flavum shingle community

SD2 Cakile maritima - Honkenya peploides strandline

SD3 Atriplex hastata - Beta vulgaris ssp. maritima strandline

SD4 Atriplex hastata - Galium aparine strandline

SD5 Elymus farctus foredune

SD6 Ammophila arenaria dune
   a **Ammophila arenaria** sub-community
   b **Elymus farctus** sub-community
   c **Carex arenaria** sub-community
   d **Senecio jacobaea** sub-community
   e **Festuca rubra** sub-community
   f **Poa pratensis** sub-community

SD7 Leymus arenarius dune
   a **Elymus farctus** sub-community
   b **Elymus repens** sub-community
   c **Festuca rubra** sub-community

SD8 Leymus arenarius - Ammophila arenaria dune
   a **Typical** sub-community
   b **Elymus farctus** sub-community

SD9 Ammophila arenaria - Ononis repens dune
   a **Brachythecium albicans** sub-community
   b **Hypnum cupressiforme** sub-community

SD10 Festuca rubra - Galium verum dune
   a **Bellis perennis** sub-community
   b **Euphrasia officinalis** agg. sub-community
   c **Thymus praecox** sub-community
   d **Hypochoeris radicata** sub-community

SD11 Ammophila arenaria - Festuca ovina - Agrostis capillaris dune
   a **Brachythecium albicans** sub-community
   b **Pleurozium schreberi - Hylocomium splendens** sub-community

SD12 Carex arenaria dune
   a **Carex arenaria** sub-community
   b **Holcus lanatus - Senecio jacobaea** sub-community
   c **Dicranum scoparium** sub-community

SD13 Carex arenaria - Cladonia spp. dune
   a **Festuca ovina** sub-community
   b **Ammophila arenaria** sub-community

SD14 Ammophila arenaria - Phleum arenarium dune
   a **Typical** sub-community
   b **Thymus praecox - Arenaria serpyllifolia** sub-community

SD15 Salix repens - Holcus lanatus dune slack
   a **Equisetum variegatum** sub-community
   b **Calliergon cuspidatum** sub-community
   c **Pulicaria dysenterica** sub-community
   d **Holcus lanatus - Festuca rubra** sub-community

SD16 Potentilla anserina - Carex nigra dune slack

SD17 Hippophae rhamnoides dune scrub
   a **Ammophila arenaria - Sonchus arvensis** sub-community
   b **Rubus fruticosus - Arrhenatherum elatius** sub-community
   c **Solanum dulcamara** sub-community
   d **Urtica dioica - Holcus lanatus** sub-community

A number of workers have categorised the dune vegetation into broad groups which relate to seral communities, (for example J.A. Wheldon 1914; Rothwell 1985; SMBC undated) particularly for use in mapping, and Edmondson, Gunn and Penney (1984) have described a much more detailed set of vegetation stands which were used for mapping Ainsdale Sand Dunes NNR. Mapping of such detailed vegetation communities however was undertaken for the first time on a coastwide basis in 1988 (Edmondson, Gateley & Nissenbaum 1988/89) using the National Vegetation Classification (NVC) survey techniques and vegetation types, as part of the Nature Conservancy Council's national sand dune survey of Great Britain (hereafter referred to as the NVC survey). This survey allows a review of the successional processes by examining the spatial relationships of vegetation types at the present time. Details of the composition of scrub and pinewood communities, other than dominant species, were not included in the NVC survey but the ground flora of the pinewoods is reviewed by Sturgess in this chapter.

The NVC survey used the plant communities described by Malloch (1985) and Rodwell (undated). Although they have since been revised (Malloch 1989), this

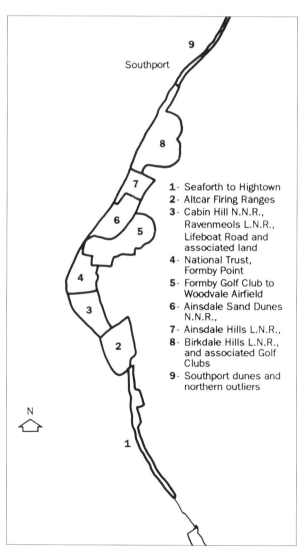

Figure 8.2 Divisions of the Sefton Coast Sand Dune Survey

chapter refers to the earlier conspectus of vegetation types (see Table 8.1) and other preliminary NVC volumes (Rodwell, undated). The survey maps and reports were presented as a series of nine volumes, each representing a convenient area of the coast (Figure 8.2). A coastwide report was also produced.

This chapter examines the results of the NVC and other surveys, investigates changes that have occurred up to the survey date and highlights uncertainties in the successional processes currently operating on the dunes.

GEOMORPHOLOGICAL HISTORY AND IMPACTS OF PEOPLE

The vegetation of the area which has survived development can be divided into:

1. Semi-natural vegetation. Vegetation types which are essentially natural in origin, or contain a significant component of sand dune species in their composition. As well as sand dune communities this includes areas such as mesotrophic (with a moderate amount of nutrients) grasslands, scrub, acidic grassland and heath which all develop at later successional stages, and also dune restoration areas planted with marram.

2. Substantially and completely modified vegetation. A whole range of vegetation types from at one extreme short mown amenity grassland which retains no natural sand dune characteristics, to abandoned agricultural areas which may eventually revert to sand dune type vegetation because of the characteristics of the soil and surrounding dunes.

Pye (1990) recognises three phases of dune morphological development on the Sefton coast, identifiable by the present-day landforms. These are

i)   Pre-1800. An irregular series of hummock dunes with incipient blowouts and parabolic dunes gradually prograding seaward, produced by the positive beach sand budget and incomplete vegetation cover.

ii) 1880-1906. A positive beach sand budget plus effective sand-trapping vegetation provided by brushwood sand-trap fencing and marram planting causing the development of a series of dune ridges parallel to the coast. These are clearly visible between Birkdale and Altcar, although are truncated by erosion around Formby Point.

iii) Post 1906. Erosion around Formby Point together with disruption of vegetation on the frontal dunes, especially by recreational pressure at beach access points, causing large transgressive sand sheets. It is

clear therefore that the vegetation of the frontal dunes has been influenced by peoples' activities for at least 200 years, and much earlier if the long history of the management of rabbit warrens is considered (see Jones *et al.* this volume).

All three phases of dune development are reflected in the vegetation types present today. The third time phase is represented at the seaward end of Fisherman's Path at Freshfield, by unvegetated advancing dunes, but at Lifeboat Road and Victoria Road, by extensive dune restoration works involving large areas of marram planting.

The parallel dune ridges of the second time phase display a typical zonation caused by succession from mobile to semi-fixed dunes. Where the coast is still accreting south and north of the erosion front around Formby Point, embryo dunes are present in front of the marram dunes.

The areas attributable to the first time phase consist of a complex mosaic of dune and slack vegetation types. The generalised trend of increased stability and senescence is reflected in the development of increased 'grassiness' and scrub on both dune and slack areas.

The long established impact of people on the coast makes the distinction between semi-natural and modified vegetation rather unclear, but it is a useful basis for description. Scrub communities are described in the semi-natural section although many of the species are introduced.

DESCRIPTION OF THE VEGETATION. 1. SEMI-NATURAL VEGETATION

SHINGLE COMMUNITIES

SD 1†[1] *Crambe maritima - Glaucium flavum* shingle community is an unlikely occurrence on a sand dune coast, but this community is becoming established on the artificial shingle of the 'brick and rubble' revetment shore at Hightown (SD 295025).

SALTMARSH

The saltmarsh vegetation, although small in extent, forms an important part of the whole coastal system. Saltmarsh plants occur in various places, particularly in young seaward dune slacks, but also on the sea wall at Blundellsands (see NVC survey) and on the beach and around Tagg's Island at Ainsdale and Birkdale. The only true saltmarsh vegetation, however occurs on the north and south sides of the Alt mouth at Hightown, the southern area being the more extensive (SD 295035). This is within the foreshore area which has been

---

†[1] SD1 refers to Shingle, Strandline and Sand Dunes community type number 1 of the National Vegetation Classification (see Table 8.1)

Figure 8.3 Common Saltmarsh-grass *(Puccinellia maritima)* forming hummocks on the beach at Birkdale, 1989.

designated as a Ramsar site and a Special Protection Area. The northern extremity of the sand dune coast grades into the large Ribble Marshes salt marsh system.

Common cord grass (*Spartina anglica* C.E.Hubb.) is dominant on the seaward edge of the larger southern Hightown marsh. A large bed of common reed (*Phragmites australis* (Cav.) Trin. ex Steudel) forms the centre of the marsh, and a red fescue zone also occurs. Smith (1984) surveyed the botanical interest of the marsh.

The origin of common cord grass on the saltmarsh is unclear. It may be the result of recent colonisation, or two early attempts by the military authorities to establish it to reduce local coastal erosion around the Alt mouth (Massey 1937). Whatever the origin, its present development at Hightown is well advanced, and it is spreading (Fairhurst 1977; Tuscon 1989). The impact on the coast of the development and growth of this saltmarsh, and of the spread of common cord grass in this area, is not known and warrants further investigation.

Common saltmarsh grass (*Puccinellia maritima* (Hudson) Parl.) occurs, forming embryo hummocks in patches on the beach at Ainsdale and Birkdale (Figure 8.3). Payne (1983a) reports the first appearance of these colonies at the Ainsdale site (south of Shore Road) in 1982, about 50m out from the seaward edge of the dunes. Although non-existent at the time of writing, this colony has persisted, apart from a break in 1987/8, since that time. This colony is unfortunately subject to heavy public pressure, particularly cars, the access point for the beach being at Shore Road. The more northerly community is over 1 km in length (SD 310155 - SD 317163 approx.) and is more stable, having been continually present since it first appeared in 1986. In 1988, species present also included sea aster (*Aster tripolium* L.), glasswort (*Salicornia* sp.) and hastate orache (*Atriplex prostrata* Boucher ex DC.) (Sturgess 1988). The hummocks reach a height of approximately 0.5m in the summer and lyme-grass (*Leymus arenarius* (L.) Hochst.) is now present. Tagg's Island, inshore from this more northerly 'green beach', originally began as a similar offshore belt of common saltmarsh grass, which first arose in 1974 and was encouraged in its growth by brushwood thatching in 1979 eventually producing an 'island' 200m in length. Beach debris was subsequently dumped on the island to produce an even bigger feature behind which a marsh has developed as a result of a consequently blocked drain.

The appearance of these transient communities is not new on the coast. Allen (1932) recorded the changes in the development of a similar vegetation type "10 yards from the base of the outermost dunes" between Freshfield and Ainsdale. Three low parallel ridges developed, each with common saltmarsh grass as the primary coloniser, and were later colonised by a range of other species including sea plantain (*Plantago maritima* L.), sea aster, arrow grasses (*Triglochin* spp.), oraches (*Atriplex* spp.), sea club-rush (*Bolboschoenus maritimus* (L.) Palla) and common reed. The vegetation first appeared in 1930 and at the time of writing in 1932 the first two ridges were separated by a large pool of "practically fresh water". The potential of these ridges on the beach is significant, not only in creating new dune ridges, but also primary dune slacks by cutting off areas of beach plain.

STRANDLINE COMMUNITIES

The NVC survey maps under-record these ephemeral communities which, although known to have been relatively extensive in May of 1988, were mostly covered by freshly blown sand before being mapped. At the northerly end of the coast, beach cleaning activities with a tractor mounted blade and car parking are the probable causes of lack of strandline communities.

SD 2 *Cakile maritima - Honkenya peploides* and SD 3 *Atriplex hastata - Beta vulgaris* ssp. *maritima* strandline communities do occur on the coast, but the more common condition is a patchy, discontinuous occurrence of a mix elements of SD2, 3 and 4 (see Table 8.1) although no cleavers (*Galium aparine* L.) was noted on the strandline in the NVC survey.

FOREDUNES

All NVC foredune communities listed were identified on the coast but were fragmented in the eroding areas around Formby Point.

SD5 *Elymus farctus* (now re-named *Elytrigia juncea*) foredune occurs over the whole seaward edge of the dunes but especially in areas north and south of the erosion front. It thins out northwards from Birkdale. This community also occurs in small patches on the leeward side of blowouts within the dune system.

SD7 *Leymus arenarius* dune occurs all along the coast but is not common in the Ravenmeols, Lifeboat Road and Freshfield area. It is especially important in the more disturbed northern and southern extremities of the system. Most of this vegetation is a more or less pure stand of lyme-grass and is not always restricted to the foredunes. In Crosby it is found around the landward margins of mown amenity grassland and in Hightown lyme grass is a component of mesotrophic grassland. SD 7a *Elymus farctus* sub-community however is always westerly in its distribution and is frequently in mosaic with SD5 and SD8. SD8 *Leymus arenarius - Ammophila arenaria* dune (both (a) typical sub-community and (b) *Elymus farctus* sub-community) is found along the seaward edge of the system but is most frequent in the Freshfield area.

MOBILE DUNES

Ammophila arenaria dune, SD 6, is the dominant community of the parallel seaward dune ridges described above, and also occurs on sand freshly deposited on the leeward side of blow-outs. Marram dunes occur along the whole length of the system apart from the disturbed northern and southern extremities. All the sub-communities occur with SD6f *Poa pratensis* sub-community occurring furthest inland. Creeping willow can occur in SD 6 dunes, and is often actively dune building.

Extensive dune restoration areas also provide artificially initiated SD6 communities.

On the leeward side of the transgressive sand dune ridges referred to by Pye (1990), semi-fixed dune is reverting to the *Ammophila arenaria* (SD 6) community type as a result of a high rate of sand accretion.

SEMI-FIXED TO FIXED DUNES

SD 9 *Ammophila arenaria - Ononis repens* dune is the most common and widespread vegetation community on the coast, occurring especially on the pre-1800 dunes described by Pye (1990). Both NVC sub-communities were recognised on the coast, but their occurrence was in relatively small stands and the composition of most of the SD 9 does not correspond closely to NVC types. Creeping willow is a very widespread and often very significant element of the community. Extensive areas of undifferentiated SD9 were mapped and two further sub-communities were described.

(a) SD 9p - This is a dense vegetation type with polypody (*Polypodium vulgare* L.) constantly occurring, and wild strawberry (*Fragaria vesca* L.), sweet vernal grass (*Anthoxanthum odoratum* L.) and the moss *Dicranum scoparium* Hedw. common associates. This community is typical of the north faces of dune ridges.

(b) SD 9r - This is characterised by a dense grassy sward. Marram is still dominant, or is co-dominant with red fescue. Other grasses more typical of mesotrophic grassland are also found, for example false oat (*Arrhenatherum elatius* (L.) P. Beauv. ex J. & C. Presl), cock's foot (*Dactylis glomerata* L.), and Yorkshire fog (*Holcus lanatus* L.). Dewberry is often abundant but is not constant. SD 9r is found increasingly to the east of the SD 9 zone, with increasing occurrence of the mesotrophic grassland species.

The identification and distribution of these two vegetation types concurs with the red fescue - dewberry dune pasture and the creeping willow - dewberry dwarf shrub dune described by Payne (1983a).

SD 14 *Ammophila arenaria - Phleum arenarium* dune is another widespread and frequently occurring community in similar areas to SD 9, often forming a mosaic with it, but more often in smaller patches and extending less far east. It is characteristic of dune ridge tops, steep dune sides and eroded areas where sand is exposed. Payne also describes this type of community in similar locations, particularly on the south facing slopes of dune ridges.

SD 10 *Festuca rubra - Galium verum* dune is an uncommon community on the Sefton coast, being mostly found in well trodden places such as footpaths and around Lifeboat Road public car park. *Thymus praecox* sub-community was also found in this area. Interestingly, Payne's model of the succession at Ainsdale makes no mention of this type of community.

ACIDIC FIXED DUNE COMMUNITIES

SD 12 *Carex arenaria* dune and SD13 *Carex arenaria - Cladonia* spp. dune occur mostly in association with open glades on the edges of pine plantations. SD12 is the more extensive, but only SD13 occurs in small patches in the open dunes.

SD 11 *Ammophila arenaria - Festuca ovina - Agrostis capillaris* dune is mostly confined to the golf courses where remnants of the eastern fringes of the sand dune system survive. In these areas other NVC calcifugous grassland types occur (*Deschampsia flexuosa* grassland, *Festuca ovina - Agrostis capillaris - Galium saxatile* grassland, *Nardus stricta - Galium saxatile* grassland and very small patches of *Juncus squarrosus* grassland), Southport and Ainsdale Golf Course (SD 319132) being the best site. On the eastern fringe of this golf course, grey hair-grass (*Corynephorus canescens* (L.) P. Beauv.) is found in an extensive sward in a mosaic of *Carex arenaria - Cladonia* spp. dune and *Festuca ovina - Agrostis capillaris - Galium saxatile* grassland.

DUNE HEATH

Acidic grasslands, and especially dune heaths are the most fragmented of all the semi-natural vegetation types, occupying as they do, the eastern fringes of the dune system where most building development has occurred. Salisbury (1925) considers that it takes 200 years for the pH of the soils on this coast to fall as low as 6.4 from its original value of 8.2 at the top of the beach. Payne (1983a) also notes that acidity is slow to develop on these dunes as the parent material is highly alkaline.

The two most extensive areas of dune heath are secondary, or presumed so. The area of Freshfield dune heath SSSI (SD 295093), which extends into Woodvale Airfield, was formerly a golf course, and Larkhill Dune Heath on the National Trust property (SD 282075), is presumed to be abandoned agricultural land (Daniels & Knights 1985). Both of these areas were mapped as the NVC community (*Calluna vulgaris - Carex arenaria* heath; (now *Carex arenaria - Calluna vulgaris* dune heath, Malloch 1989). Areas of this community also occur on Formby Golf course, where it is mown to a height of approximately 10 cm. More natural areas of this community occur extensively on Southport and Ainsdale Golf Course, often mixed with acidic grassland and small areas of another heath community, *Calluna vulgaris - Deschampsia flexuosa* heath. These areas however occur in the hollows and old dune slacks rather than on the ridges.

DUNE SLACKS

Slack vegetation was extensively reviewed by Smith (1978). He noted that the "north Merseyside dunes are particularly well endowed with slacks". The older ones at Birkdale and Ainsdale have a mainly east-west orientation suggesting an origin from large blow-outs (secondary dune slacks) occurring in Pye's pre-1800 phase of dune development. Younger, primary dune slacks occur at Ainsdale and are associated with the later phase of dune development where successive dune ridges parallel to the coast have cut off former beach plain surfaces. Smith points out that south of Formby Point natural dune slacks have been largely eliminated by extensive modification for asparagus growing, industrial waste tipping and military uses. Artificially created wetlands have however replaced natural dune slacks in the southern area, resulting from borrow pits, bomb craters, sand-winning and vehicle tracks.

New dune slack formation is now rare on the Sefton coast and Smith (1978) considers that there has been little formation of slacks during most of this century. A small secondary dune slack is being created in a mobile area on the Ainsdale NNR/LNR boundary and small blow-outs down to damp sand are dotted through the frontal dunes on Ainsdale LNR (Figure 8.4). The large blow out known as the Devil's Hole at Ravenmeols (SD 278054) has now deflated down to wet sand. A small area of beach plain has been isolated by sand accumulation around fencing on Birkdale LNR just north of Shore Road, potentially creating an artificial primary dune slack, and Tagg's Island (SD 311153), a little further north has cut off an area of freshwater marsh. These however are isolated examples.

Small scrapes (pools) for natterjack toad (*Bufo calamita* L.) have been dug throughout the dune system, but in 1976 five larger and deeper ponds were dug on Ainsdale Sand Dunes NNR and one on Birkdale LNR. These excavations were saucer-shaped, and although unsuitable in the long term for natterjack toad breeding sites, have successfully initiated the early successional stages of damp and wet slack vegetation which natural processes have not produced.

The NVC conspectus used for the 1988 survey lists only two slack vegetation types ; SD 15 *Salix repens - Holcus lanatus* dune slack and SD 16 *Potentilla anserina - Carex nigra* dune slack. Of these SD 15 is by far the most common and widespread, but the diversity of the slacks so classified is obscured by their division into only four sub-communities. The range of vegetation types covered by the SD 15 category includes the early successional stages, such as is found in the excavations; mature wet slacks dominated by tall creeping willow and a *Calliergon cuspidatum* (Hedw.) Kindb. moss layer ; low growing species-rich wet slacks containing many of the coastal rarities such as marsh helleborine (*Epipactis palustris* (L.) Crantz.) and grass-of-Parnassus (*Parnassia palustris* L.); and the drier, older slack types which are less species rich and include more grasses such as red fescue. SD 15d *Holcus lanatus - Festuca rubra* sub-community represents this older phase of slack vegetation development and is by far the most widespread and frequent type on the coast.

SD 16 contains virtually no silverweed (*Potentilla anserina* L.) on this coast. It is typical of older, more acidified slacks which have remained wet, and is often found as a central stand in a large slack surrounded by SD15. Some of the larger stands are transitional with mire-type communities. As with the dry dunes, the highly calcareous nature of the dune-sand buffers development of acidity in the slacks.

In some of the much wetter areas in slacks, together with ditches, bomb craters and ponds, emergent plants such as yellow flag (*Iris pseudacorus* L.), reed canary-grass (*Phalaris arundinacea* L.), common reed, glaucous bulrush (*Schoenoplectus tabernaemontani* (C.C.Gmel.) Palla), branched bur-reed (*Sparganium erectum* L.), bulrush (*Typha latifolia* L.) and water horsetail (*Equisetum fluviatile* L.) dominate. Such communities are described by Blanchard (1952), Smith (1978) and Payne (1983a).

The two major sources of variation in the slack vegetation are age and hydrology. These two variables are often correlated, since sand and organic matter accumulate as the slacks get older, causing them to become drier. Added to these are: the effects of colonisation and persistence by those plants the propagules of which by chance first arrived on the incipient slack sand surface; the nature of creeping willow; and the impact of rabbit grazing. See also Jones, this volume.

Meikle (1984) describes the polymorphism (different forms) of creeping willow, ranging from slender, prostrate, hairless sub-shrubs to robust, erect or ascending shrubs with silky-haired leaves, and concludes that it currently has no workable taxonomy. Blanchard (1952) distinguished two distinct forms at Ainsdale, and related them to successional stages; firstly a small semi-prostrate creeping form typical of

Figure 8.4 Slack formation, Ainsdale Local Nature Reserve, 1988.

plants colonising a new slack area and secondly an upright bushy form present when colonisation is complete. These forms are clearly recognisable in the field, but the extent to which they are determined by genetic or environmental differences is not known. Jones (1980) investigated the polymorphism of creeping willow, assigning scores to specimens according to their affinity with either *Salix arenaria* or *Salix repens* forms as described by Rechinger (1964). Barton (1981) continued this work and found some correlation between the form of the plant and habitat, but this was largely associated with the slack/dune contrast.

The relationship with hydrological conditions is also unclear. Blanchard (1952) suggests that duration of winter flooding, especially in the early part of the growing season, is more significant in affecting the growth of creeping willow than the depth of submergence. Payne (1983a) suggests that there is a significant competitive advantage for tall plants in areas of prolonged flooding in having the growing tips above water level at the time of flowering and leaf bud burst. He concludes that in wet slacks, creeping willow is tall and dominant and "has probably been so for many years". On the Sefton coast, where creeping willow often dominates both dune and slack environments, and is present at both early and late successional stages, the variation in the form and impact of this plant, operating alongside the other major physical and biological variables makes analysis of the successional sequence of the vegetation difficult.

Rabbit-proof exclosures were installed in 1974 in four species-rich slacks on Ainsdale NNR (Edmondson 1991) to investigate the impact of grazing on slack vegetation. Creeping willow, as expected, increased in the exclosures relative to the control plots in the vegetation outside. The contrast was however, much greater in the young, wet slacks than in the older drier ones, suggesting that control of succession by light grazing pressure is more successful in these conditions. Change in species diversity in the exclosures parallels this, with a clear loss in the younger, wetter sites which is not shown in the older, drier ones. In one of the latter sites one slack specialist, round-leaved wintergreen (*Pyrola rotundifolia* ssp. *maritima* (Kenyon) E.F.Warb.), was more successful in the exclosures. These results illustrate that many factors affect the variation in slack vegetation.

Grasses increase in cover in the exclosures, but the increase relative to control conditions is less after ten or more years. The abundance of different grass species in exclosures also consistently changes over time, with a loss of creeping bent grass (*Agrostis stolonifera* L.) and a gain in either red fescue or smooth meadow-grass, both of which are typical of the older, drier SD 15d community described above.

The factors outlined above are further compounded by longer term changes in the climate causing changes in the levels of the dune water table. A significant illustration of this is the occurrence in the late 1960s and early 1970s of a drier phase . This has been described by Clarke (1980) and illustrated by the long-term water table data monitored by the Nature Conservancy Council on the Ainsdale NNR (see Figure 8.5). Figure 8.5, showing wells 7 and 11, also demonstrates that the annual fluctuation of the water table can vary. Well 7 which has a significantly smaller fluctuation is situated in the landward end of a very large dune slack relatively near to the sea, in contrast to well 11 which is in a smaller more landward slack. Payne (1983a) describes the lesser fluctuation as being characterised by surface run-off to the seaward end of the slack, rather than pooling of the water table to the surface. The proximity of the water table to the surface for much of the year in this area creates a very short, species-rich vegetation (termed "wet bryophyte" slack by Payne) of which mosses form a significant component. Exclosures in this slack however, demonstrate that rabbit grazing is important in maintaining this vegetation type.

Payne (1983a) has proposed a model for dune slack succession (see Figure 8.7) and gives a detailed description of each of the communities he identifies.

MESOTROPHIC GRASSLANDS

Mesotrophic grassland is extensively found on the coast, where it is a successional stage developing from a range of both dune and slack communities, especially SD 9,10 and 15. It is also often associated with areas of scrub. Most of it is a form of the NVC community *Arrhenatherum elatius* coarse grassland, with false-oat and cock's foot grasses common and umbellifers such as wild parsnip (*Pastinaca sativa* L.) also present. Payne (1983a) describes this community as running along the edges of larger slacks and totally colonising some slack hollows.

SCRUB

Only a small proportion of the scrub on the coast is the result of succession by species native to the coast.

In the 1988 survey, only SD 17 *Hippophae rhamnoides* dune scrub was identified as a distinct NVC community. Sea buckthorn (*Hippophae rhamnoides* L.) is however only one of a number of species of woody plants which have been successfully introduced over the last 150 years or so in attempts to stabilise the dunes and have since naturalised and spread extensively. Apart from sea buckthorn, poplars, especially white poplar (*Populus alba* L.) and balsam poplar (*P. candicans* Aiton) form the most extensive areas.

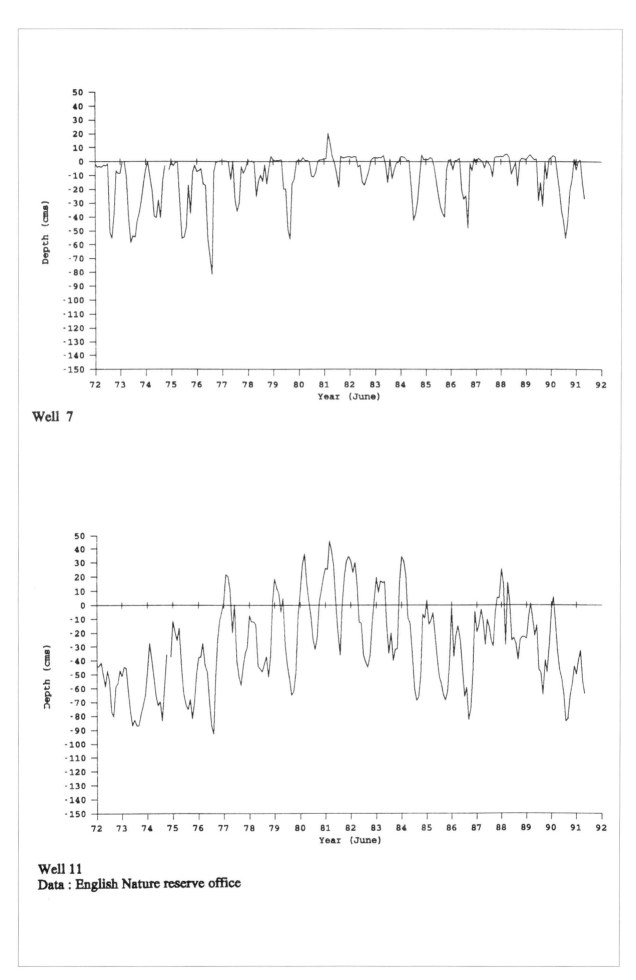

Well 7

Well 11
Data : English Nature reserve office

Figure 8.5 Time series plots of water table depths for the period 1972-1991, Ainsdale Sand Dunes NNR. Data: English Nature.

Figure 8.6 Dune habitats of the Sefton Coast. Photographs by David Woodfall.

a) Foredune vegetation (lyme grass and sea-rocket) on blown sand south of Fisherman's path, Ainsdale.

b) Mobile dunes (Marram grass) at Cabin Hill NNR

c) Mobile/fixed dune transition showing a decrease in the area of bare sand. Cabin Hill NNR.

d) Fixed dune flora, with marram grass. creeping dewberry, ragwort, rose-bay willowherb and polypody fern. Cabin Hill NNR.

e) Mature wet/damp slack with meadowsweet. Ainsdale NNR.

f) Sea buckthorn scrub growing on fixed dunes. The plant also invades drying slacks. Ainsdale LNR.

g) Birch Woodland. Ainsdale NNR.

h) Blowout. Ainsdale NNR.

74

i) Wet slack. Ainsdale NNR.

k) Dune heath at Freshfield.

Since 1954, when myxomatosis first arrived on the coast (Jones *et al.* this volume) these species, together with the native species (especially willows and birches (*Betula spp.*), and hawthorn (*Crataegus monogyna* Jacq.) have undergone a massive increase. Summarising slack vegetation surveys in 1960, 1971 and 1976, Simpson (1990a) records an "explosive spread of *Hippophae rhamnoides*", expansion of other deciduous scrub types and invasion by regenerating pines.

Scrub is extensive and widespread coastwide, although is rather more sparse at the more disturbed northern and southern extremities and also on Ainsdale NNR. In the NVC survey the scrub areas were mapped mostly by the dominant woody species but additional notes were

l) Pine Woodland. Ainsdale NNR.

made for many of the areas, listing the shrubs and the dominant herb layer species. No attempt has been made to classify these extensive communities, which vary significantly in their impact on the vegetation. For example, relatively old, extensive white or balsam poplar stands which have invaded dune ridges, contrast markedly with mixed birch-hawthorn scrub which has invaded a dry slack area. The former often retains a ground-layer plant community similar to an SD14 or SD 11 community, but the latter may be rapidly colonised by mesotrophic herb and grass species such as rose-bay willowherb (*Chamerion angustifolium* (L.) Holub.), stinging nettle (*Urtica dioica* L.) and false oat.

j) Wet slack vegetation. Grass-of-Parnassus and water mint. Ainsdale NNR.

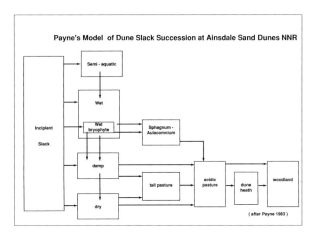

Figure 8.7 Payne's Model of Dune Slack Succession at Ainsdale Sand Dunes NNR (After Payne 1983a).

Scrub development appears to accelerate the process of enrichment of the soil with plant nutrients, particularly by the annual leaf-fall and in sea buckthorn by nodules on its roots which are able to fix nitrogen into the soil from the air.

Habitat management programmes have cleared much scrub, especially sea buckthorn, and monitoring on Ainsdale NNR records re-establishment by some dune plants especially on the ridges. Clearance sites in slacks are more likely to return to scrub (Simpson 1990a; Wheeler *et al.,* this volume).

The impacts of these large scrub areas on a whole range of seral communities is still to be assessed.

DECIDUOUS WOODLAND

The Sefton coast woods were surveyed in 1982 by Gray and Clitherow who recorded species lists for the canopy and ground flora of all sites from Formby south to Cabin Hill.

No deciduous woodland on the coast has developed purely as a result of natural succession to a climax condition. Some of the scrub described above is now developing towards a woodland condition, but the birch - hawthorn communities are the only natural type. A large stand of alder (*Alnus glutinosa* (L.) Gaertner) woodland occurs in a slack area beside Fishermans Path on Ainsdale NNR (SD 285095). Using cores taken from the trees, the age of the trunks in this wood were estimated in 1975 to be 40 to 50 years old (M. Hughes quoted in Robinson 1975). The alder stand is not on the Ordnance Survey map of 1848, but is shown on a later edition of about 1870. It is assumed that it was planted and then coppiced at about 50 years old (Robinson 1975). Although originally planted, this stand is spreading into an adjacent slack area by natural regeneration. A much smaller slack with alder woodland occurs on the National Trust site.

The main areas of deciduous woodland are planted and occur on the eastern side of the dunes in the Formby and Ravenmeols area, often surrounded by areas of pine plantation. The majority is dominated either by a species of poplar (*Populus alba* L., *P. candicans* Aiton, *P.* x *canescens* (Aiton) Smith, *P. nigra* L. or *P. tremula* L.) or by sycamore (*Acer pseudoplatanus* L.), although usually other species are mixed in, the most frequent being hawthorn, pedunculate oak (*Quercus robur* L.), crack willow (*Salix fragilis* L.) and Wych elm (*Ulmus glabra* Hudson), plus pines (*Pinus* spp.). Norway maple (*Acer platanoides* L.), horse chestnut (*Aesculus hippocastanum* L.), alder, silver birch (*Betula pendula* Roth) and ash (*Fraxinus excelsior* L.) occur less frequently.

Bramble (*Rubus fruticosus* agg.) is very common in the shrub layer. Sycamore regeneration is frequent and elder (*Sambucus nigra* L.) is occasional.

Although more extensive than in the pine woods, the ground flora is not botanically diverse or significant. The ivy cultivar (*Hedera helix* L. 'Hibernica') is widely naturalised throughout these woodlands and is often the dominant constituent of the ground flora. Other common species are ground elder (*Aegopodium podagraria* L.), rose-bay willowherb and stinging nettle.

A small but potentially more interesting area of silver birch - pedunculate oak woodland has been created by planting, mostly in the early 1970s, and by natural colonisation in an area cleared of pine plantation at the north end of Ainsdale NNR (SD 301109). This area has not been colonised by the species typical of nutrient-rich conditions described above. The ground flora is mixed, but large areas are dominated by sand sedge and there is much birch regeneration. This is an excellent area for macrofungi.

DESCRIPTION OF THE VEGETATION. 2. MODIFIED VEGETATION

THE PINEWOODS

There are about 269 hectares of woodland on the Sefton coast, occupying approximately 22% of the total area of the dune system (Doody 1989). The majority of the woodland is Corsican pine (*Pinus nigra* ssp. *laricio* Maire) and Scots pine (*P. sylvestris* L.), although Austrian pine (*P. nigra* ssp. *nigra* Arnold), maritime pine (*P. pinaster* Aiton) and lodgepole pine (*P. contorta* Douglas ex Loudon) are also present. The trees were planted to provide shelter and as a timber crop, and more recently recreation and conservation have become important functions. Planting began in 1887 and has continued to the present day, with most of the woodlands being planted before the 1930s. The history of the woodlands and their management has been described by Garbett (1990), Gresswell (1953), Macdonald (1954) and JCAS (1990).

The flora of the pine woodland is very different from the dune vegetation which previously occupied the area. The evergreen canopy casts a dense shade, and the accumulating layer of needle litter causes significant soil changes (James & Wharfe 1989) and inhibits seed germination (Greenow 1989). Pine woodland has a relatively low diversity of plant species, and the uniformly species-poor vegetation may cover large areas. The woodland vegetation has been described by Gray and Clitherow (1982).

Despite their low number of plant species the woods do possess some botanical importance. Dune helleborine (*Epipactis leptochila* var. *dunensis* (T. & T.A.Stephenson) Godfrey) and pendulous-flowered helleborine (*E. phyllanthes* G.E.Smith), both nationally rare species, are found throughout much of the woodland area. The pinewoods now contain the major part of the local dune helleborine population, which is originally associated with *Salix repens* in dune slacks (Gray & Clitherow, 1982).

In the densest woodland very few higher plants are able to grow, and the ground flora may be a sparse cover of bryophytes such as *Hypnum cupressiforme* Hedw., *Lophocolea* spp. and *Brachythecium rutabulum* (Hedw.) Br. Eur. amongst the needle carpet.

In younger, thinned plantations and especially where light is able to penetrate at woodland edges, the ground cover may be dominated by sand sedge, sometimes together with Yorkshire fog or the moss *Dicranium scoparium* Hedw.

The highest amount of ground cover and species-diversity are found in the older pinewoods which have been periodically thinned, the dominant species often being bramble and broad buckler fern (*Dryopteris dilatata* (Hoffm.) A.Gray), associated with mosses such as *Eurhynchium praelongum* (Hedw.) Br. Eur., *Plagiothecium undulatum* (Hedw.) Br. Eur. and *Hypnum cupressiforme* Hedw.

Disturbance can influence the vegetation, and where there has been a fire or turning over of the needle litter, especially where light can reach the woodland floor, species such as rose-bay willowherb, common ragwort (*Senecio jacobaea* L.), stinging nettle, and violets (*Viola* spp.) can be seen.

A more drastic form of disturbance is clear-felling or heavy thinning. Where this has been carried out, the conditions allow the growth of many more light-demanding species. Other woodland trees may regenerate naturally, especially those whose seeds are brought in by birds. Species include elder, hawthorn,

dog rose (*Rosa canina* L.), holly (*Ilex aquifolium* L.), *Sorbus* spp., oaks, sycamore and white poplar. The ground flora may contain species such as rose-bay willowherb, sand sedge, ground-ivy (*Glechoma hederacea* L.), red campion (*Silene dioica* (L.) Clairv.), Yorkshire fog, creeping soft-grass (*Holcus mollis* L.) and the mosses *Dicranum scoparium* Hedw., *Polytrichum formosum* Hedw. and *Eurhynchium praelongum* (Hedw.) Br. Eur. The second rotation woodlands invariably have a richer ground flora and greater structural diversity and are generally of greater conservation value.

The planting of so many trees has inevitably caused some changes in un-forested areas. These problems include the self-seeding of pines into unplanted areas, and the lowering of the watertable by as much as one metre (R.K.Pegg, unpublished data). The subsequent drying of dune slacks has been associated with loss of species diversity and an increase in birch invasion (Atkinson 1988). Plans to remove large areas of poor quality woodland from the Ainsdale NNR in an attempt to restore vegetation more typical of a sand dune system, were put into operation in 1992 with a first phase of 4 ha.

AMENITY GRASSLAND

The most significant amount of amenity grassland on the open dunes is the combined area of tees, greens, and fairways on the five golf courses. Apart from the morphological alteration of the dunes, all of these areas, but especially the greens, are heavily managed, by continual mowing, watering and treatment with herbicides and artificial fertilisers. This results in the golf courses being a patchwork of bright green and the more natural browns and paler greens of the surrounding sand dune vegetation. Total loss of sand dune vegetation occurs, and it is replaced by mesotrophic grassland, the majority dominated by the NVC community *Lolium perenne* mesotrophic grassland, both *Lolium perenne - Plantago lanceolata* and *Lolium perenne - Poa pratensis* sub-communities are common. Only infrequently are the grass swards influenced in their composition by the dune or acid grassland characteristics of adjacent communities.

A large expanse of open dunes was bulldozed and seeded to create this type of grassland in the early 1970s. An area approximately 3.5 km long and on average about 250 m wide, stretches in a continuous strip from the Seaforth Docks in the south to the Coastguard station at Hall Road in the north. This area must demand considerable financial resources in its maintenance and has no nature conservation value. Areas of formal parkland with a similar sward occur in the same region in Blundellsands and Crosby and also at Southport.

A large area of flat, mown grassland has been created from the dunes on the firing ranges at Altcar. Largely, this again is rye-grass dominated grassland, but there are some interesting areas which are the only sites on the coast for green-winged orchid (*Orchis morio* L.) and cowslip (*Primula veris* L.).

Within the built-up areas of Formby, Ainsdale and Birkdale is a considerable area of amenity grassland on former dunescape, comprising areas such as road verges, school playing fields and other similarly maintained areas. The NVC survey did not cover all of this greenspace, but the sward at one site visited indicates that such a survey is justified on nature conservation grounds (although much of the area is probably rye-grass dominated mesotrophic grassland). The low, regularly mown sward on the road verges in the housing area between the Coastal Road and Kenilworth Road at Ainsdale (SD 304120) is a drought-tolerant turf consisting of silver hair-grass (*Aira caryophyllea* L.), soft brome (*Bromus hordeaceus* L.), buck's-horn plantain (*Plantago coronopus* L.), common stork's-bill (*Erodium cicutarium* (L.) L'Hér.), hairy hawkbit (*Leontodon saxatilis* Lam.), glabrous rupture-wort (*Herniaria glabra* L.) white clover (*Trifolium repens* L.), hare's-foot clover (*Trifolium arvense* L.), lesser trefoil (*Trifolium dubium* Sibth.), dove's-foot crane's-bill (*Geranium molle* L.), little mouse-ear chickweed (*Cerastium semidecandrum* L.) and the moss *Tortula ruraliformis* (Besch.) Ingham, almost all species of dune grassland. Buck's-horn plantain, which occurs in almost every area sampled on these verges is rare on the dunes, silver hair-grass is uncommon on the dunes and glabrous rupture-wort, a rare plant nationally, has not been recorded on the dunes and is not listed in Savidge, Heywood and Gordon (1963).

TOBACCO WASTE TIPS

Large areas of the dunes on the National Trust site have been used for dumping tobacco waste, largely on old asparagus fields (Figure 8.8). Some of this, together with a small area on Lifeboat Road, is now exposed on the eroding face of the frontal dunes. The largest area is 4.5 ha in extent (SD 273077) and the total area is approximately 7 ha. The tobacco waste is an organically rich substrate with high moisture retention, totally different from dune sand. Much of the waste is colonised by extensive stands of stinging nettle, with great hairy willow-herb (*Epilobium hirsutum* L.) co-dominant in parts and cleavers abundant. Other species are mixed in but almost all are either ecologically similar tall herbs or ruderals.

In places, sand has covered the waste and marram has colonised. In 1988, an apparently anomalous feature, that of common reed on dunes, was explained by the presence of tobacco waste beneath the surface sand. This feature has since been eroded by the sea.

The tobacco waste represents a significant area of non-dune vegetation on the open dunes.

ASPARAGUS FIELDS

Rimmer (1986) estimates that asparagus growing has been conducted on the Sefton coast for at least 100 years, and probably much longer, and that during the early part of this century it reached its peak with 100 hectares in cultivation. (see also Jones *et al.* this volume) Asparagus was grown on land levelled from the dunes, virgin sand being preferred, which was fertilised with animal manure.

The land can be continuously cultivated for 20 years and is then laid fallow. Although many abandoned asparagus fields are clearly visible on the ground and in old air photographs, there appears to be no coast-wide map of all areas previously farmed for asparagus, or the dates at which they were abandoned. Figure 8.9 gives an example of the scale of farming at Formby Point in 1945 and 1982. Many previously farmed areas have now been built on as Formby has expanded, or have been subject to sand-winning or tobacco waste dumping. Asparagus farming now has almost completely died out.

The nature of the vegetation on old asparagus fields appears to depend on the time since abandonment and the position of the site.

Large areas on Lifeboat Road, in open dunes relatively near the coast (150-800m), which have apparently been abandoned a considerable time , are covered by a red fescue dominated dune grassland, whereas another area on the same site, 800-925m from the coast is covered by mesotrophic grassland which is being invaded by rose-bay willowherb and bramble. The majority of the abandoned fields, including sites on Ravenmeols Hills LNR, Lifeboat Road and National Trust land are covered by mesotrophic grassland, sometimes with ruderals or red fescue grassland mixed in. A site on Ainsdale NNR which is surrounded by pines has a mix of more acidic communities including marram - red fescue - common bent dune. This site may be managed in future to encourage the development of dune heath (D. Wheeler pers. comm. 1991).

ANALYSIS - TOWARDS A MODEL OF DUNE SUCCESSION

DRY DUNES

The early successional stages at the top of the beach, where conditions are stressful for the growth of most plants, parallels that of many dune systems, where decreasing stress is matched by increasing species diversity with distance from the coast. The characteristic successional series of sand couch-grass to

Figure 8.8 Area of tobacco waste tipping, Formby Point. Tipping was mainly confined to disused asparagus fields between Blundell Avenue and Victoria Road (see Figure 8.9). The area of tipping is distinguished by a lush growth of stinging nettles.

marram dunes, which then acquire an increasing cover of red fescue and a range of other typical sand dune plants is clear. This can be seen north and south of the Formby Point erosion front where accretion is occurring.

At the erosion front, sand couch-grass dunes are missing, and this plant is then more common on the lee of eroded dunes where sand exposed by the waves has been blown inland. To the lee of the large transgressive sand sheets, the successional series also varies as semi-fixed vegetation is reverting to marram dunes with the invasion of large amounts of sand.

An alternative early successional sequence also occurs, which might, with management, become more important. This involves the development on the beach of common saltmarsh grass plants which, with sand accumulation around the grassy patches, eventually coalesce and become sufficiently stable and high for the colonisation by other terrestrial plants such as sand couch-grass, lyme-grass and marram. Algae are probably important precursors to the colonisation by common saltmarsh grass.

Next in the series is a mosaic of marram - restharrow dune and marram - sand cat's-tail dune, with mosses such as *Tortula ruraliformis, Ceratodon purpureus,*

Brachythecium albicans and *Hypnum cupressiforme* often being important sand surface binders.

The subsequent development of the vegetation involves an increased cover of grasses and range of herbs, but also dewberry and creeping willow.

This stage is represented by extensive areas of undifferentiated SD 9 and SD 9r mapped in the NVC survey, and the broad band of red fescue - dewberry, and creeping willow - dewberry types described by Payne (1983a) at Ainsdale. This vegetation type replaces the SD 10 *Festuca rubra - Galium verum* dune which is so widespread on systems which are more grazed, e.g. Aberffraw in Gwynedd and Sandscale in Cumbria. The lack of grazing is almost certainly the cause of the absence of SD 10 and the widespread occurrence of grassy, shrubby SD 9. However SD 10 vegetation does occur in moderately trampled areas such as around car parks and on footpaths.

Trampling pressure thus appears to replace the stress or disturbance caused at other sites by grazing.

It seems probable that the widespread occurrence of the grassy and shrubby SD 9 vegetation has arisen since the advent of myxomatosis in the mid-1950s. The rabbit population was certainly much higher

79

previously, having a significant impact on the mobility of the dunes. J.A. Wheldon noted in 1915 that "rabbits were very much in evidence" on walking through the Ainsdale and Birkdale area, a description entirely suitable for the rabbit population at Aberffraw at the present. He also noted the highly mobile state of the marram dunes with "some higher dunes half cut away" the sand having been blown into neighbouring hollows. The aerial photograph of Ainsdale LNR and NNR in Gresswell (1953) shows the dunes generally to be in a much more mobile condition than at present with bare sand on most dune ridges. The wide belt of bare sand at the base of dune ridges around slack edges, which is so characteristic and consistent on grazed dune systems is clearly seen around nearly all the slacks in this photograph but is now absent or very narrow. Newlands, Thompson and Robinson (1987) state quite categorically that " the development of deciduous scrub ... is a post myxomatosis phenomenon." It would seem unlikely that such a significant release of grazing pressure would not have a similarly dramatic impact on the grassland communities.

The widespread occurrence of this grassy/dwarf shrubby community devalues the conservation value of the dunes. Firstly, it is less species-rich than the red fescue - herb rich communities and secondly, it is indicative of the over-stable condition of the dunes. Lack of dune mobility results in less diversity of vegetation types, compared with more dynamic systems in which conditions change cyclically from stable to mobile and back to stable cover. Also there will be no formation of secondary dune slacks, or the movement of dune ridges across dune slack surfaces as described by Ranwell (1958) at Newborough Warren in Gwynedd. This results in progressive senescence and loss of diversity in the existing dune slacks.

The extensive growth of scrub on dune ridges and slacks has accelerated the problem by further stabilisation, loss of species diversity and enhanced addition to the nutrient budget of the dune soils.

The present and future successional sequence subsequent to this grassy/shrubby vegetation is of significance because of its widespread occurrence. Mesotrophic grassland is developing in a number of sites, but is more common around scrub margins and in old dry dune slacks. It is possible that such development could be more widespread in the future, particularly if the deposition of nitrogen pollution from the atmosphere is increased. Colonisation by scrub is also common.

Later stages of dune grassland succession when most calcium has been leached from the soil, would be expected to tend towards short, more acidic vegetation communities such as *Ammophila arenaria - Festuca*

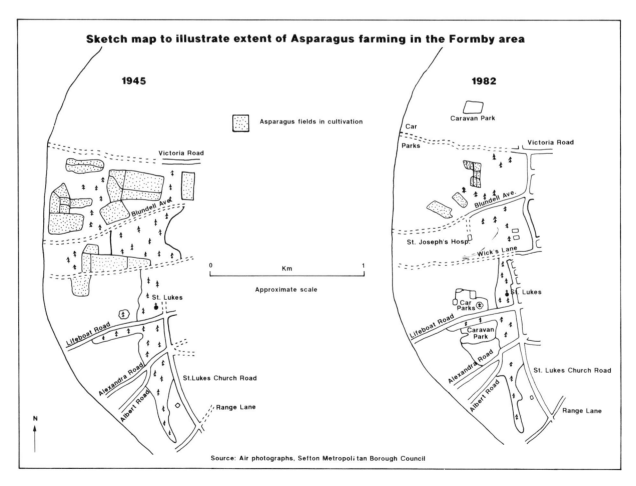

Figure 8.9 Sketch map to illustrate extent of asparagus farming in the Formby area. (Source: Air photographs, Sefton Metropolitan Borough Council).

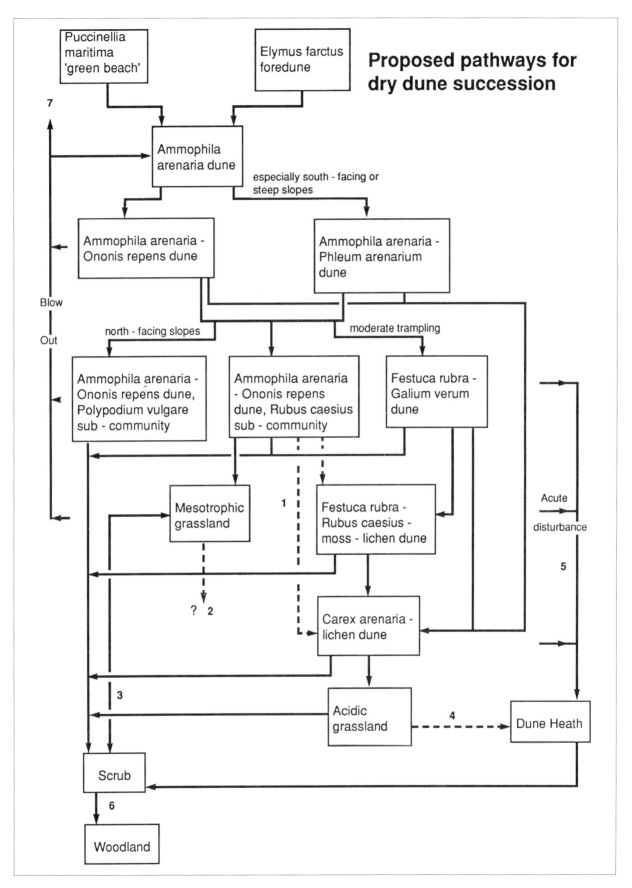

Figure 8.10 Proposed pathways for dry dune succession.

Notes: *1 The succession to acidic communities needs further investigation; tighter nutrient budgets in vegetation with a relatively large biomass, plus enhanced water retention, may reduce rates of leaching. 2 Development of acidic communities from this stage seem less likely than 1. 3 Increased nutrient enrichment from scrub communities causes development of an encircling ring of mesotrophic grassland. 4 The most landward natural dune ridges are vegetated by calcifugous grassland, with dune heath only in the surrounding lows. 5 The most extensive areas of the dune heath occur on areas disturbed by complete alteration of the dune morphology eg. agriculture, golf course construction. 6 Some mature scrub is almost at the 'woodland stage'. Other areas of woodland are planted. 7 Secondary dune slacks may be caused by deflation down to the water table.*

ovina - Agrostis capillaris dune or *Carex arenaria - Cladonia* spp. dune, and eventually acid grassland. Although these communities do occur on the Sefton coast they may have developed at times when a different type of grassland community was predominant. Malloch (1985) describes *Ammophila arenaria - Festuca ovina - Agrostis capillaris* dune as replacing the *Festuca rubra - Galium verum* community when sands have become extensively decalcified. The *Festuca rubra - Galium verum* zone is replaced on the Sefton coast, however, by the dwarf shrub/grass SD 9r vegetation described above. Payne (1983a) describes the inland edge of this dwarf shrub/grass zone as being characterised by the gradual disappearance of creeping willow and the development of short red fescue and dewberry growing in a carpet of mosses and lichens, typically heavily rabbit grazed. This type of vegetation however is not widespread and again may have arisen prior to the impact of reduced grazing pressure or on previously bare sand well back in the dune system. Furthermore Payne's analysis is necessarily interrupted at about this stage because of the disruption of the sequence by conifer plantations, the coastal road (built along the line of the old Cheshire Lines railway in 1968) and residential development. The next 'zone' he describes is the acidic grassland vegetation found extensively on Southport and Ainsdale Golf Course which is much further inland.

A coast-wide systematic soil survey investigating nutrient status and pH might help to predict the likelihood of these acidic dune communities developing from the widely occurring dwarf shrub/grass community or the mesotrophic grassland which is becoming increasingly widespread. Malloch (1989), discussing an *Ammophila arenaria - Arrhenatherum elatius* community with an increased nutrient status, says "it is not too clear how it relates to dune zonation".

Carex arenaria dune and *Carex arenaria - Cladonia* spp. dune, which would represent a stage towards development of acidic dune grassland, is mostly found in association with the pine plantations where soil conditions have been considerably altered.

It seems probable that the areas of acidic grassland found most abundantly on Southport and Ainsdale Golf Course developed in the past either from vegetation similar to the short red fescue - dewberry - moss - lichen community described by Payne or from sand sedge - lichen communities, although it is not possible to follow this temporal sequence spatially on the ground. It is even possible that this area was part of an earlier phase of dune development previous to the blow-outs and large parabolic dunes characteristic of Pye's (1990) pre-1800 phase of dune development. Modification of the pre-existing landforms by golf course construction makes this possibility difficult to substantiate.

There appears to be no development of dune heath on the dune ridges in this area, although ling can be dominant in the old slacks. Heath does develop on other parts of the system where disturbance by peoples' activities has occurred.

Any of these dry dune communities may be subject to scrub encroachment, especially by the introduced poplars. A model of pathways of dry dune succession is proposed in Figure 8.10, which includes an indication of the less certain routes.

DUNE SLACKS

Dune slack succession is difficult to summarise because a number of factors constantly change and interact to produce the vegetation of any one slack at any one time. As with dry dune succession the earlier stages are clear. Very wet slacks and pools are rapidly colonised by Charophytes, and subsequently by aquatics or semi-aquatics such as the water crowfoot (*Ranunculus trichophyllus* Chaix.) and various-leaved pondweed (*Potamogeton gramineus* L.). In wet to damp slacks a species rich community containing many regionally scarce species can develop quite quickly, shown by the colonisation of the scrape margins on Ainsdale NNR (Simpson 1990f). Early colonists are creeping bent-grass and jointed rush (*Juncus articulatus* L.) and are soon joined by species such as few-flowered spike-rush (*Eleocharis quinqueflora* (F.Hartm.) Schwarz), yellow sedge (*Carex viridula* ssp. *viridula* Michx.), brookweed (*Samolus valerandi* L.), bristle club-rush (*Isolepis setacea* (L.) R.Br.) and bog pimpernel (*Anagallis tenella* (L.) L.), all low-growing species which cannot compete in a taller, denser sward. Creeping willow is always an early coloniser in all but the wettest slacks, but at this stage remains in the low, prostrate form without becoming competitively dominant.

The younger slacks are certainly the more species-rich and have the highest nature conservation value botanically. Increasing age brings increasing dominance by creeping willow and loss of species diversity in slacks with a wide range of hydrological conditions, unless it is controlled by heavy grazing pressure. Payne (1980a) considers that rabbit grazing may only be effective in controlling creeping willow if other preferred food is in short supply. He quotes a report to the Nature Conservancy reporting that "by 1957 (prior to myxomatosis) some slacks ... were in some cases overgrown by creeping willow and other vegetation." The succession towards species-poor creeping willow dominated slacks therefore may not solely be a post-myxomatosis phenomenon on this coast[2]. Exclosures

---

[2] The first records and spread of myxomatosis, which would probably have killed 99% of the rabbit population is crucial here. Jones *et al.*, this volume (Appendix to chapter 1) quote a reference to myxomatosis from 1954.

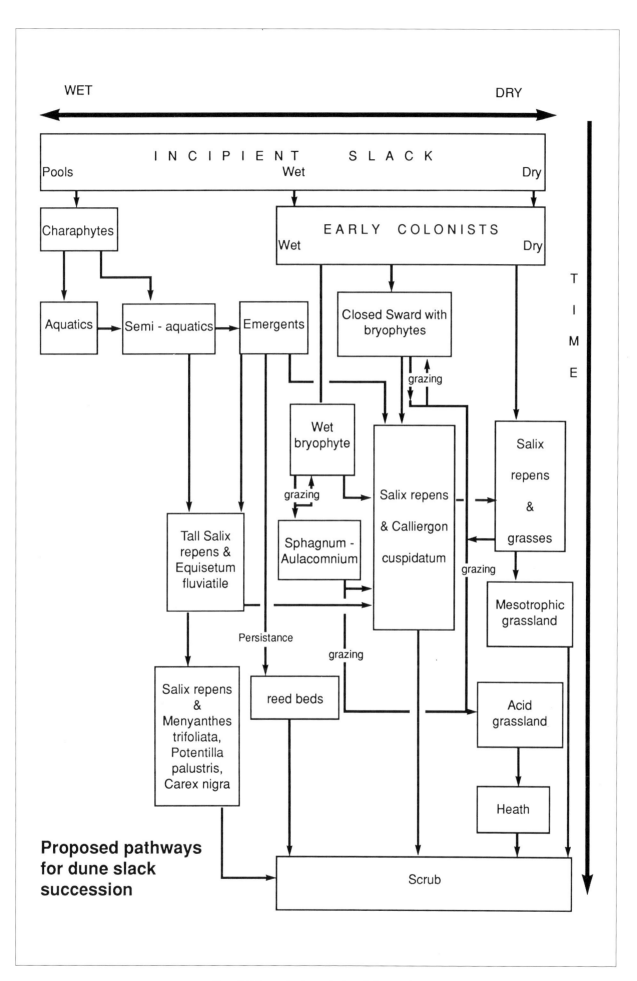

Figure 8.11 Proposed pathways for dune slack succession.

83

on the Sefton coast show that rabbits are significantly affecting dune slack succession, but grazing pressure is not sufficiently high to arrest the widespread development of species-poor slacks dominated by creeping willow. The lack of new slack formation is another important factor. The introduction in 1990 of sheep grazing and in late 1991 of cattle grazing to Ainsdale NNR is an important step in the management of the ecological resources of the dunes, potentially altering the successional processes and revitalising the dynamics of the dune geomorphology. The change in 1991 to summer grazing by cattle on the recently only winter-grazed areas of slack on Cabin Hill NNR (Simpson 1991a) will also be interesting.

The "wet bryophyte" slack type described by Payne (1983a), if sufficiently heavily rabbit grazed will be colonised by hummocks of the mosses *Aulacomnium palustre* Hedw. and *Sphagnum plumulosum* Röll, indicating the development of more acidic conditions on the characteristic peat layer.

In older slacks which remain wet, species associated with creeping willow are water horsetail, marsh pennywort (*Hydrocotyle vulgaris* L.) and the moss *Calliergon cuspidatum* (Hedw.) Kindb. These slacks may eventually become more acidic and plants such as bogbean (*Menyanthes trifoliata* L.), common cotton-grass (*Eriophorum angustifolium* Honck.), marsh cinquefoil (*Potentilla palustris* (L.) Scop.) and common sedge occur (SD 16-type vegetation).

If a slack becomes drier associated species are grasses such as red fescue, Yorkshire fog and smooth meadow-grass. This condition is very widespread and commonly becomes transitional to false-oat coarse mesotrophic grassland. As with dry dunes, the question as to whether this dense, grassy vegetation will develop towards acidic grassland and eventually heath is difficult to answer.

Ling has become established in a few dune slacks on the landward edge of Ainsdale NNR, but these are surrounded by pine plantations and presumably are significantly influenced by them. Payne's (1983a) model of dune slack succession includes a sequence from "tall pasture" to "acidic pasture" to dune heath. He describes a stage where red fescue decreases in importance and common bent-grass and sheep's fescue become common, and in slacks in the pine plantations lichens and mosses such as *Racomitrium lanuginosum* (Hedw.)Brid., *Dicranum scoparium* Hedw., *Hypnum cupressiforme* Hedw. and *Polytrichum juniperinum* Hedw. become important. As with the dry dune succession, however this transitional stage towards the acidic communities is uncommon.

Scrub may encroach upon dune slack communities at almost any stage or condition except semi-aquatic. Wet slacks may be invaded by willows, damp slacks by sea buckthorn and damp to dry slacks by hawthorn or birch spp. mixed scrub or pine seedlings.

A refinement of Payne's model of slack succession is proposed by Edmondson (1991) (see Figure 8.11) Analysis of new slack survey data at Ainsdale NNR confirm that age and hydrology are the dominating influences on the nature of slack vegetation. Other factors however, were shown to be significant, including soil pH, the condition of creeping willow and proximity to the slack margin.

Although models of successional processes are a vital aid to understanding and management of dune plant communities, the vegetation at any one time and place is a function of the history of physical, biological and human factors that have operated through time at that particular place, and will be unique. The further that succession progresses from the early stages which are dominated by the severe physical stress and disturbance of the backshore environment, the greater will be the variation in plant responses to the range of conditions experienced, including increased significance of competition between plants.

Sally Edmondson (Review co-ordinator)

Liverpool Institute of Higher Education,
Environmental & Biological Studies,
Stand Park Road,
P.O. Box 6
Liverpool L16 9JD

A full list of contributors is given in Appendix 2.

CHAPTER NINE

Clear-Felling Dune Plantations: Studies in Vegetation Recovery on the Sefton Coast

P. W. Sturgess

INTRODUCTION

Afforestation of sand dunes is associated with ecological changes including loss of flora and fauna, soil change, a fall in level of water tables, and seeding into surrounding duneland (Sturgess, in press; Atkinson 1988). In response to these effects some dune managers are attempting to restore sand dune habitat of greater conservation value by removing areas of pine woodland from several nature reserves.

This report is based on studies of cleared sites at Ainsdale Sand Dunes National Nature Reserve (Ainsdale NNR), and on National Trust land in Formby. The Ainsdale NNR dune woodlands were planted between 1897 and 1960, mostly with Corsican pine (*Pinus nigra* ssp. *laricio* Maire). Woodland covers 120 hectares of the nature reserve (JCAS 1990), over one third of the total area (Figure 9.1). The majority of the tree clearance was carried out during the second World War and in creating fire-breaks between 1977 and 1981. The study sites had been afforested for 30-70 years prior to felling, consequently losing almost all of their natural flora and developing an acidic needle layer. The ground-flora of the woodlands is described by Edmondson *et al.* (this volume). Trees were felled leaving the stumps *in situ,* but removing the logs and branches. Litter was not removed, although it would have been disturbed during felling.

VEGETATION CHANGES

Vegetation data was collected using National Vegetation Classification techniques (Malloch 1985). Sample areas of woodland, unplanted dunes and clear-felled sites were examined using 2x2 metre quadrats. A total of 310 quadrats were used for this study.

The abundance of each species was recorded using Domin values as an estimate for plant cover. Slope, aspect (compass direction), vegetation height, vegetation cover, bare sand and depth of the organic soil horizons were also noted for each quadrat.

The main trends in vegetation quality within the data were identified using detrended correspondence analysis (DECORANA), an ordination technique.

Figure 9.1 Aerial view of Ainsdale Sand Dunes NNR, showing the area afforested and the distribution of frontal and rear woodland. English Nature's long term intention is to remove the area of frontal woodland starting a first phase in 1991/92.

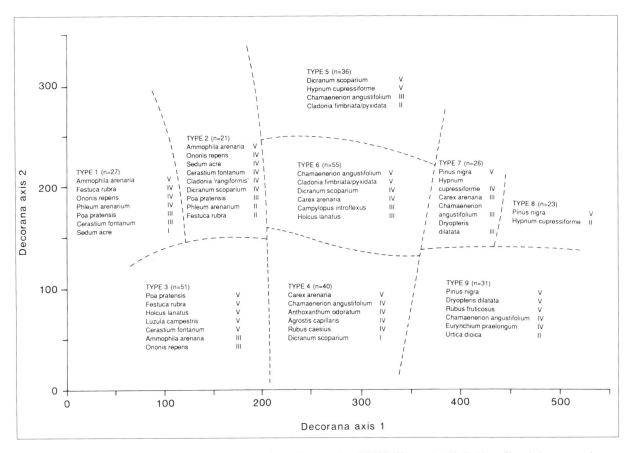

Figure 9.2 **TWINSPAN** summary diagram, showing the positions of vegetation types along **DECORANA** axes 1 and 2. Positions of boundaries are approximate.

Quadrats which have very similar plant species with similar abundances are placed very close together on ordination diagrams. Vegetation types were identified using Two Way Indicator Species Analysis (TWINSPAN) which also assisted description of the plant communities.

Figure 9.2 shows the distribution of quadrat data along the primary and secondary DECORANA axes. Nine vegetation types are identified. Positions on the ordination diagram may be related to environmental factors. Table 9.1 shows that axis 1 is largely related to tree-cover, with higher values given to quadrats with older woodland, a deeper organic soil, low species diversity and low percentage ground vegetation cover. On axis 2 high values are given to quadrats with a shallow organic soil and a relatively high proportion of lichens and mosses. Low values are given to quadrats with deeper soil and taller vegetation. This may be related to water and/or nutrient availability.

Figure 9.3 shows that quadrats from recently felled woodlands occupy an intermediate position along DECORANA axis 1, between the woodlands and the

TABLE 9.1.
Linear regression statistics for DECORANA axes 1 and 2, with recorded variables. Percentage data has been arcsine transformed. (= p<0.005, * = p<0.05, NS = not significant)**

	AXIS 1			AXIS 2		
	Correlation	Explained Variance (R²)	Degrees Of Freedom	Correlation	Explained Variance (R²)	Degrees Of Freedom
Woodland age	+	.630	308 **	+	.035	308 **
Years felled	-	.021	308 *	-	.023	308 *
Soil depth	+	.208	158 **	-	.151	158 **
Percentage Vegetation Cover	-	.261	208 **	-	.006	208 NS
Percentage Bare Sand	-	.071	244 **	+	.092	244 **
Vegetation Height	+	.057	255 **	-	.029	255 *
Number of species	-	.410	308 **	-	.018	308 *
Number of Moss species	+	.087	308 **	+	.121	308 **
Number of Lichen species	-	.009	308 NS	+	.326	308 **
Slope	-	.066	253 **	-	.004	253 NS

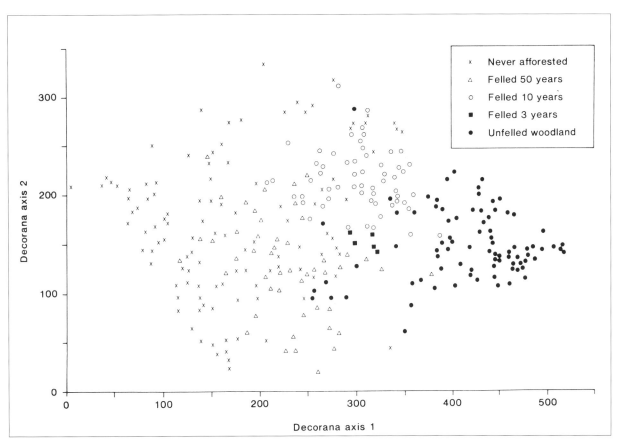

Figure 9.3 **DECORANA** diagram, showing length of time after felling

unplanted dunes. The vegetation is dominated by rose-bay willowherb (*Chamerion angustifolium* (L.) Raf.), ragwort (*Senecio jacobaea* L.) and mosses and lichens (particularly *Dicranum scoparium* Hedw., *Campylopus introflexus* (Hedw.) Brid., *Hypnum cupressiforme* Hedw. and *Cladonia* spp.). Quadrats from the older plantations felled for 10 years tend to have a high score on axis 2, with a bryophyte and lichen dominated ground flora, probably indicating a low availability of nutrients. Several cleared sites are now dominated by scrub vegetation where birch and pine seedlings have become established. Many quadrats from sites felled during the war are very similar to the unplanted dunes, although they tend to have a lower species diversity with more tall grasses, rose-bay willowherb, sand sedge (*Carex arenaria* L.), *Dicranum scoparium* and *Cladonia* than dunes which have never been afforested.

SOILS

Samples of the organic (L,F,H) layer and the mineral soil at 0-5cm, 5-15cm and 15-25cm depth were taken from a total of 68 soil pits throughout the study area. Methods of chemical analysis are described by Sturgess (1991). The results of the analyses are summarised in Figure 9.4.

A feature seen in most of these profiles is the sharp distinction between the organic litter and the mineral soil. Organic layers tend to have a lower pH, and higher levels of nitrogen and available phosphate. This is true of the unplanted dunes, but not to such a great extent as in the woodlands. The mineral soil below the needle layer is little altered by 70 years of afforestation; most changes appear to be limited to the top 10 centimetres.

The amount of organic matter in clear-felled sites is lower than in the pinewoods, showing that organic material is being lost. There is also a reduction in the amount of phosphate and ammonium-nitrogen. Total nitrogen appears to increase 10 years after felling; this proportional increase is usual as carbon is lost more quickly through respiration, than nitrogen which remains held in microbial biomass and other unavailable forms (Staaf & Berg 1982). Soil profiles from the recently felled sites show changes to a greater depth than young woodlands felled 50 years ago. This is at least partly the result of soil development proceeding further in the older plantations (James & Wharfe 1989). Following felling there will be an increase in the movements of some minerals as the higher effective rainfall promotes decomposition and leaching, and plants colonise, which grow roots and begin to recycle nutrients (Atkinson & Sturgess 1991); this may be why the profiles for nitrogen and phosphate generally even out with time since felling.

Figure 9.4 also shows changes following removal of tree stumps by bulldozer. The micropodzol is completely broken up, as organic material is buried and calcareous sand is brought to the surface; the resulting

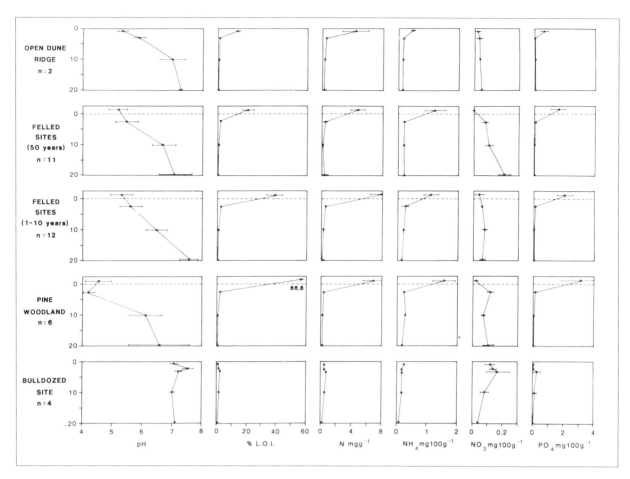

Figure 9.4 Summary of results of soil analyses. Vertical scale shows depth in centimetres. Organic horizons are shown above the dotted line.

profile seems closer to that of grey, or even mobile dunes (see James, this volume).

SEEDBANK

Woodland and unplanted dune seed-banks were examined using a glass-house germination technique. Soil samples were taken from three woodland sites and three nearby unplanted grey dune sites at Ainsdale, in August, 1990.

Samples were spread over trays of sterile seed compost under glasshouse conditions and watered only with distilled water. Seedlings were identified and removed over a period of 3 months. The results of the study are summarised in Table 9.2.

TABLE 9.2.
Ainsdale Seed-bank Study. Total numbers of buried viable seeds. Totals are from three 500 cm³ soil samples for each soil depth.

	GREY-DUNES		WOODLAND			
Soil depth(cm)/horizon	0-2	3-5	L	F	H	O-5
Total Seeds Germinated	379	257	13	28	4	6
Mean seeds per sample	126.3	86.6	4.3	9.3	1.3	2.0
Mean species per sample	12.6+	5.3+	2.3	2.6	1.3	2.0

The soil samples from grey dunes produced large numbers of seedlings, closely reflecting the surface vegetation in composition and including a high diversity of typical 'dune' species. Woodland samples gave rise to relatively few seedlings, those present were mostly 'weed' seeds, notably rose-bay willowherb (53%), from the F horizon.

The woodland sites at Ainsdale once supported a flora similar to the dunes which were never afforested (Salisbury 1925; Blanchard 1952), and would therefore have possessed a diverse dune seed-bank. Most of this has been lost during 70 years under afforested conditions. Species apparently able to survive for longer periods include the relatively large seeds of sand sedge and violets (*Viola* spp); these are usually among the first species to recolonise a felled site.

Seed supply of some species may be increased following afforestation. The most obvious being pine, but bird-distributed tree species such as elder, holly and hawthorn are also increased, indicated by the presence of seedlings throughout the woodlands. In the absence of a ground flora the major seed input appears to be as wind dispersed seeds such as rose-bay and other willowherb species, and various composites. Such seeds do not have a long dormancy (Granstrom 1987), they are present by virtue of their high mobility and their production in large numbers outside the plantation. In the event of the woodland being felled it

88

is this weed-rich woodland seedbank which will provide the most significant immediate contribution towards the revegetation of the site.

DISCUSSION

Afforestation of sand dunes results in almost total exclusion of the original vegetation. Restoring a diverse dune flora to areas which have supported woodland for many years is not possible simply by clear-felling as the ecosystem has been altered substantially, both physically and biologically. There has been a major change to the soil, now covered by needle litter. The low pH of this organic layer may be sufficient to prevent successful growth of many dune plants characteristic of young, calcareous dunes, even if there were a suitable seed source. The high organic content retains water much better than bare sand, and this may be an important factor in the establishment of scrub, particularly birch, on clear-felled sites.

In the older, thinned plantations, there is often a ground flora characterised by sand sedge, bramble (*Rubus fruticosus* agg.), broad-buckler fern (*Dryopteris dilatata* (Hoffm.) A.Gray), or rose-bay willowherb, usually with mosses. Following clear-felling, some of these species such as sand sedge and rose-bay willowherb may quickly become dominant, presumably benefiting from the post-felling nutrient release and an absence of competition.

Immediately after clear-felling there is a large release of soluble nitrogen from decomposing litter (Gosz *et al.* 1973; Vitousek 1981; Williams 1972), but this is only available to established plants and plants quick to germinate. In the absence of a ground flora most of this will be lost from the system by leaching (Berg & Staaf 1981). After the initial breakdown the litter decays more slowly (Sturgess 1991). Some sites have an organic layer up to 10cm deep ten years after clear-felling. Remaining nitrogen and phosphate is largely held in unavailable forms within the humus and the microbial community. Plants colonising the bare litter during this time tend to be mosses and lichens, which may form large carpets. The presence of higher plant species such as birch may increase the rate of litter breakdown and nutrient cycling as leaf litter decays more quickly than pine needles (Nykvist 1959), providing nutrients in forms available to plants and decomposers.

The length of time under woodland conditions is of great importance. The plantations felled fifty years ago were only about 30 years old and may have retained much greater proportion of their dune seed-bank, accumulated less litter, and not exhausted the buffering capacity of any calcium carbonate in the upper soil surface. At a recently felled 30 year old plantation at Whiteford (West Glamorgan) many of the original sand dune species have returned within ten years (Sturgess 1991), and in less than two years where the litter layer was removed. This situation may help to explain why young woodlands felled fifty years ago on the Sefton coast are now predominately grassland rather than scrub woodland or moss carpets. It highlights the benefits of removing trees while they are young, and also of the importance of removing the needle litter in order to reduce the initial nutrient level, to remove the weed seedbank and to allow any original seedbank to germinate.

Peter Sturgess

Department of Environmental and Evolutionary Biology,
University of Liverpool
P.O.Box 147
Liverpool L69 3BX

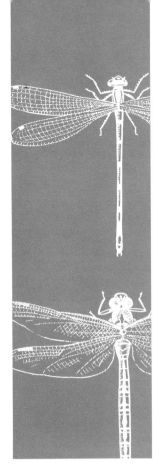

SECTION 5

ANIMAL

AND PLANT GROUPS

CHAPTER TEN

Animal and Plant Groups

D. Atkinson, M. Bird, T. M. Eccles, M. R. Edmondson, S. E. Edmondson, C. Felton,
M. A. Garbett, P. S. Gateley, A. S. Gunn, R. A. Hall, M. Hull, S. Judd, D. A. Nissenbaum,
P. J. Rooney, D. E. Simpson, P. H. Smith and K. W. Wood

INTRODUCTION

The large number of authors contributing to this section reflects the diversity of animals and plants and the specialisms required to study each in detail. The sheer volume and diversity of material, often widely scattered in files and libraries, has forced us to concentrate mainly on cataloguing the work done on specific animal and plant groups, thereby providing a database to help future studies. The commentaries on the various groups are thus unavoidably brief. Because many of the references are unpublished, tables have been produced to help the reader, listing relevant sources of information about particular groups. Omissions, of course, are bound to occur. Details of field reports not listed individually may be extracted from the natural history journals and reports indicated in Table 10.1.

In this section we have tried to indicate those gaps in our knowledge which, if filled, would be particularly valuable for the management of the dune system. The text also gives prominence to species of high amenity or conservation value e.g. natterjack toad (*Bufo calamita* L.), sand lizard (*Lacerta agilis* L.), red squirrel (*Sciurus vulgaris* L.) and the orchids (Orchidaceae). A specialist chapter at the end of this section by Cooke also gives more detail on sand lizard habitat.

TABLE 10.1
Some Local Natural History Society Publications

Lancashire Bird Report
(published by the Lancashire and Cheshire Fauna Society)

Northwestern Bird Report
(published by the Merseyside Naturalists' Association)

Proceedings of the Liverpool Naturalists' Field Club

Lancashire Naturalist 1907-14

Lancashire and Cheshire Naturalist 1914-1951

Northwestern Naturalist (New Series 1-3) 1953-1955

The Naturalist

South West Lancashire Ringing Group, Annual Report 1971-

Report of the Southport Scientific Society

Report of the Southport Society of Natural Science

Lapwing
(published by the Lancashire Trust for Nature Conservation)

Annual Report and Proceedings of the Lancashire and Cheshire Entomological Society

MAMMALS

RED SQUIRREL (*Sciurus vulgaris* L.)
M. A. Garbett

The thriving population of red squirrels at Formby has spread from Freshfield north to Hesketh Park in Southport and south to Crosby. Their existence is due at least partly to introductions since World War II. The main block of coastal woodlands was planted between 1893 and 1930: up to this point the only red squirrels to be found were residing on the estates of Ince Blundell and Little Crosby Hall (E. Hardy, pers. comm.).

About 1942, European red squirrels were liberated probably at Woodvale or Freshfield. In about 1950 a pet shop in Liverpool was selling Russian red squirrels as fashionable pets. There have been several suggestions that a number of these were released. They probably mixed with the local population to colonise the young pine plantations (E. Hardy, pers. comm.). Since then the population has multiplied at an enormous rate (see also Robinson 1972) which has been assisted by supplementary feeding by the public.

The hundreds of thousands of human visitors to the area each year have apparently caused the squirrels to lose their timidity, resulting in extremely bold approaches to visitors at the National Trust Reserve. The presence of the squirrels has an important influence on the management of the Reserve (Clements & Lutley 1987).

Although there are two short studies, (Rice-Oxley 1991; Hughes 1991), this population would benefit from further investigation. Answers to the following questions would be particularly helpful:

What is the minimum size of suitable conifer woodland needed to support a population which is regularly given supplementary food? Red squirrels appear to have 'favourite' trees for cone feeding and regular routeways among the tree branches - can these be identified and thus be protected?

Is the average life-span and breeding success greater than in populations which do not have supplementary feeding?

Given that squirrel density is extremely high at Freshfield and that the pine woodland is aged and suffers from maritime exposure, would planting native deciduous trees (e.g. oak) help provide an important native food source, or could this facilitate an eventual take-over by grey squirrels (Kenward & Holm 1989)?

OTHER MAMMALS
P. J. Rooney

There has been little systematic work on the other mammals of the Coast. Much of the information available and the summary presented here is based on casual observations. Observations on mammals in general include those of Simms (1968), Anon (1972e) and Aldridge (1973a, b, 1974, 1975c).

On Ainsdale Sand Dunes NNR, locations of sightings have been mapped and trapping techniques have been employed on common shrew (*Sorex araneus* L.), pygmy shrew (*Sorex minutus* L.), field vole (*Microtus agrestis* (L.)), wood mouse (*Apodemus sylvaticus* (L.)) and bank vole (*Clethrionomys glareolus* (Schreber) (Bennett 1981; Fox 1972; Harris & Nance 1974; Whitticase 1985).

Woodmice are the most frequently trapped and are present in all habitats sampled. They are most frequent in pinewoods, and are the only animal trapped in modest numbers in deciduous woodland (Bennett 1981). Common shrews are associated with pine woodland, and bank and field voles are concentrated more in dune slack areas (Whitticase 1985). Further work is required to determine the effects of the changing dune habitats on these small-mammal communities.

One water shrew (*Neomys fodiens* (Pennant)) was recorded in 1966 in Massam's slack ditch, and the water vole (*Arvicola terrestris* (L.)) had not been recorded on Ainsdale Sand Dunes NNR for several years since 1967 (Musgrave 1974). Although the status of these animals prior to the last known records is unclear, their absence may be the result of a lowered water table and increased disturbance.

Badgers (*Meles meles* (L.)) have not been seen since 1966 when a family party was spotted near Fishermans Path (Robinson 1985). Badger tracks were identified in the same area in 1967, and on the Birkdale dunes in 1971 (Robinson 1985).

A red deer (*Cervus elaphus* L.) was observed on Ainsdale NNR in 1966 and a stag was present along the Coast during 1990 and 1991.

Stoats (*Mustela erminea* L.) weasels (*M. nivalis* L.), moles (*Talpa europaea* L.), hedgehogs (*Erinaceus europaeus* L.), foxes (*Vulpes vulpes* (L.)) and brown hares (*Lepus capensis* L.) have all been observed on the Coast (Anon 1972a-d; Payne 1978c, d). Apart from the mapping scheme on Ainsdale NNR during the 1970s, no systematic records appear to exist for these animals.

If their abundance and distribution were better known, it might be possible to study, for instance, how stoat and weasel populations are reacting to changes in ground vegetation cover, or how the close proximity of housing development affects the density of foxes.

The dune area is an important feeding habitat for bats, but offers little natural roosting opportunity. Bat boxes have recently been erected in the pine woodland along the Coast. Noctules (*Nyctalus noctula* (Schreber)), pipistrelles (*Pipistrellus pipistrellus* (Schreber)) and long-eared bats (*Plecotus auritus* (L.)), have been recorded using ultra-sonic detectors, and a species of mouse-eared bat (*Myotis* sp.) may occur. A long-eared bat roost is known on Ainsdale NNR and the pipistrelle roosts in housing adjacent to the dune system (P. Rooney, pers. obs.; see also Anon. 1990).

Considering the ecological impact that a large population of rabbits (*Oryctolagus cuniculus* (L.)) can have on sand dunes (Aldridge 1976b; Boorman & Fuller 1982; Edmondson 1987; Edmondson *et al.,* this volume), this species has been remarkably little studied locally. The first myxomatosis outbreak probably occurred in 1954 (Jones *et al.*, appendix 1, this volume). Aldridge (1973b) noted that by 1971 numbers were still below the pre-myxomatosis level. Rabbits with myxomatosis were seen on Ainsdale NNR between 1973 and 1977 (Anon 1975c, 1976), and the disease still occurs though its importance varies between years. Grazing exclosures erected in the northern part of Ainsdale NNR in 1974 continue to be studied by S. E. Edmondson (see Edmondson *et al.*, this volume) though further detailed work on the rabbit populations would also be very useful, especially for exploring the possible use of these animals for improving grassland management.

Feral cats (*Felis catus* L.), the common rat (*Rattus norvegicus* (Berkenhout)) and the house mouse (*Mus musculus* L.) are undoubtedly present although no written records have been found.

BIRDS
K. W. Wood

Early records of birds of the dunes include those of Byerley (1856), Mitchell (1885, 1892) and Wrigley (1893). The coast adjacent to the dunes is of international importance for birds, particularly the Mersey, Alt and Ribble estuaries, and Seaforth Nature Reserve. But no present-day sand dune site has been designated a nature reserve specifically because of its birds, although many reports have included the birds of the dunes (Table 10.2). Other information may be found in the Lancashire Bird Report, published by the Lancashire and Cheshire Fauna Society, and in regular articles and reports of field visits by E. Hardy in the Liverpool Daily Post (Saturdays), and by F. Goodier in the Formby Times. Felton (1966) lists 128 species that

TABLE 10.2:
Some Ornithological References

Subject Area / Location of Source	General	Breeding Bird Censuses and Studies	Winter Bird Studies	Particular Species or Groups	Ringing
ASD NNR	Campbell (1954, 1955), Hardy (1959) Anon (1968,1969a,b, 1975a,b) Lassey (1968), Boston (1968b, 1969a,b) Aldridge (1971a,b, 1972a, 1976a) Aldridge and Musgrave (undated) Brewster (1981) McLardy (1987) Wood (1984-86) Smith (1983c) Cross (1987)	Anon (1979b, 1981-1982, 1989) Boston(1968a,1970a,d)	Anon 1977, 1979a), Wood (1982-84, undated)	Wood(1978)	Wolfenden (1986)
English Nature, Regional Office, Blackwell	Smith & Henderson (1955), Smith (1957), Davies & Whatmough (1966), Merchant Taylors Field Club (1968)	Smith (1967)	Simms (1963) (1936), Fearon & Duckels (1966)	Williams	
S W Lancs Ringing Group Annual Reports	Wolfenden (1980)	Duckels (1973b)	Thomas (1973)	Thomas (1973) Wolfenden (1973,1978, 1979a,b,1984 1985,1989), Kennedy (1976, 1977a,b), Williams (1977), Duckels (1978,1989), Fletcher (1987), Pennington (1986,1987)	Duckels (1973a 1978,1989), Thomas (1973), Wolfenden (1973,1978, 1970a,b, 1984,1985, 1989), Kennedy 1976,1977a, b)Williams (1977,1978) Pennington (1986,1987) Fletcher (1987)
NWBFDB	Williams (1939, 1942), Williams (1974), Smith (1978)	Duckels (1974) Peace (1977)			
Libraries and Society proceedings	Byerley (1856), Mitchell (1885, 1892), Wrigley (1893), Holder (1920), Wagstaffe (1932, 1934, 1935), Hardy (1941, 1979), Oakes (1953), Felton (1966), Spencer (1973), Riley (1983).				

Note that references mentioned in one row of Table 10.2 are not repeated in lower rows although some references may be found in more than one location.

ASD NNR is Ainsdale Sand Dunes NNR; S W Lancs Ringing Group Annual Reports can be obtained from A. S. Duckels, 16 The Spinney, Freshfield, L37 7EL; NWBFDB is North West Biological Field Data Bank, housed in Liverpool Museum.

have been recorded in the dunes including vagrants, regular migrants and breeders. Between 1967 and 1975, 103 species were recorded (Aldridge 1976a) on Ainsdale NNR. Nesting and migratory species from different habitats and sites are given in Table 10.3 (after Hardy 1979).

Threats to birds have come from a lowering of the water table, with consequent loss of wet slack and water meadows; possibly from the loss of some good open sites due to the decline in asparagus farming; and most importantly from human disturbance in its various forms (A. S. Duckels, pers. comm.) Ground-nesting birds such as snipe (*Gallinago gallinago* L.) lapwing (*Vanellus vanellus* (L.)) and partridge (*Perdix perdix* (L.)) are prone to disturbance by visitors, especially with dogs, and in the 1970s a short-eared owl (*Asio flammeus* Pontoppidan) was reported killed by a dog at Hightown (A. S. Duckels, pers. comm.).

The value of the dunes for migrants is shown in a study by Lassey (1968) and in reports from 'Bird Ringing in South West Lancashire', published every one or two years from 1972 by the S. W. Lancashire Ringing Group. Subjects that have been studied by ringing include the passage of warblers (Pennington 1987), and the natural history of siskins (*Carduelis spinus* (L.)) (Duckels 1989) and skylarks (*Alauda arvensis* L.) (Wolfenden 1978, 1979b, 1981-84, 1989) in the dunes.

The magpie (*Pica pica* (L.)) population was studied in 1977 and 1978 (Wood 1978). It has increased greatly in recent years, reflecting the increase nationally (Marchant *et al.* 1990) but possibly also aided locally by scrub development.

Common Bird Censuses were performed annually at the Ainsdale NNR during the 1970s (see Table 10.2); these have provided useful base-line data.

Currently however, large-scale systematic monitoring of birds throughout the dunes is not being carried out to assist dune management, despite the sensitivity of birds to disturbance and the large army of ornithological volunteers potentially available to help.

Systematic monitoring in different habitats and at different times of year would help understand changes in status of breeding and wintering species caused by habitat threats and by dune management. It should also be possible to compare current status with that indicated in past literature. Further detailed studies of particular species would also provide useful information:for instance on the importance of the dunes for nesting shelducks (*Tadorna tadorna* (L.)) and the short-term use made of the area by migrants and seasonal visitors such as wheatears (*Oenanthe oenanthe* (L.)) and snow buntings (*Plectrophenax nivalis*(L.)).

TABLE 10.3
'Birdwatching in Lancashire' Hardy (1979) lists nesting and migratory species under three headings, viz:-

I. AINSDALE NATIONAL NATURE RESERVE:

Open dunes

NESTERS: Stonechat, Whinchat, Whitethroat, Reed Bunting, Corn Bunting, Shelduck, Sedge Warbler, Grasshopper Warbler, Redshank, Snipe, Partridge, Mallard, Oystercatcher, Skylark.

VISITORS: Harriers, Merlin, Short-eared Owl, Little Grebe, Teal, Garganey, Gadwall, Heron, Tree Pipit, Corncrake, Water Rail, Buzzard, Green Sandpiper, Fieldfare, Redwing.

RARITIES: Little Bunting, Red-rumped Swallow, Black-eared Wheatear, Stone Curlew, Yellow-browed Warbler, Nightingale, Firecrest, Rough legged Buzzard, Red-footed Falcon, Mealy Redpoll, Bee Eater.

Pine woods

NESTERS: Turtle Dove, Stock Dove, Collared Dove, Goldcrest, Coal Tit, Long tailed Tit, Willow Tit, Jay, Magpie, Redpoll, Great-spotted Woodpecker, Treecreeper, Long-eared Owl, Tawny Owl, Crossbill, Nightjar, Woodcock.

VISITORS: Crossbill, Woodcock, Siskin, Woodpigeon.

II. FORMBY POINT & DUNES (INCLUDING CABIN HILL)

NESTERS: Shelduck, Whinchat, Stonechat, Whitethroat, Ringed Plover, Oystercatcher, Great-spotted Woodpecker,Treecreeper, Long tailed Tit, Nightjar.

VISITORS: Ring Ouzel, Tree Sparrow, Reed Warbler, Grasshopper Warbler, Wren, Goldcrest, Harrier Species, Merlin, Short-eared Owl, Shoveler, Finch flocks, Larks, Pipits, Sparrowhawk, Green Sandpiper.

RARITIES: 1st British Eleanora's Falcon (Cabin Hill Aug. 1977), Red-breasted Flycatcher, 'Ortolan', Rough-legged Buzzard, Osprey, Nightingale, Bearded Tit, Great Grey Shrike, Black Redstart, Hoopoe, Golden Oriole, Avocet, Richard's Pipit, Red-throated Pipit, Shore Lark, Wryneck, Mealy Redpoll, Greenland Redpoll, Crossbill, Melodious Warbler, Barred Warbler, Raven, Firecrest, Wood Lark, Waxwing.

III. HIGHTOWN DUNES

NESTERS: 45 species including Stonechat, Shelduck, Oystercatcher, Ringed Plover, Whitethroat, Corn Bunting, Reed Bunting, Goldfinch, Tree Sparrow, Grasshopper Warbler, Whinchat, Redpoll, Snipe, Redshank.

VISITORS: Subalpine Warbler, Short-eared Owl, Greenshank, Whimbrel, Redstart, Ring Ouzel, Twite, Reed Warbler.

RARITIES: Serin, Little Bunting, Crane, Montagu's Harrier, Hoopoe.

REPTILES
R. A. Hall and D. A. Nissenbaum

SAND LIZARD (*Lacerta agilis* L.)

The sand lizard is endangered in Britain and is fully protected on Schedule 5 of the Wildlife and Countryside Act, 1981. It has also been identified as one of the few European species to merit further strict protection of 'important sites and local races' (Bern Convention, December 1987 meeting).

Most British sand lizards occur on the heathlands of southern England, but a small isolated population survives on dunes on the Sefton Coast (NCC 1983; Corbett 1988a; Spellerberg 1988). The Sefton population is known to have declined substantially this century, the reasons for this have been much discussed e.g. Jackson (1978a, 1979); Beebee (1978b).

TABLE 10.4

Major Reference Sources for Reptiles on the Sefton Coast (see also Table 12.1).

Arnold (1973)
Beebee (1978b, 1979)
Boston (1970)
BHS Conservation Committee (1973, undated)
British Trust for Conservation Volunteers (1979)
Bruce (1972, 1973)
Cooke (1980, 1981, 1982, 1986b,c,d, 1987a,b,c, 1988, 1989a,b, 1991, this volume)
Corbett (1974, 1985, 1987, 1988a, b)
Corbett & Tamarind (1979)
Dent (1986)
Gresswell (1953)
Hall & Nissenbaum (1987)
Hall (1988b,f)
Horne (1979)
Jackson (1976, 1978a,b, 1979)
Jackson & Yalden (1977, 1979)
Lees (1976)
Lunn & Wheeler (1989)
Musgrave (1974)
Nature Conservancy Council Wardens (Undated, 3 reports; 1978-1988; 1981)
NCC (1983)
Nissenbaum & Hall (1988)
Nissenbaum (1988, 1989, 1990)
Page (1911)
Pearsall (1934)
Prestt, Cooke & Corbett (1974)
Ratcliffe (1977)
Simms (1966, 1969)
Simpson (1989c, 1990b)
Smith, P. H. (1975, 1978, 1980, 1982a, 1983a, b)
Smith, M. (1952, 1973)
Wheeler (1987)
Wilkinson *et al.* (1953)
Wright & Cooke (1982)
Yalden (1980a, b)

A number of projects have been undertaken to assess the status, distribution and requirements of the sand lizard. Lunn and Wheeler (1989) summarised current understanding of its status, identifying 13 colonies which have yielded a total of 228 sightings in the period April 1986 to August 1989. Cooke (this volume) describes recent studies of sand lizard habitat.

Habitat management has been carried out at six known sites of importance, with some success.

Since 1978, a joint Nature Conservancy Council/British Herpetological Society captive breeding project has been running, with the aim of providing young lizards for reintroduction into the wild. To the end of 1989, a total of 227 lizards have been released at three coastal sites.

Table 10.4 contains a list of major reference sources.

Gaps exist in our knowledge and understanding of sand lizards on the Sefton Coast:

i)   Present distribution and status of sand lizards.
ii)   Habitat requirements of sand lizard:- further work required.
iii) Habitat management: management prescriptions for all known and potential sites should be drawn up.
iv)   Re-introduction: the present programme and its success should be evaluated and reviewed.

A conservation strategy for sand lizards on the Sefton Coast is in preparation (May 1991) and incorporates the points identified above. The strategy will be available to all coastal agencies and will define the necessary resource input for sand lizard conservation.

OTHER REPTILES

Besides the sand lizard, only common lizards (*Lacerta vivipara* (L.)) are known to occur on the Sefton coast. The present distribution and status of this species still needs to be determined. A few old records of slow worm (*Anguis fragilis* L.) are known from the Formby town area, and occasional releases from captivity of species such as garter snake *(Thamnophis sirtalis)* have occurred (records in Liverpool Museum).

AMPHIBIANS
D. E. Simpson

The first records of amphibians made by visiting naturalists include an early field visit to the Bootle area, reported in *The Naturalist* 1838, where natterjack toads were "found in great abundance". Observations and surveys have been continued to the present day and recent surveys give much detailed information of distribution and population levels (Tables 10.5 & 10.6).

NATTERJACK TOAD (*Bufo calamita* L.)

Natterjack toads have undoubtedly attracted the most study due to their rarity. Apart from the now annual breeding season surveys (Table 10.5), a number of major published studies have been produced on distribution and status (Smith, Harris & Hancock 1972; LNT 1972; Smith & Payne 1980). The general decline of the species locally has also been described (Corbett & Beebee 1975).

TABLE 10.5.
Natterjack Survey References

Birkdale
Aldridge, Musgrave, Twyman 1973
Smith, S. H., Lambert 1973
Robinson 1977
Houston 1981
SMBC, Sefton Ranger Service 1985-90

Ainsdale
NC Warden, 1967, 1971
Smith, P. H., Harris, Hancock 1972
NC/NCC Wardens 1972-1975
Aldridge, Musgrave, Twyman 1973
Smith, S. H., Lambert 1973
NCC Wardens 1976a, b, 1977-90
Robinson 1977
Smith, Payne 1980
Houston 1981
Paull 1984
SMBC, Sefton Ranger Service 1985-90

Formby Point (includes: National Trust, Lifeboat Rd, Ravenmeols)
Smith, P. H., Harris, Hancock 1972
Smith, P. H. 1976* (1972-76), 1979-90
Roberts, 1981
SMBC, Sefton Ranger Service 1990a

Cabin Hill/Altcar
Smith, P. H., Harris, Hancock 1972
Cook 1976
Smith, P. H. 1977-80, 1989
Davis 1981
NCC Wardens, 1985a-90a

Hightown
Anon 1985
Hancock 1972
Smith, Payne 1980
SMBC, Sefton Ranger Service 1985, 1987

Sefton Coast
SMBC, Sefton Coast Management Scheme 1987-90

NB Reference years are recording years except * where recording years are shown in brackets.

For abbreviations see Table 10.6

Studies of breeding biology have included the species' hybridisation with the common toad both in the laboratory and field (S. H. Smith 1974b), and mate choice behaviour (Arak 1982, 1988a,b). It was shown that female natterjacks selected larger, deeper-voiced males. Physiological research has shown a growth inhibition effect by common toad (*Bufo bufo* L.) tadpoles on natterjack tadpoles (Nicolle 1988), apparently caused by an unpigmented alga passed in excreta. General observations that warm, wet weather is especially important for spawning, particularly later in the season, were confirmed by Pierce (1989). Two short general studies of breeding activity have also been carried out on the Coast (Cook 1976; Greeno 1987).

Studies of natterjack populations have looked at numbers at excavated pools at Ainsdale NNR using mark-recapture techniques (Smith & Flynn 1977); the initial use of these pools by adults (Smith & Bownes 1978); population changes across the dune system (Davis 1985); and the use of body length measurements to assess the proportion of individuals of different ages in local populations (Smith 1990).

A large amount of pool excavation work for natterjacks was carried out in the 1970s and these were studied to assess their success and successful design features (NCC Wardens (undated, three reports) Wheeler 1984a; Beebee 1985; Aitcheson 1987; see also Wheeler *et al.*, this volume).

Mathias (1971) described differences between the niches of the natterjack and common toads. More recent work includes that by Beebee & Denton (1988-89, 1989-90, 1990-91), which confirmed that the natterjacks are adapted to mobile dune and short turf habitats whilst common toads were adapted to living in the rank, scrubby vegetation in fixed dune slack (see abstract from Beebee & Denton, p.150 this volume).

Natterjack toad corpses have been analysed for radionucleides as part of a national investigation (Horrill & Livens 1987), though only extremely low levels were recorded from Sefton coast specimens.

OTHER AMPHIBIANS

As mentioned above, common toads have featured in comparative studies linked to natterjack research (Nicolle 1988).

Table 10.6 list breeding surveys undertaken for common toad, common frog *(Rana temporaria* L.), great-crested newt *(Triturus cristatus* (Laurenti) Dunn) and smooth newt *(Triturus vulgaris* (L.) Dunn). The changing status of great crested newt on Ainsdale Sand Dunes NNR has been monitored since 1976 (Wheeler & Carty 1985; Wheeler 1986b), and for the other species since 1980 (Simpson 1990b).

Palmate newt *(Triturus helveticus* (Razoumowsky) Dunn.) has been recorded at Hightown (Hancock 1972), though there are no recent records.

The large amount of amphibian research, particularly related to natterjacks, both on the coast and elsewhere (Beebee 1983), has provided managers with most of the information they require for effective conservation. Future research is likely to concentrate on in-house monitoring of populations, particularly of the natterjack toad and great-crested newt, including their response to management.

TABLE 10.6
Other Amphibian Survey References

Ainsdale

NC Warden 1967
NC/NCC Wardens 1972-75
Aldridge, Musgrave, Twyman 1973
Smith, S. H., Lambert 1973
Smith, S. H. 1974b
NCC Wardens 1977-90

Formby Point (includes: National Trust, Lifeboat Rd., Ravenmeols)

Smith, P. H. 1979-1990

Cabin Hill/Altcar

Smith, P. H. 1977-80
NCC Wardens 1985a-90a

Hightown

Hancock 1972
SMBC, Sefton Ranger Service 1985
Anon 1985

Abbreviations used in tables 10.5 and 10.6

LNT Lancashire Naturalists' Trust
NCC Nature Conservancy Council
NNR National Nature Reserve
SMBC, Sefton Metropolitan Borough Council

FISH
D. E. Simpson

Very little information has been gathered on this group, mainly because fish are so scarce in the dune system. No literature has been found on the subject. All information here, therefore, results from comments gathered from staff and research workers presently working on the Coast. A review is given of the history and status of fish on the dune system, site by site.

Prior to human interference in the dune system, it is unlikely that many fish were present, as water bodies present in the dune slacks were ephemeral.

On what is now Ainsdale and Birkdale Hills LNR the Sands Lake (SD 301129) was created, around 1900, by deepening 'Bulrush' slack. Coarse fish and trout have been introduced, though there are no details of species (J. A. Houston pers. comm.). In recent years a flat-fish was observed (J. Sharpe, pers. comm). The lake is rather brackish, being linked to the beach by pipeline for drainage purposes. For many years fishing was allowed here but this is now prohibited. In the 1940s bombs dropped by the German airforce created several small deep permanent pools on the Birkdale Hills. These have

since been unofficially stocked with perch (*Perca fluviatilis L.*), roach (*Rutilus rutilus L.)* and tench (*Tinca tinca L.)*. Three-spined sticklebacks (*Gasterosteus aculeatus L.*) are also present, though these may have naturally colonised (R. A. Hall, pers. comm). Tagg's Island (SD 311153), created in 1981, contains three-spined sticklebacks which appear to live in the drainage ditch towards the road (J. Sharpe, pers. comm).

On Ainsdale Sand Dunes NNR, carp (*Cyprinus sp.*) and goldfish (*Carassius auratus (L.))* have been observed in the Large Pond (SD 302112), created in 1972. Carp have also been observed recently in excavation 13B, created in 1977 (D. J. Wheeler, pers. comm.).

Wicks Lane Lake, Formby (SD 278071) was created as a playpool in 1978. This lake has been unofficially stocked over the years. In recent years it has been drained and cleaned out on several occasions. The following species were recorded: roach, rudd (*Scardinius erythrophthalmus (L.))* , perch, tench, goldfish, carp, eel (*Anguilla anguilla (L.))* and three-spined stickleback (J. A. Houston, pers. comm.). Only the latter two species are likely to have colonised naturally. Three-spined sticklebacks and roach have been recorded in the 'newt ponds', excavations 2, 3 and 4 at Lifeboat Road. The latter species was almost certainly introduced (P. J. Rooney, pers. comm.).

Royal Birkdale, Hillside and Southport & Ainsdale Golf Courses all contain permanent pools and fish have been observed in several of them (D. A. Nissenbaum, pers. comm.).

Apart from the sites mentioned above, there are no records of fish in the sand dune area. A full survey of fish species in all water bodies, and studies of the effect of fish populations on other aquatic species, notably natterjack toads and great crested newts would be valuable.

INVERTEBRATES

The scheme for classifying rare and endangered species used in the Invertebrate Sites Register (Parsons 1987a) will be referred to several times. Therefore, relevant details are summarised in Table 10.7.

BEETLES (COLEOPTERA)
T.M. Eccles

The Sefton Coast has a unique and internationally important coleoptera fauna. Many species are at the northernmost limit of their geographical range, and at least two species have been found nowhere else in Britain. The beetles of the dunes have been the subject of study by coleopterists for over a century; indeed there can be few other areas in North West England where coleoptera have been so well documented (Table 10.8).

TABLE 10.7
Species status categories: Invertebrates (from Parsons 1987a)

British Red Data Books

RDB1 Endangered. Taxa in danger of extinction and whose survival is unlikely if the causal factors continue to operate. Included are taxa whose numbers have been reduced to a critical level or whose habitat has been so drastically reduced that they are deemed to be in immediate danger. Also included are taxa which are believed to have become extinct recently, but if rediscovered will need special protection.

RDB2 Vulnerable. Taxa believed likely to move into the endangered category in the near future if causal factors continue to operate. Includes taxa which are still abundant but are under threat from serious adverse factors throughout their range.

RDB3 Rare. Taxa with small populations that are not at present Endangered or Vulnerable but are at risk. These taxa are usually very localised within a restricted geographical area or in habitats which are thinly scattered over a more extensive range.

Nationally Notable

Notable A (Na) known from 30 or fewer 10km squares.

Notable B (Nb) known from 100 or fewer 10km squares.

Although these criteria can be applied directly to a few well recorded groups such as the butterflies, the majority of invertebrates are insufficiently known for this to be meaningful. Therefore, estimates of the 'notability' have also been made.

In the Diptera, a group in which widespread interest is a recent phenomenon, no attempt to distinguish between Notable A and B has been made and species are simply graded 'Notable'.

As Table 10.9 shows, there are two endangered species (Red Data Book category 1 (RDB1) (Shirt 1987)), one vulnerable (RDB2) and three rare (RDB3). In addition, there are 55 nationally notable species (13 Na and 42 Nb; Parsons 1987a).

TABLE 10.8.
Coleoptera: Some Major References

Aldridge (undated)
Burrows, Fielding & Goodwin (1966)
Chaster & Burgess Sopp (1903)
Denton (1990)
Eccles (1978, 1990)
Ellis (1889)
Flint (1959-1962)
Fowler & Donisthorpe (1887-1913)
Johnson (1966, 1976)

It is possible to deduce changes in the fauna which reflect changes in habitat. Wetland species in particular, have declined as a result of the general drying out of the area.

The most important community of beetles, in terms of naturalness, rarity and fragility, is that associated with the thin strip of mobile dunes. The true arenicolous species (specalising in sandy habitats) occur here and

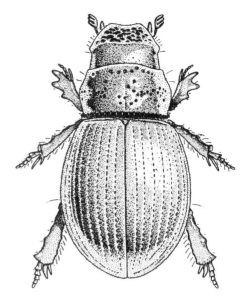

Figure 10.1 *Psammodius caelatus* (Le Conte) (x15)

they include certain highly specialised species of the family Scarabaeidae (Scarabaeids) such as *Aegialia rufa* (F.) which has been accorded Red Data Book Category 1 status - 'Endangered'. *Aegialia rufa* is known from very few continental localities, and apart from old records from the Barmouth district, and a few century-old records from Wallasey, the Sefton Coast would appear to be the only British locality. In the course of over a decade of fieldwork, I personally have come across only four examples. Its largely subterranean habits mean that it is seldom found by fieldworkers using ordinary collecting techniques. The closely related *Psammodius asper* (F.) appears to have declined in numbers for no very apparent reason; it was recorded as "common on the sandhills" (Chaster & Burgess-Sopp 1903), but the only recent record is my own, of a single example found in October 1977 on the mobile dunes of Ainsdale NNR.

This group of burrowing arenicolous scarabaeids includes the very common black *Aegialia arenaria* (F.), which is one of the most typical species of the mobile dunes. The group is characterised amongst other things, by the absence of wings - a condition which might lead one to suppose that they have very limited powers of dispersal and a lack of ability to colonise new areas. This is not borne out however by the example of the recent immigrant species *Psammodius caelatus* (Le Conte) (Figure 10.1), which originates from the western seaboard of North America. Since its discovery by Johnson in 1972 (Johnson 1976), it has spread along the dune system and is now well established all along the Sefton Coast. The dung feeding *Aphodius brevis* Erichson is yet another scarabaeid, which in this country is endangered (Red Data Book 1), and known only from the Sefton Coast. The re-introduction of grazing by sheep as a management technique may benefit this rare species.

TABLE 10.9.
Endangered[1], Vulnerable[2] and Rare[3] Beetles

Species	Family	Location (and year)
Aegialia rufa [1] (F.)	Scarabeidae	Southport (1906) Formby (1963)
Aphodius brevis [1] (Erichson)	Scarabeidae	Massam's slack N to Fisherman's Path (1962)
Hypocaccus rugiceps [2] (Duffschmid.)	Histeridae	Ainsdale (1985)
Cicindela hybrida [3] L.	Carabidae	Ainsdale (1984)
Dryocoetinus alni [3] (Geog.)	Scolytidae	Formby (SD2707) (1987)
Trypopholeus asperatus [3] (Gyll.)	Scolytidae	Ainsdale (1980s)
Dryops griseus [3] (Erichson)	Dryopidae	Ainsdale (1977)
Arena tabida [3] (Kiesenwetter)	Staphylinidae	Cabin Hill (1988)

Information from Parsons (1987a) and T. M. Eccles (pers. obs.). Only dated and confirmed records are included. Precise locations are often not recorded..

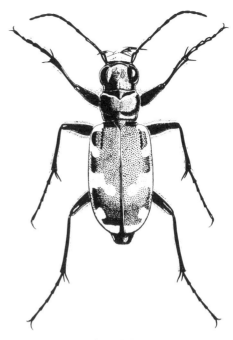

Figure 10.2 *Cicindela hybrida* (L.) (x5)

Among the more conspicuous insects of the mobile dunes is the tiger beetle *Cicindela hybrida* (L.) (Figure 10.2), a species with a very localised and discontinuous distribution in Britain, (Red Data Book 3) associated exclusively with the larger sand-dune systems. It favours exposed sun-baked slopes where it hunts its insect prey. It flies actively in warm sunshine and can be extremely difficult to capture. The report by Aldridge (undated) describes the distribution and ecology of this species, although it is incorrectly referred to as *C. maritima*. A handsome metallic green and brown variety of the large chafer *Euchlora dubia* (Scop.) occurs on the dunes, with the unicolorous green 'type' form occurring much more rarely. These larger insects are easy to find, patient of observation and provide interesting and ready material for those engaged in interpreting the natural history of the dunes to the public.

The littoral zone provides a habitat for the Red Data Book 3 species *Arena tabida* (Kiesenwetter) which was discovered by myself in April 1988 at Cabin Hill. The tiny wingless *Diglotta mersa* (Holiday), which has been found at Hightown is a species which inhabits the strandline and is also adapted to withstand twice daily immersion by the sea. The small area of saltmarsh at the mouth of the River Alt at Hightown is the habitat for two weevils viz. *Polydrusus chrysomela* (Olivier) and *Notaris bimacalatus* (F.) which are found only in this type of situation. All these littoral species are of course vulnerable to pollution, especially oil spillages, and overzealous tidying-up of beech debris removes their hiding places.

The boundary between the unstable 'yellow' and stable 'grey' dunes has its own characteristic 'suite' of coleoptera. Typical of these are the xerophilous species (dry habitat specialists) *Phylan gibbus* (F.) and *Melanimon tibiulis* (F.) of the family Tenebrionidae both of which have thick darkly pigmented cuticles. The peculiar *Notoxus monocerus* (L.) occurs here, and where creeping thistle *(Cirsium arvense* (L.) Scop.) has gained a foothold, the large weevil *Cleonus piger* (Scop.) may be found clinging to the plants where it is superbly camouflaged in spite of its size, or else making characteristic regular tracks on the bare sand.

The stable dunes have a rich fauna with components of xerophilous, mossland and, where dune slacks occur, wetland beetles. The large ground beetle *Carabus nitens* (L.) is a species of damp situations and has a beautiful coppery green colour. It appears to be on the verge of extinction, with only one confirmed record in the past thirty years (C. Johnson pers. comm.). It was described as occurring "locally in the Freshfield district" at the turn of the century (Chaster & Burgess-Sopp 1903). Coleopterists of the last century found it in abundance, but their over-collecting may have contributed to its demise. Phytophagous (plant-feeding) species abound on the varied and abundant dune flora. Most clumps of common dog violet (*Viola riviniana* Rchb.) will harbour the tiny blue/black weevil *Orobitis cyaneus* (L.) which looks like a piece of animated lead-shot, and a careful search of birdsfoot trefoil (*Lotus corniculatus* L.) may yield examples of the weevil *Tychius flavicollis* Stephens or the obscure *Orthochaetes setiger* (Beck), the latter usually encrusted with dirt, making it very difficult to detect in the field.

Human activities have had a profound effect on the coleopterous fauna of the dunes. There have undoubtedly been extinctions of primary species caused by habitat destruction, but species now occur which were unknown to earlier workers. The introduced pines have an assemblage of beetles associated with them which are not mentioned in early accounts. These are usually to be found on recently dead or moribund trees, and include commercial pests such as the pine shoot-borer *Tomicus piniperda* (L.), and the large pine-weevil *Hylobius abietis* (L.). The striking black, white and red *Thanasimus formicarius* (L.) is a predator of these and other wood-feeding beetles.

Where forestry activity has left truncated stumps of coniferous trees, their breakdown and decay is hastened by the activities of two sombre looking wood-boring longhorn beetles viz. *Asemum striatum* (L.) and *Arhopalus tristis* (F.), the latter a large insect, up to 30mm in length. Most stumps will show evidence of these beetles in the form of exit holes about a centimetre across.

Another legacy of former human activity is the prettily marked asparagus beetle *Crioceris asparagi* (L.), which may be found with its slug-like larvae on the elegant fern-like foliage of mature asparagus plants which have naturalised on the stable dunes, (see Edmondson *et al.*, this volume).

Amongst the shrub species, birch (*Betula* sp.) has the rare weevil *Curculio betulae* (Stephens), and the leaf-rolling weevil *Deporaus betulae* (L.). White poplar (*Populus alba* L.) has the uncommon chrysomelid *Zeugophora subspinosa* (F.). No beetles appear to have any direct association with the invasive sea buckthorn, but the balsam poplar *Populus candicans* (Aiton) is the host for several interesting species.

The way in which the balsam poplar is managed provides an interesting example of the conflicts of interest which arise whenever interventive habitat management is embarked upon. Among the reasons that may be advanced for clearing poplar thickets is that they are invasive and compete for space with the indigenous flora, and in any case there can be little harm in removing this obviously alien species. The balsam poplars however support a unique community of insects including one 'Red Data Book' species which would be destroyed by clearance. The trees have a stunted appearance and seldom attain any appreciable size but this is attributable as much to the depredations of the goat moth (*Cossus cossus* L.) as to the effects of salt spray and prevailing winds. The goat moth larvae bore into the woody tissues of the trees usually just a little above ground level. The sap-feeding nitidulid beetle *Soronia punctatissima* (Illiger) may be found in and around the larval galleries of the goat moth, no doubt attracted there in the first place by the pungent 'goaty' smell of the large pink larvae. The sap oozing from the wounds caused by the goat moth also attracts the fine weevil *Cryptorhynchus lapathi* (L.); this is a very cryptically coloured and easily overlooked species, in spite of its comparatively large size of up to 1 centimetre.

The unhealthy poplars are also host to the Red Data Book 3 (Rare) bark beetle *Trypophloeus asperatus* (Gyllenhal) which makes borings under the bark of branches of 1-2 centimetres thickness. Arbitrary and uninformed clearance of the poplar scrub is damaging to the invertebrate interest - other potentially damaging operations could be cited. Only through regular survey

TABLE 10.10
Vulnerable and Rare Diptera

Species	Family	Location (and year)
Xanthandrus comtus (Harris)	Syrphidae	Freshfield dune heath (1986)
Cheilosia mutabilis (Fallen)	Syrphidae	Formby Point, Ainsdale (1987)
Melangyna guttata (Fallen)	Syrphidae	Freshfield (1961, 1986)
Limonia ventralis (Schummel)	Tipulidae	North of Fisherman's path, SD3013 (1959, 1973)
Gnophomyia viridipennis (Gimmert)	Tipulidae	Fisherman's path (1963)
Orimarga juvenilis (Zetterstedt)	Tipulidae	Ainsdale (1933)
Phalacrocera replicata (Linnaeus)	Tipulidae	Massam's slack and northwards (1959)
Nephrotoma quadristriata (Schumm.)	Tipulidae	Ainsdale or Birkdale (1973)
Bolitophila rossica (Landrock)	Mycetophilidae	Ainsdale (1970)
Chaetomus flavotestaceus (Zett.)	Heleomyzidae	Ainsdale NNR (1954)
Chyliza fuscipennis (Robineau-De)	Psilidae	"Rear slack", Ainsdale (1959)
Coenosia pygmaea (Zett.)	Muscidae	Massam's slack (1959)
Dexiopsis minutalis (Zett.)	Muscidae	Massam's slack (1962)
Colobaea distincta (Meigen)	Sciomyzidae	Freshfield (1969)
Pherbellia grisescens (Meigen)	Sciomyzidae	Ainsdale (1957)
Mycetobia pallipes (Meigen)	Anisopodidae	Fisherman's path near golf course (1963)

Information from Parsons (1987a). Only dated and confirmed records are included. Precise locations are often not recorded. Only *Xanthandrus comtus* is vulnerable (RDB2); the rest are rare (RDB3).

and monitoring can the necessary data on which management decisions are based, be accumulated. Fortunately in the case of coleoptera, a great deal of information is available, and through management plans and the implementation of the prescriptions continued in them, the remarkable coleoptera fauna of the Sefton Coast would seem to be - to use a word which can never become too clichéd in this context - sustainable.

TRUE FLIES (DIPTERA)
D. Atkinson

Early records of true-fly species from Formby were given by Wright (1941). The true flies were more thoroughly surveyed between 1959 and 1962 in the Freshfield Entomological Survey (Brindle 1962). Since then, records from different parts of the Coast have been added (Burrows *et al.* 1966; Cross 1989; Godfrey 1989; Franks 1990; Palmer 1988).

Fifteen species are rare (RDB3; Table 10.10; Parsons 1987a). At least one of these, the cranefly *Limonia ventralis* (Schummel), is specifically associated with coastal ponds and ditches (Parsons 1987a).

The hoverfly *Xanthandrus comtus* (Harris) (Figure 10.3), recorded in 1986 on Freshfield Dune Heath, is vulnerable (RDB2; Parsons 1987a). It is normally associated with meadows or scrubby areas (Parsons 1987a), and may not therefore be a coastal or dune heath specialist.

Figure 10.3 *Xanthandrus comtus* (x3)

In addition, 77 species are nationally notable (Nb, Parsons 1987a). At least one of these, *Orygma luctuosum* is typically found on the strandline, and at least two (*Achalcus flavicollis* (Meigen) and *Odontomyia viridula*) are indicative of reedbed, fen, carr or grazing marsh (Parsons 1987a).

BUTTERFLIES AND MOTHS (LEPIDOPTERA).
M. Hull and M. Bird

Ellis (revised by Mansbridge 1940) and Leech & Michaelis (1957) provide early reviews of the lepidoptera occurring in the area. Other references are given in Tables 10.11 and 10.12.

TABLE 10.11
Some References to Lepidoptera.

Aldridge (1975a)
Anon (post -1970, post -1983)
Boston (1970b, c)
Burrows, Fielding & Goodwin (1966)
Carty (1986a, b)
Ellis (revised by Mansbridge 1940)
Hall (1988a)
Hancock (1970)
Harper (1988)
Harrop (1990)
Leech (1967/68, 1969/70)
Leech & Michaelis (1957)
Michaelis (1957)
Parsons (1987b)
Wallace (1981)
Wright (1941)

Out of a total of 699 species recorded in the area, 22 were butterfly, 342 were species of macro-lepidoptera and 335 belonged to the micro-lepidoptera (Leech & Michaelis 1957). Despite the length of time for which the lepidopterous fauna have been studied in this area, records are still too few to determine the true status of many of the species recorded.

There is an undated record of the vulnerable (RDB2) sandhill rustic moth (*Luperina nickerlii gueneei* Doubl.), and records of the rare (RDB3) belted beauty (*Nyssia zonaria* Schiff (D & S)) only up to 1915. The latter is probably not now present but may have been overlooked as the moth should be searched for early in the year in March and early April. However, recent investigations by M. Hull suggest that its current scarcity and vulnerability to increased trampling disturbance may warrant a re-evaluation of its Red Data Book Status.

Nineteen nationally notable species (one Na and eighteen Nb, excluding undated observations) have been recorded (Parsons 1987a). Some of these, such as the sand dart moth (*Agrotis ripae* Hubn) are coastal dune specialists. The larvae of this species feed on the roots of plants growing in sandy areas with almost no trace of humus. Other nationally notable dune specialists include the Portland moth (*Ochropleura praecox* (L.)) and the shore wainscot (*Mythimna litoralis* (Curt.)) (Figure 10.5a).

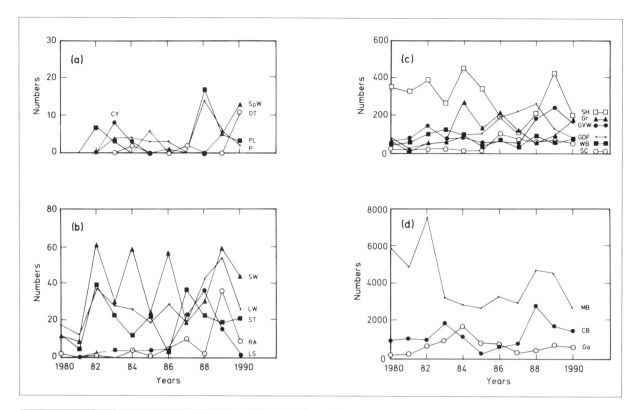

Figure 10.4 Butterfly numbers. Ainsdale Sand Dunes NNR 1980-90 based on transect counts (the same route is followed in each survey). Data provided by Mick Bird.

	KEY		(c)	SH	Small Heath
(a)	SpW	Speckled Wood		Gr	Grayling
	OT	Orange Tip		GVW	Green-veined White
	PL	Painted Lady		DGF	Dark Green Fritillary
				WB	Wall Brown
(b)	SW	Small White		SC	Small Copper
	LW	Large White			
	ST	Small Tortoiseshell	(d)	MB	Meadow Brown
	RA	Red Admiral		CB	Common Blue
	LS	Large Skipper		Ga	Gatekeeper

In 1980, a transect was set up by NCC wardens on Ainsdale NNR to monitor butterfly populations from the beginning of April to the end of September (see Pollard, Hall & Bibby 1986 for methods).

Since 1982, M. Bird has carried out the monitoring. The status of each species is shown in Table 10.13 and numbers are plotted in Figure 10.4.

Recent felling and thinning of woodland areas may assist butterfly species such as the speckled wood (*Pararge aegeria* L.) (Figure 10.5b), which appears to be becoming established on the transect. A variety of

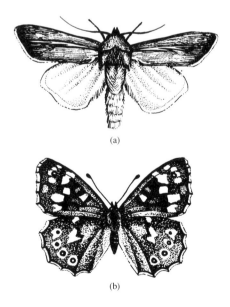

Figure 10.5 (a) *Mythimna littoralis* (x 1.5) (b) *Parage aegeria* (actual size).

vegetational heights is also likely to be beneficial to allow both egg-laying and roosting.

TABLE 10.13.
Relative Abundance of Butterflies, based on an Annual Census at Ainsdale NNR from 1980 to 1990

Species	Common Name	Status	Relative Abundance
Ochlodes venata	Large Skipper	B	Scarce
Colias croceus	Clouded yellow	NB	Rare
Pieris brassicae	Large white	NB?	Frequent
Pieris rapae	Small white	NB?	Frequent
Pieris napi	Green-veined white	B	Common
Anthocharis cardamines	Orange-tip	B	Scarce
Lycaena phlaeas	Small copper	B	Common
Polyommatus icarus	Common blue	B	Abundant
Vanessa atalanta	Red admiral	B	Occasional
Cynthia cardui	Painted lady	B?	Occasional
Aglais urticae	Small tortoiseshell	B	Frequent
Inachis io	Peacock	B?	Occasional
Polygonia c-album	Comma	NB	Rare
Argynnis aglaja	Dark green fritillary	B	Common
Pararge aegeria	Speckled wood	B?	Scarce
Lasiommata megera	Wall brown	B	Common
Hipparchia semelle	Grayling	B	Common
Pyronia tithonus	Gatekeeper	B	Abundant
Maniola jurtina	Meadow brown	B	Abundant
Coenonympha pamphilus	Small heath	B	Abundant

KEY TO STATUS: B-Breeds on reserve: B? Breeding status unknown: NB? Doubtful breeder: NB Not breeding.

TRUE BUGS (HEMIPTERA)

The two sub-orders which comprise the hemiptera, the heteroptera (which includes shield bugs and water bugs) and the homoptera (which includes aphids and plant hoppers), will be discussed in turn.

HETEROPTERA
S. Judd

The heteroptera are under-recorded and little studied. Unlocalized historic species records are cited by Whittaker (1906) and Britten (1930). Flint (1964) provides the only species list, which is restricted to Ainsdale NNR. Voucher specimens, collected mainly by Judd, are housed in the Liverpool Museum. Judd's (1986) Lancashire checklist includes new county records from the dunes, whilst Parsons (1987a) highlights Red Data Book (RDB) and Nationally Notable (N a & b) species.

The rare (RDB3) *Monosynamma bohemani* (Fallen) and notable (Nb) *Monosynamma sabulicola* Wagner are both associated with creeping willow (*Salix repens* L.) and recorded from Ainsdale NNR. Members of this genus are difficult to identify and records must be treated with care (Parsons 1987a). Two other notable (Nb) species are recorded; the ant mimic *Systellonotus triguttatus* (L.) (Figure 10.6) associated also with, amongst other plants creeping willow, was recently recorded from Altcar Rifle Ranges; whilst *Polymerus palustris* (Reuter) is recorded from Ainsdale NNR and is associated with marsh bedstraw (*Galium palustre* L.).

HOMOPTERA
D. Atkinson

Fairly recent reviews and detailed studies of the homoptera include those of Whittacker (1965) and Payne (1978b, 1979a,b, *ca*. 1980, 1980b, 1981a,b, 1982a) on leafhoppers, and Sutton (1982) on the psyllids on hawthorn (*Crataegus monogyna* Jacq.).

No Red Data Book or Nationally Notable species of homoptera has so far been recorded. However, several plant-hoppers are near the northern limits of their known ranges, such as *Agallia laevis* Ribaut, a local coastal species (Payne 1982a).

According to Payne (in Parsons 1987a), the main areas of interest for finding leafhoppers are the dune slacks, with some of the larger ones containing over 50 species.

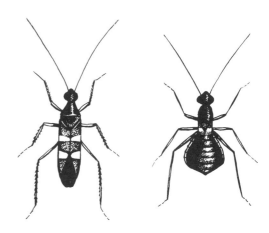

Figure 10.6 *Systellonotus triguttatus* (x6). Male (left) female (right).

BEES, ANTS AND WASPS (HYMENOPTERA)
D. Atkinson

Species lists for this under-recorded group include those of Askew (l969,1981) Holmes (1971), Payne (l978b) and Parsons (1987a). Askew (1981) lists observations of the solitary pompiloid wasps in the vice-counties of Cheshire and Lancashire, which includes the Sefton Coast

TABLE 10.14.
Rare Hymenoptera

Species	Family	Location (and year)
Arachnospila wesmaeli	Pompilidae	Ainsdale (l976-78)
Cleptes nitidulus	Chrysididae	Ainsdale (l976-78)
Colletes cunicularius	Colletidae	Ainsdale (l976-78)
C. marginatus	Colletidae	Ainsdale (1976)
Podalonia affinis	Sphecidae	Ainsdale (1976)
Psen littoralis	Sphecidae	Ainsdale (l976-78)
Stelis ornatula	Megachilidae	Ainsdale (l985)

Information from Parsons (1987a). All species are included in Red Data Book 3. Only dated and confirmed records are included. Precise location are often not recorded.

Of seven hymenoptera species listed as rare in the British Red Data Book (RDB3; Shirt 1987) three have recently been provisionally re-catalogued as nationally notable (Na; Table 10.14; Falk 1991). Parsons (1987a) also includes one nationally notable (Nb) species from the coast. Of these the spider wasp *Arachnospila wesmaeli* (Thompson), the solitary wasps *Podalonia affinis* (Kirby) and *Psen littoralis* (Bondroit) and the mining bees *Colletes cunicularius* (L.) and *C. marginatus* Smith are confined in Britain almost totally to areas with open sand, usually near the coast (Falk 1991).

The solitary wasp *Psen littoralis* largely confined to western coastal dune systems as far north as Sandscale Haws is associated with the marram zone and its adults freely visit flowers such as spurges (*Euphorbia* spp.) (Falk 1991)

Figure 10.7 *Colletes cunicularius* (female x2)

The vernal bee *Colletes cunicularius* (Figure 10.7) appears to be confined in Britain to north-west England and Wales (Falk 1991). O'Toole (1974; 1989) showed that these mining bees from isolated British populations, typified by those at Hightown Dunes and Meadows SSSI, were sufficiently different from continental ones to be placed in a separate subspecies (*celticus*). This species seems to favour old blow-outs undergoing secondary colonisation by plants such as marram grass (*Ammophila arenaria* Link), restharrow (*Ononis repens* L.) and creeping willow (*Salix repens* L.) with plenty of exposed sand and little or no bryophyte (moss and liverwort) cover (O'Toole 1974). This bee nests in aggregations on south facing slopes, and forages on catkins and creeping willow (O'Toole 1974, 1989).

DRAGONFLIES (ODONATA)
R. A. Hall

The seasonally flooded slacks and various man-made pools of the coast provide suitable habitats for dragonflies. A review of historical records, data held on file at Ainsdale NNR,together with a collation of recent sightings, has been produced by Hall and Smith (1991). Table 10.15 identifies the major reference sources.

TABLE 10.15.
Sefton Coast Dragonflies - Major Reference Sources.

Askew (l988)	Ford (1953)	Hall & Smith (1991)
Bird (1986)	Hall (1986)	Payne (1976a)
Bird (1987)	Hall (1987)	Sephton (1989)
Carty (l985)	Hall (l988e)	Sumner (1985)

A total of fourteen species has been recorded, ten of which breed. The status of each species is summarised in Table 10.16.

Ainsdale NNR is by far the most important single site for Odonata, all fourteen species having been recorded there.

This reflects the presence of many ponds dug for nature conservation since the early 1970s and a degree of observer bias.

Some species have only been recorded since these ponds were dug, for example the azure damselfly (*Coenagrion puella* (L.)) (Figure 10.8a) and the emperor dragonfly (*Anax imperator* Leach) (Figure 10.8b), while others have shown marked population increases, for example emerald damselfly (*Lestes sponsa* Hansemann).

There are still gaps in our knowledge, particularly of the golf courses, where access is restricted and a number of water bodies occur which could support dragonflies.

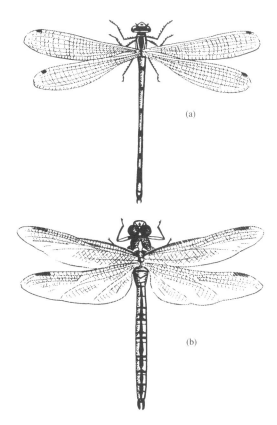

Figure 10.8 (a) *Coenagrion puella* (x1.5) (b) *Anax imperator* (x0.66)

TABLE 10.16.
Species of Odonata Recorded. Nomenclature follows Hammond (1983)

Sub-order Zygoptera		**Damselflies**
o	*Coenagrion puella* (L.)	azure blue
x	*Enallagma cyathigerum* (Charpentier)	common blue
	Pyrrhosoma nymphula (Sulzer)	large red
x	*Ischnura elegans* (van der Linden)	blue-tailed
x	*Lestes sponsa* (Hansemann)	emerald
	Sub-order Anisoptera	**Dragonflies**
o	*Aeshna cyanea* (Müller)	southern hawker
o	*A. grandis* (L.)	brown hawker
o	*A. juncea* (L.)	common hawker
o	*Anax imperator* Leach	emperor
	Libellula depressa L.	broad-bodied chaser
x	*L. quadrimaculata* L.	four-spotted chaser
	Sympetrum danae (Sulzer)	black darter
	S. sanguineum (Müller)	ruddy darter
x	*S. striolatum* (Charpentier)	common darter

x = *common breeder;* o = *scarce breeder;* = *vagrant..*

GRASSHOPPERS AND CRICKETS (ORTHOPTERA)
D. Atkinson

Only four species - three grasshoppers and a groundhopper - have been recorded (Bunn 1968; Payne 1978b; Felton & Jones 1982; Atkinson 1985). None is rare or nationally notable.

During the 1980s intensive studies of the mottled grasshopper (*Myrmeleotettix maculatus* (Thunb.)) and the field grasshopper (*Chorthippus brunneus* (Thunb.)) on sites at Ainsdale Sand Dunes NNR investigated influences on their life cycles, local distribution and abundance (Atkinson 1985; Atkinson & Begon 1987a, b, 1988a, b; Cherrill 1987; Cherrill & Begon 1989a, b, 1991; Wall 1985).

OTHER INSECT ORDERS
D. Atkinson

Other insect orders are under-recorded (see Brindle 1962; Keitch 1969; Payne 1978b). Only two nationally notable species (one Na and one Nb) are recorded in The Invertebrate Sites Register (Parsons 1987a). The latter species, the lacewing *Chrysopa abbreviata* Curtis, recorded at Formby and around the Massam's Slack area is a coastal dune specialist (Parsons 1987a).

SPIDERS (ARACHNIDA)
C. Felton

Species mentioned in this section have been observed by the author, unless other references are given. Further information can be found in Mackie (1967)

The majority of the spiders occurring on the Sefton dunes are generally common throughout Britain and only a small number can be considered typical coastal species. However, several that are present are rare and local on Merseyside and of these, a few are rare nationally. Of these *Mecopisthes peusi* (Wanderlich) lives amongst marram grass on the outer dunes, particularly between Freshfield and Ainsdale. This is the only known site in the vice-county of Lancashire and one of a small number of sites in Britain. Two other species belonging to this large family, *Mioxena blanda* (Simon) recorded once at Formby Point (Locket & Millidge 1953) and *Lepthyphantes insignis* (O.P-C) also recorded once at Southport, are both rare species in Britain. Of the larger spiders on the outer dunes, the locally rare crab-spiders *Xysticus sabulosus* (Hahn) and *Philodromus fallax* (Sundevall) are both cryptically patterned, which might account partly for their apparent rarity here.

The attractive jumping spider *Attulus saltator* (Simon) is a scarce species in Britain and mainly coastal, occurring generally along the whole length of the dunes. Another coastal species is *Argenna patula*

(Simon) which in recent years has been recorded only at Formby Point. The little harvestman *Odiellus meadeii* (O.P.-C.) occurs sparingly in the dunes and is very local in Britain.

The wet slacks support a wide variety of spiders and amongst the less common species is *Trochosa spinipalpis* (F.O.P.-C.) taken once at Hightown (Mackie 1961-62). Another wet-slack species is *Halorates distinctus* (Simon) a rarity recorded at Formby Point. The drier scrub areas around the slacks are the habitat of *Agelena labyrinthica* (Clerck). The large webs of which are often conspicuous on creeping willow (*Salix repens L.*) and other plants. This species seems to be restricted to these dunes on Merseyside.

The so-called nursery-web spider *Pisaura mirabilis* (Clerck) is widespread and common on the open dunes but strangely, it is rare or absent from much of 'S. W. Lancashire'.

Tall grasses and umbellifers are favoured by the very local *Agalenatea redii* (Scopoli) which forms scattered colonies in a variety of places, including a deserted asparagus field at Formby Point.

A very rare and mainly southern jumping spider *Euophrys herbigrada* (Simon) is known only from an unverified specimen at Freshfield (Mackie 1967). Unfortunately, this specimen cannot be traced and this nationally notable (Nb) species may be dropped from the Lancashire list. The spider *Enoplognatha latimana* Hippa & Oksala, discovered at Freshfield in 1984 (S. Dobson, pers. comm.) is a new Lancashire record. This species is comparatively new to the British fauna and although records of it are increasing it is still rare in Britain.

Other local rarities which occur generally on the dunes outside the conifer plantations include *Cheirachanthium erraticum* (Walckenaer), *C. virescens* (Sundevall) and *Scotina gracilipes* (Blackwall).

The conifer plantations support numerous spiders, some of which do not occur anywhere else on the dunes but few can be considered rare. However, there are several Lancashire records of *Atea sturmi* (Hahn), a species found mainly on evergreen trees and which lives on the lower foliage of Corsican pine (*Pinus nigra* ssp. *laricio* Maire) at Ainsdale and Freshfield. The harvestman *Oligolophus hanseni* is a dark-coloured, short-legged species that is common in the conifer plantations but scarce elsewhere on Merseyside. Two large common spiders, *Amaurobius similis* (Blackwall) and *A. fenestralis* (Stroem), occur under bark of pine trees here. The former species is usually associated with man-made objects such as buildings and walls, whilst the latter species is normally found on trees. However, in the pines, *A. similis* is much the commoner species.

Ostearius melanopygius (O.P.-C.) long established in Britain, together with *Lepthyphantes nebulosus* (Sundevall) and the house spider *Tegenaria saeva* (Blackwall) are all strongly associated with made-made situations that are present on the outer dunes.

OTHER INVERTEBRATES
D. Atkinson and C. Felton

Most other invertebrate groups are under-recorded, and the records are scattered (Table 10.17).

The calcareous dunes support large numbers of snails, which require calcium to build their shells. Among the most abundant are the brown-lipped banded snail (*Cepaea nemoralis* (L.)) and *Candidula intersecta* Poiret. *Cepaea nemoralis* shells can be yellow, pink or brown with zero, one, three or five dark bands in each whorl.

TABLE 10.17
Invertebrates (excluding insects and arachnids*): Some References

Group	References
Aquatic invertebrates (general)	Galliford (1952, 1963, 1979, 1981, 1984), Young & Williams (1968), Bevercombe (1969), Cox (1970), Bevercombe *et al* (1973), Jones (1978), Kirkham (1978), Griffiths (1979), Whitehead (1985), Chatwin (1986).
Molluscs	Grensted (1922), McMillan (1969)
Other Terrestrial Species	Felton & Jones (1982), Daws (1990), Felton (1991

*Some sources also include information on insects and arachnids as part of their accounts of invertebrates.

The common slug *Deroceras caruanae* (Pollonera) which lives under bark in alder groves and the centipedes *Lithobius melanops* (Newport) and *L. microps* (Meinhert) which are found in dune hollows, are all usually found in association with people.

Galliford (1952, 1963, 1979, 1981, 1984) has monitored the presence of various aquatic invertebrates on Ainsdale NNR, and reported the nationally notable (Nb) water flea (Cladoceran) *Lathonura rectirostris* (O.F.M.) (Parsons 1987a). Also, as far as Galliford was aware "not one organism characteristic of brackish water has been recorded from these pools" (Galliford 1952).

As recently as 24 March 1991, C. Felton (in litt.) recorded at Cabin Hill "large number of the rare (RDB3) woodlouse *Armadillidium album* under old drift-line debris, especially planks of wood deeply embedded in the sand".

108

This species was previously recorded locally on salt-marsh in the Alt estuary in 1973 (Parsons 1987a), and under drift wood at Ainsdale (Daws 1990). Thus an activity as apparently innocuous as removing old drift wood from the upper shore could significantly affect the scattered populations of at least one rare and apparently specialist coastal species (see also section on beetles, this chapter).

FLOWERING PLANTS (ANGIOSPERMAE)

S. E. Edmondson, M. R. Edmondson, P. S. Gateley, P. J. Rooney and P. H. Smith

An indication of the diversity of this group is given by the NNR species lists (Gateley 1987c and Payne 1982b, updated in the file) recording 435 species for Ainsdale Sand Dunes and 313 for the smaller Cabin Hill site, although some of these are introductions.

Of the native species recorded at Ainsdale, 32% are confined to slacks and the remainder are from the whole range of dry dune communities, including woodland. At Cabin Hill where the variety of dune slack types is far less, 24% are confined to slacks.

A breakdown of the dry dune, slack and introduced species at these two sites is shown in Table 10.18.

Many species are recorded in target notes made during the NVC survey (see Edmondson *et al.* this volume). The fullest account coastwide of the species present is given in Savidge, Heywood & Gordon (1963), which reviews all records of past and present occurrences. Green (1933) gives an earlier account.

This section reviews only those species or groups that are of particular interest because of rarity or unusual and changing distributions, plus those which have been the subject of previous interest or research. Unless otherwise stated, records are from observations made during the course of the NVC survey.

Flowering plants at Hightown Dunes and Meadows, Ravenmeols Dunes, Lifeboat Road and Ainsdale and Birkdale Hills LNR have been classified according to their rarity at a national, regional and local level. Species previously recorded on the system but now thought to be extinct are recorded in Table 10.19; uncommon or rare species from these sites are presented in Table 10.20.

BROAD-LEAVED CENTAURY (*Centaurium latifolium* Sm. Druce)

This species was only known from the Sefton coast. It was first collected in 1801 from Crosby and the last known record is from Freshfield, 1871 (Savidge, Heywood & Gordon 1963). The exact cause of the extinction of this endemic species is unknown but over-collecting by 19th century botanists may well have contributed to its disappearance.

CREEPING WILLOW (*Salix repens* L.) AND ITS HYBRIDS

This plant forms a significant part of many vegetation communities on the coast, both dry dune and slack communities. At one extreme it is actively dune building, at the other, it is the dominant plant in the species-poor later stages of wet dune slack succession (see Edmondson *et al.* this volume).

Its taxonomy is poorly understood, (Rechinger 1964; Meikle 1984). Two forms occur on the dunes, *S. repens* var. *repens* L. and *S. repens* var. *argentea* (Sm.) Wimm. & Grab. but the relationship between these varieties is not clear. Creeping willow hybrids also occur on the dune system (Payne 1977). *Salix* x *doniana* Sm. (*S. purpurea* x *repens*) and *Salix* x *friesiana* Anderss. (*S. repens* x *viminalis*) both occur at their only English localities on the Sefton Coast.

An understanding of the genetics, physiology and ecology of creeping willow would be a significant aid to the understanding and conservation management of vegetation on the dune system.

TABLE 10.18.
Composition of the Angiosperm Flora at the Two NNRs.

	Total No. of Species	Introductions		Total No. of Native Species	Slack Species	
		No. of species	% of total		No of species	% of native species
Ainsdale Sand Dunes	435	64	15	371	117	32
Cabin Hill	313	36	12	277	67	24

Note

i. *Introductions include all species which are not native to the coast - this includes deliberate introductions as well as naturalised and garden escape species.*

ii. *Slack species include those which are confined to slack and aquatic habitats.*

TABLE 10.19
Species Previously Recorded But Now Thought to be Extinct.

SPECIES	NOTES
Antennaria dioica	"a fine patch on the sand dunes on the Formby side of Freshfield" plus populations in Ainsdale and Birkdale, 1953. No subsequent records.
Centaurium latifolium (Sm.) Druce	Thought either to be an endemic to the coast or a variety of *C.erythraea*. Last recorded near Freshfield Station in 1872, but formerly scattered rarely over the southern dunes, to the northern edges of Liverpool. Now known only in herbaria (Stansfield 1936).
Coeloglossum viride	see section on Orchidaceae
Pinguicula vulgaris	Recorded from Massam's Slack (S end of ASDNNR) 1914. No subsequent records.
Plantago media	Recorded at Formby Golf Course, Formby sand dunes and Southport seawall. No recent records.
Platanthera bifolia	see section on Orchidaceae
Salvia verbenaca	Reported from dry pastures and sand dunes between Waterloo and Little Brighton. Recorded as "very rare or extinct" in 1963. No recent records.
Senecio erucifolius	Formerly frequent, no recent records.
Spiranthes spiralis	See section on Orchidaceae.

Unless otherwise stated, all records in this table from Savidge, Heywood & Gordon (1963). ASDNNR - Ainsdale Sand Dunes National Nature Reserve.

BALTIC RUSH (*Juncus balticus* Willd.) AND ITS HYBRIDS

A plant of wide distribution worldwide, Baltic rush is here at the southern limit of its range, at its only site in England. It was first found at Birkdale in 1913 (Savidge, Heywood & Gordon 1963). Several attempts at transplants have been made but as yet without success (Smith 1984b).

Smith (1984b) reviewed the status of the species from data collected during a survey in 1982. The main conclusions were as follows:

Baltic rush was found to occur at ten sites in two groups at Birkdale. The spread of the plant seems to be aided in this area by public pressure on the dunes.

Its growth and associated plant species suggest that it is best suited to open damp-slack communities probably representing an early stage in the vegetation succession. Despite the increased use of the dunes for recreational purposes in recent years, with consequent damage to many plant communities, Baltic rush appears to be surviving well and is even spreading. Several factors may have contributed to this success, these include;

i)   Baltic rush has a high resistance to mechanical damage.

ii)   Damage caused to potential competitors by trampling, horse riding and motor-cycle riding favours the establishment of young Baltic rush plants

iii) The drying of the dune system in the early 1970s allowed wind erosion of exposed dry sand, making new damp-slacks available for the growth of new colonies.

iv)   The seeds germinate readily and are sticky, aiding dispersal.

During the NVC Survey carried out in 1988, Baltic rush was again recorded from the same area.

In 1989/90, McKinnell (1990) repeated Smith's (1984b) survey. He found that Baltic rush had become extinct at one site but had spread to three new ones in the same general area. Furthermore, the area occupied by patches of the plant had increased from 133m^2 to 348m^2.

Two extremely rare hybrid rushes, *J. balticus* x *J. effusus* and *J. balticus* x *J. inflexus* have been found, the latter being endemic to the north-west of England (Stace 1972). Both of the hybrids are sterile (Stace 1970), and in contrast to *J. balticus*, both hybrids have been transplanted successfully (Smith 1984b). The most successful transplant sites are at the edge of wet-slacks with sparse vegetation. Once established, both hybrids compete well with other vegetation.

The hybrid *J. balticus* x *J. effusus* has been found at three sites in Hightown (1966, 1973) and Ainsdale (1933) (Savidge, Heywood & Gordon 1963). These sites have since been lost due to housing development or coastal erosion. Transplants to the Altcar Rifle Range (1977) and five sites on Ainsdale NNR have met with some success, with plants surviving at several of the sites in 1982. This hybrid is now thought to exist at transplant sites only (Smith 1984b).

TABLE 10.20.
Rare Flowering Plants from Four Sites on the Sefton Coast.

STATUS	SPECIES	HDM	RMD	SITES LBR	ABSH	(A + B)
L	*Anacamptis pyramidalis*		•		•	A+B
R L	*Atriplex laciniata*	•	•		•	B
R L	*Atriplex littoralis*				•	B
L	*Baldellia ranunculoides*			•	•	B
R L	*Beta vulgaris* ssp. *maritima*				•	B
R L	*Blysmus rufus*				•	B
L	*Calystegia soldanella*	•			•	B
NsR	*Centaurium littorale*	•			•	B
R	*Centaurium pulchellum*				•	B
NsRL	*Crambe maritima*	•				
L	*Dactylorhiza purpurella*	•			•	B
R L	*Eleocharis uniglumis*				•	A+B
NrR	*Epipactis leptochila* var. *dunensis*	•	•	•	•	A+B
R	*Epipactis palustris*	•	•	•	•	A+B
Ns R	*Epipactis phyllanthes*			•	•	A
Ns R	*Equisetum variegatum*	•	•	•	•	A+B
Ns?	*Euphorbia paralias*	•	•	•	•	A+B
Ns?	*Euphorbia portlandica*	•	•	•	•	A+B
L	*Glaucium flavum*	•				
L	*Atriplex portulacoides*	•				
Ns	*Hydrocharis morsus-ranae*			•		
NsR	*Hypochaeris glabra*				•	A+B
L	*Inula conyzae*				•	B
NsRL	*Juncus balticus*				•	B
NRL	*Juncus balticus x inflexus*				•	B
R L	*Juncus subnodulosus*				•	B
R	*Monotropa hypopitys* ssp. *hypophegea*		•			A
L	*Oenanthe lachenalii*				•	B
R	*Orobanche minor*		•		•	B
R L	*Potamogeton gramineus*				•	B
NsR	*Pyrola rotundifolia*	•	•		•	B
Ns RL	*Coincya monensis* ssp. *monensis*	•			•	B
L	*Rosa pimpinellifolia*	•				
N?L	*Salix x friesiana*		•	•		A+B
R	*Schoenoplectus tabernaemontani*			•		A+B
R L	*Schoenus nigricans*				•	A+B
L	*Thalictrum minus* ssp. *arenarium*		•			

Site abbreviations: HDM Hightown Dunes and Meadows, RMD Ravenmeols Dunes Local Nature Reserve, LBR Lifeboat Road, ABSH Ainsdale and Birkdale Sand Hills Local Nature Reserve (A = Ainsdale, B = Birkdale)

Rarity criteria

Nr National - rare, recorded from only 1-15 10 km squares in GB (Red Data Book), Ns National - scarce 16-100 10 km squares, R Regional 1-10 10km squares in NW NCC Region (5% or less of 10 km squares) L Local 1-5 localities in vice County in Region 59, Lancs. (v. rare or rare in Savidge, Heywood & Gordon 1963) Data from Mick Brummage, June 1991.

Two colonies of the hybrid *J. balticus* x *J. inflexus* were found in wet-slacks at Birkdale and Ainsdale in 1952 (Stace 1970). This plant shows considerable hybrid vigour, growing up to 2m high. Transplants were made into two sites in Ainsdale NNR and were growing well in these sites in 1982 (Smith 1984b). The Birkdale clone, despite being damaged in 1975 was also growing well and spreading in 1982, and was still present in 1988 (Edmondson *et al.* 1988/89).

A third clone of this hybrid, morphologically different from the Ainsdale and Birkdale clones was found at Lytham St. Annes LNR (Stace 1970).

ORCHIDS (ORCHIDACEAE)

Most published information on the orchids of the Sefton coast dates back to the early part of the century and is reviewed by Savidge, Heywood & Gordon (1963) and Gray (1980). This account of the family's current status is based on personal observations by P. H. Smith since 1968 and unpublished reports.

In recent years, fourteen species of orchid have been identified in the dune system (Table 10.21). However, according to Savidge, Heywood & Gordon (1963), three others occurred in the past. These, together with

111

their last dated records are: autumn lady's tresses (*Spiranthes spiralis* (L.) Chevall.) (1903), frog orchid (*Coeloglossum viride* (L.) Hartman) (1890) and lesser butterfly orchid (*Platanthera bifolia* (L.) Rich.) (1957). The record for lizard orchid (*Himantoglossum hircinum* (L.) Sprengel) from 1954 (Savidge, Heywood & Gordon 1963) is now believed to be an error, the specimen not collected locally.

TABLE 10.21.
Status and Habitats of Orchids Recently Recorded in the Sefton Coast Dune System.

Species	Status	Habitat				
		FD	Sl	DG	Sc	CW
Epipactis helleborine	r				•	
Epipactis leptochila var. dunensis	f	•	•		•	•
Epipactis phyllanthes	o	•	•			•
Epipactis palustris	c		•			
Listera ovata	o			•		
Listera cordata	r					•
Orchis morio	lf			•		
Anacamptis pyramidalis	lo	•				
Gymnadenia conopsea	lo			•		
Ophrys apifera	o	•	•			
Dactylorhiza fuchsii	o			•	•	
Dactylorhiza praetermissa	o			•	•	
Dactylorhiza purpurella	lo			•	•	
Dactylorhiza incarnata	c					

r = rare; o = occasional; f = frequent; c = common; l = locally.

FD = fixed dune; Sl = dune slack; DG = dune grassland Sc = dune scrub; CW = conifer woodland.

Most extant species are associated with dune slacks, fixed dunes and grasslands. Several are widespread and common in the dune system. They include early marsh orchid (*Dactylorhiza incarnata* (L.) Soó), mainly of the endemic coastal subspecies *D. incarnata* ssp. *coccinea* (Pugsley) Soó and the marsh helleborine (*Epipactis palustris* (L.) Crantz), which includes a few of the beautiful white variety *ochroleuca*. Other species are rare; broad leaved helleborine (*Epipactis helleborine* (L.) Crantz), for example is represented by two small stands at Lifeboat Road, Formby (Gateley 1990) and some plants on the Formby Golf Course (Gray & Clitherow 1982).

Of particular interest is the occurrence of both northern and southern floristic elements. Thus, this is one of the few areas of the country where both northern marsh (*Dactylorhiza purpurella* (Stephenson & T.A. Stephenson) Soó) and southern marsh orchid (*D. praetermissa* (Druce) Soó) are found. Perhaps the most surprising orchid to be discovered in the dunes is the lesser twayblade (*Listera cordata* (L.) R.Br.) a northern species which has a small population under conifers at Ainsdale.

The only British Red Data Book species of orchid (Perring & Farrell 1977) is the dune helleborine (*Epipactis leptochila* var. *dunensis* Stephenson & T.A.Stephenson) which is found quite widely in slacks, on fixed dunes and in or near conifer plantations. In the latter habitat, it grows with the superficially similar pendulous-flowered helleborine (*E. phyllanthes* G.E.Sm.) (see also Travis 1943). During a detailed survey in 1988 and 1989, Gateley (1990) counted 870 specimens of dune helleborine and 251 of pendulous-flowered helleborine between Hightown and Birkdale.

As most of the orchid species favour open dune habitats, the main threat to their populations is probably the increasing maturation of the dune system and the rapid development of dune scrub in most areas. Increased recreational trampling and flower picking can be a problem at some sites. Gateley (1990) discusses the implications of conifer woodland management for the conservation of dune and pendulous-flowered helleborines.

SHARP CLUB-RUSH (*Schoenoplectus pungens* (Vahl) Palla)

A very rare plant in western Europe, sharp club-rush is known to occur at only one other site in the British Isles, a pond margin on Jersey (Savidge, Heywood & Gordon 1963).

It was first recorded at Ainsdale in 1928 (Travis 1929) "found in a hollow among the dunes near the sea-coast in the vicinity of Formby". It then existed as a patch of approximately 25 square yards. Travis subsequently found specimens of it in his records, which had been collected at the same site in 1909 but incorrectly identified. The associated plants were creeping willow, grass of Parnassus (*Parnassia palustris* L.) round-leaved wintergreen (*Pyrola rotundifolia* L.), and grey club-rush *Schoenoplectus tabernaemontani* (C.C.Gmel.) Palla, all typical of wet-slacks. As the sharp club-rush had obviously been there for a long time, were in good condition, and since no aliens were present, Travis concluded that the colony was native, although Clapham, Tutin and Moore (1987) record it as "introduced in Lancashire".

Blanchard (1952) reported that local areas of the northern part of Massam's Slack South, in what she referred to as "the damp *Salix repens* association", were co-dominated by common cotton-grass (*Eriophorum angustifolium* Honck.), and sharp club-rush. It was also found further south in the same slack, growing in a peat cut, from which it was spreading to the surrounding drier area.

The colony in the northern part of the slack, close to Fishermans Path, still existed in 1972 (Aldridge 1972b). At this time it consisted of 39 plants (of which 12 were in flower) covering an area of approximately 20 x 15 feet (*ca*.28m²). It was noted that the plants were shorter than in the 1950s, were subject to rabbit grazing and were often chlorotic.

The colony in Massam's Slack South was extinct by 1978 (Payne 1978c). A group of transplanted plants which had established at the edge of the Large Pond at Ainsdale at an unknown date, consisted at this time, of 40 mature plants (see also NCC Wardens, undated). These plants were initially damaged by rabbit grazing, and were later protected by exclosures. A healthy stand of sharp club-rush exists by the pond at present.

GREY HAIR-GRASS (*Corynephorus canescens* (L.) P. Beauv.)

A grass of mainly east coast distribution in Britain, this is recorded from Norfolk, Suffolk, Moray and Inverness. The only western record from mainland Britain, other than S. Lancashire, is from Glamorgan (Clapham, Tutin & Moore 1987). Rose (1989) states that its only native British locality is East Anglia, the Scottish records being introduced plants.

Grey hair-grass was first recorded on the Lancashire coast in 1928 "in some plenty at two places at Formby" (Travis 1929). Travis states that J.A.Wheldon first noted it in 1919, "among the rough and high dunes of the pinewoods near the Formby Golf Links", but did not know what it was.

It was subsequently recorded from Freshfield in 1929 (Green 1933). There is some debate as to whether or not it is native. Clapham, Tutin & Moore (1987) record it as introduced to this site, but Travis (1929) supports the view that it is native, stating : "It is found on the unconsolidated outer series of dunes where marram grass and pine trees have been planted. It is probably native and grows amongst such species as *Ammophila arenaria, Carex arenaria, Erodium cicutarium, Euphorbia paralias, Viola canina* and *Senecio jacobea*."

It was reported to have become extinct at one of these sites in 1937 (Savidge, Heywood & Gordon 1963).

Extensive stands were recorded on Southport and Ainsdale Golf Club in 1988 (Edmondson *et al.* 1988/89), where it occurs as "large swathes of *Corynephorus canescens* dominated dune with much

Agrostis capillaris and mossy tufted sward". It also occurs in the same area as a co-dominant with sheep's fescue (*Festuca ovina L*) , and in an area of "very low vegetation dominated by mosses (generally *Polytrichum juniperinum*), along with plants such as *Ammophila arenaria, Hypochoeris radicata, Anthyllis vulneraria, Carex arenaria, Sedum acre* and *Cladonia spp.*".

This site, being entirely composed of very low dunes, seems to differ significantly from the earlier sites of grey hair-grass, where it was reported to grow on high dunes. It is also some distance from these earlier sites. This grass is also found in abundance on railway track ballast near Ainsdale (D. A. Nissenbaum *in lit.*).

Marshall (1965) has shown that this species declines in vigour on stable dunes. This would appear to raise doubts about the long term viability of this grass on its present sites, although observations indicate it to be well established and under no threat from competitors.

OTHER FLOWERING PLANTS

Grass-of-Parnassus (*Parnassia palustris* var. *condensata* Travis & Wheldon) and round-leaved wintergreen (*Pyrola rotundifolia* ssp. *maritima* (Kenyon) E.F.Warb.) (Figure 10.9) are nationally uncommon but frequent in the dune slacks on the Sefton coast. They occur however in differing conditions; grass-of-Parnassus occurs in damp, low-growing slacks whereas round-leaved wintergreen, unlike many other slack specialities, occurs in older slacks amongst relatively dense stands of creeping willow (see Edmondson *et al.*, this volume), a situation also shown at Kenfig by Jones and Etherington (1989).

Figure 10.9 *Pyrola rotundifolia.*

113

TABLE 10.22
Species with very Local Distributions on the Sefton Coast

10.22a - Plants occurring on dry dune habitat

Species	Notes
Allium scorodoprasum	One small colony, probably introduced on edge of Fishermans Path (ASDNNR). (Not recorded on the dunes in Savidge, Heywood & Gordon 1963)
Anthriscus caucalis	Formerly more widespread (Travis), now the only known stand is under willow scrub on CHNNR (Gateley 1987c)
Aphanes inexspectata	On more acidic substrates, on eastern edge of ASDNNR, and some golf courses.
Atriplex laciniata	A few recent strandline records at BLNR and RLNR (P. H. Smith, pers. comm.)
Briza media	Very sparsely distributed except on parts of CHNNR and Hightown dunes. Occasionally occurs in damp slacks.
Campanula latifolia	One small stand in the southern part of RLNR.
Cerastium arvense	Known only from ASDNNR Payne (1982b)
Centaurea scabiosa	A few plants in main entrance verges at Altcar rifle ranges, probably introduced.
Ceratocapnos claviliculata	Probably introduced with *Pinus* roots, dotted through eastern edge of ASDNNR pine plantations
Crambe maritima	A small colony recently established on artificial shingle shore at Hightown, together with *Glaucium flavum*. Neither known elsewhere though past records (Travis) indicate they occurred sporadically along the strandline.
Festuca rubra x *Vulpia fasciculata*	ASDNNR (nationally rare) (P. H. Smith, pers. comm.)
Filipendula vulgaris	A small colony at Hightown (introduced?)
Genista tinctoria	Known only from edge of coastal road, BLNR.
Gentianella campestris	Not as widespread as *G. amarella*. Mainly in ASDNNR, and extends to ALNR and BLNR in small numbers.
Glaucium flavum	see *Crambe maritima*
Herniaria glabra	Not recorded from the dunes proper, found in the short mown sandy verges of Kenilworth Rd. Ainsdale, built through former high dunescape. Not recorded in Travis
Inula conyzae	Very sparsely scattered over the dunes, mainly in the open areas of ASDNNR and ALNR.
Ornithopus perpusillus	On disturbed acidic sandy areas and sparse acidic swards on the eastern fringes
Pimpinella major	One record only on CHNNR.
Poa compressa	Formerly frequent on part of CHNNR where its current status is unknown, most recently recorded on Lifeboat Rd. (Liverpool Botanical Society field trip 1990). Easily overlooked.
Primula veris	Only record is a large colony on one of the Altcar rifle ranges. Hall (1988c)
Pyrola minor	Recorded as extinct in Travis, but is listed by Payne (1982b) and was recorded in the N.V.C. survey in slacks surrounded by conifers on ASDNNR.
Coincya monensis ssp. *monensis*	Occurs in large numbers in disturbed areas around Southport Marine Lake. Also recorded on a disturbed sandy verge near the entrance to Blundellsands Key Park and one site in the Birkdale frontals. (Smith & Hall 1991)
Rosa rubiginosa	Not recorded in Travis, but becoming naturalised and increasingly common in mixed scrub on ALNR and BLNR. Presumably introduced by birds.
Sanguisorba officinalis	One plant in RLNR
Saxifraga tridactylites	Common on parts of Altcar Rifle Ranges and CHNNR, but very sparsely distributed elsewhere.
Silene maritima	Only scattered stands on the seaward edges of ALNR and BLNR
Succisa pratensis	On more acidic dunes on eastern edge of ASDNNR
Thalictrum minus arenarium	Sparsely scattered, mainly in in south of the system, the largest populations being in RLNR and Blundellsands Key Park.
Trisetum flavescens	Apparently restricted to two areas of the dunes, a meadow on CHNNR and on Lifeboat Rd.

10.22b Plants occurring in damp to aquatic habitats

Baldellia ranunculoides	Increasing with permanent water areas newly created in the 1970's. Spreading over ASDNNR, ALNR and BLNR.
Berula erecta	In wet slacks in ASDNNR and ALNR.
Blysmus compressus	In a few slacks at BLNR, Lifeboat Road and CHNNR (P. H. Smith, pers. comm.)
Blysmus rufus	In one slack on BLNR. *B. compressus* and *Juncus balticus* occur in the same slack. A second locality at Southport Esplanade was destroyed by tipping in the early l980s (P. H. Smith, pers. comm.)
Catabrosa aquatica	In ditches in the Woodvale area
Centaurium pulchellum	Is at its northern limits, cf. *C. littorale* at its southern limits. The two species overlap here but *C. pulchellum* is much less common in only a few western slacks.
Cornus sanguinea	Absent from the increasing scrub growth. Occurs in one slack on BLNR.
Cyperus longus	Patches in two slacks in ALNR, apparently introduced (P. H. Smith, pers. comm.)
Eleocharis uniglumis	At least one slack, ASD NNR; difficult to identify (P. H. Smith, pers. comm.)
Geum rivale	One site only on Altcar Rifle Ranges.
Juncus subnodulosus	Sparsely present on CHNNR and BLNR.
Littorella uniflora	Recorded as extinct in Ratcliffe (1977). As *Baldellia ranunculoides,* has benefitted from excavations in slacks. Now forms dense patches in shallow water in CHNNR and ASDNNR.
Monotropa hypopitys	Occurs sporadically, depending on the season. Most frequent in older slacks with well developed *Salix repens* cover on ASDNNR, ALNR and BLNR.
Oenanthe fistulosa	Now well established in wet slacks and scrapes in ASDNNR, ALNR and BLNR.
Oenanthe lachenalii	Only in some western slacks on BLNR.
Osmunda regalis	One young plant in damp acidic sand, Hillside golf course.
Parentucellia viscosa	Apparently declining as sites become too densely vegetated. Increase on its location on ASDNNR has been effected by management. It occurs in two other sites in the Freshfield area and on CHNNR (Hall 1988d, Smith 1982b).
Pedicularis palustris	One slack only on BLNR.
Potamogeton gramineus	As *Baldellia* and *Littorella,* has benefitted from excavations. Rare but increasing over ASDNNR and BLNR.
Ranunculus lingua	Only recent records are in ditches on edge of BLNR.
Rumex hydrolapathum	Decreasing as a result of its former sites (mostly ditches) becoming drier. Has not colonised the excavations.
Schoenus nigricans	One clump only in the same site as *Pedicularis.*
Thalictrum flavum	Very rare in wet areas. Only recent record is Hightown.
Trifolium fragiferum	Largely confined to westernmost slacks in BLNR (P. H. Smith, pers. comm.)
Typha angustifolia	One slack only on BLNR.

N.B. Plants discussed in separate sections are not listed here.

ALNR - Ainsdale Local Nature Reserve; ASDNNR - Ainsdale Sand Dunes National Nature Reserve BLNR - Birkdale Local Nature Reserve; CHNNR - Cabin Hill National Nature Reserve; RLNR - Ravenmeols Local Nature Reserve; Travis - Travis's Flora of South Lancashire (Savidge, Heywood & Gordon 1963)

Species with limited distributions on the Sefton coast are listed, together with notes on their distributions, in Table 10.22. A number of species typical of calcareous dune systems which are surprisingly rare on the Sefton coast are presented in Table 10.23. A few have previously been more frequent and are apparently the victims of the increasingly mature, stable and ungrazed condition of the dunes. Some species common on dunes in the south of England, e.g. travellers' joy (*Clematis vitalba* L.) which is known here at two sites as an introduction, and stinking iris (*Iris foetidissima* L.) would not be expected in this more northerly location (see also Holder 1924).

A large number of introduced and alien species occur on the coast. Of the intentionally introduced plants, the tree and shrub species, which were planted earlier this century in attempts to stabilise the dunes are the most prominent. These include a variety of *Alnus, Populus* and *Salix* species which are referred to by Edmondson *et al* (1988/89), Gateley (1987c), Payne (1982b), and Savidge, Heywood & Gordon (1963). Of these, white poplar (*Populus alba* L.) and balsam poplar (*Populus candicans* Aiton) are particularly prominent forming extensive stands on the dry dunes, and willows are actively colonising slacks. Sea buckthorn (*Hippophae rhamnoides* L.) was also introduced, spread rapidly (Ranwell 1972b; Nesbitt 1981; Simpson 1990a) and has been the subject of extensive clearance programmes. Tree lupin (*Lupinus arboreus* Sims) has also become naturalised although is sparsely distributed. A number of tree species have been planted

TABLE 10.23
Plants Typical of British Calcareous Dune Systems, Rare on the Sefton Coast.

Species	Notes
Calystegia soldanella	Well established small stands on ALNR and BLNR and at Hightown but showing no signs of increase
Echium vulgare	Occurs sparsely in Hightown dunes, and rarely on ASDNNR and RLNR. Formerly more frequent (Wheldon 1913a, Anon 1920)
Galium verum	Occurs throughout but is hardly ever common enough to be part of the typical fixed dune *Festuca rubra - Galium verum* (Malloch 1989)
Ligustrum vulgare	Very rare, only isolated clumps on ALNR and the Lifeboat Rd. site.
Lithospermum officinale	Only scattered plants in a small area of Hightown dunes and Altcar rifle range dunes.
Rosa pimpinellifolia	Small colonies between West Lancashire Golf Course and the shore. Abundant in the Key Park at Blundellsands
Thymus polytrichus	As *Galium verum*, typical of fixed dune grassland, but here only sparsely distributed patches in Hightown, Altcar, Lifeboat Rd. and Birkdale. Elsewhere it is rare.

ALNR - Ainsdale Local Nature Reserve ASDNNR - Ainsdale Sand Dunes National Nature Reserve BLNR - Birkdale Local Nature Reserve

in the woodlands in the Formby and Ravenmeols area, (Edmondson *et al.* 1988/89, this volume; Gray & Clitherow 1982), sycamore (*Acer pseudoplatanus* L.) being particularly common.

Other species are still being introduced as landscape plantings on golf courses especially in the Birkdale and Hillside area, and also on Lifeboat Road.

Some herb species are introductions of long standing and have become widely naturalised. Examples are horse-radish (*Armoracia rusticana* P.Gaertn., B.Mey. & Scherb.) and soapwort (*Saponaria officinalis* L.) which occur in disturbed areas, Michaelmas-daisy (*Aster* sp.), tansy (*Tanacetum vulgare* (L.) Bernh.) and goldenrod (*Solidago* sp.) common in mesotrophic grassland, (i.e. with only moderate amounts of nutrients) pond weeds (*Elodea* spp.) in open water, spring beauty (*Montia perfoliata* (Willd.) Howell), common in woodland and woodland edge, ivy (*Hedera helix* ssp. *hibernica* (Kirschner) D.C.McClint.) widely naturalised on banks and woodland floor, white melilot (*Melilotus alba* Medic.) common on disturbed ground at the south end of the system and evening primroses (*Oenothera biennis* L., Figure 10.10, and *O. erythrosepala* Borbas) which are extensively found throughout the mobile to semi-fixed dunes and readily hybridise (see Wheldon 1913b; Rostanski 1982; Ash & Clitherow 1983). Asparagus (*Asparagus officinalis* L.) occurs widely on the dunes, the result of its cultivation on the coast which until relatively recently was widespread (see Edmondson *et al.*, this volume).

Of more restricted distribution are buttonweed (*Cotula coronopifolia* L.) established on one site in Southport, hairy bindweed (*Calystegia pulchra* Brummitt & Heywood) found at one site near the mouth of the Alt, Pyrenean lily (*Lilium pyrenaicum*, Gouan), at one long established site on Ainsdale NNR and blue-eyed grass

(*Sisyrinchium bermudiana* L.), a long standing introduction (Savidge, Heywood & Gordon 1963) now known only in the western edges of the southern parts of the system. Hungarian brome (*Bromopsis inermis* (Leysser) Holub) is found at Altcar Rifle Range, Cabin Hill NNR and in the Ainsdale buffer strip (east of the coast road), and tuberous pea (*Lathyrus tuberosus* L.) has a long-established flourishing colony at Ravenmeols LNR (P. H. Smith, pers. comm). Bloody crane's-bill (*Geranium sanguineum* L.), was once part of the native flora (Savidge, Heywood & Gordon 1963): latterly it has apparently been introduced, becoming naturalised at Hightown and Ravenmeols LNR (P. H. Smith, pers. comm.). One female plant of Spanish catchfly (*Silene otites* (L.) Wibel), a very uncommon Breckland species, has been present near the entrance of Ainsdale NNR for about 10 years.

Figure 10.10 *Oenothera biennis* (x 0.75)

116

Some plants occasionally occur on the strand-line where seeds have been deposited. Wheat (*Triticum aestivum* L.) and oat (*Avena sativa* L.) cultivars, plus *Tropaeolum majus* L. and sunflower (*Helianthus annuus* L.) were recorded by Edmondson *et al.* (1988/89). Sturgess (1988) has recorded a number of aliens occurring at Tagg's Island.

Garden escapes recorded in the NVC survey target notes are shown in Table 10.24. Although the listing of species was not a primary aim of the survey, a high proportion of those encountered was recorded and therefore this serves to give a coastwide picture of the scale of this type of introduction. Spring species such as *Narcissus* cultivars and snowdrop (*Galanthus nivalis* L.) which are known to occur were not recorded. Although recorded above as widely naturalised, Michaelmas-daisies and goldenrod are also listed in this table as it seems clear that they are still being introduced in garden rubbish. The introduction and establishment of these garden escapes is a particular problem where dunes abut garden fences for example in Ainsdale and Birkdale. Another source of these introductions is from gardens of abandoned houses for example around Alexandra Road in the Formby area.

Nationally recognised plant pests are not common on the Sefton coast but are present. In the NVC survey (Edmondson *et al.* 1988/89) Japanese knotweed *(Fallopia japonica* (Houtt.) Ronse Decr.) was recorded in Divisions 1, 3, 7 and 9 (see Table 10.24 for explanation of divisions) but only formed extensive stands in division 3. Rhododendron (*Rhododendron ponticum* L.) occurs in the woodlands in divisions 3 and 4. Giant hogweed *(Heracleum mantegazzianum* Sommier & Levier), and Himalayan balsam (*Impatiens glandulifera* Royle), were recorded as isolated occurrences in division 8. A potentially more serious problem is the arrival on the coast in 1976 of the New Zealand water stonecrop (*Crassula helmsii* (Kirk) Cockayne) on Ainsdale NNR (Payne 1976b, 1978a). It is now carpeting the edges of various water bodies in the NNR and at Lifeboat Road.

CONIFERS AND ALLIES (PINOPSIDA)

No species of gymnosperm is native on the Coast. Yew (*Taxus baccata* L.) is rare, and one specimen of juniper (*Juniperus communis* L.) has been recorded on Ainsdale NNR, but is no longer present (Robinson 1973; Payne 1982b). Extensive areas of pine-woods are present, mostly Corsican (*Pinus nigra* ssp. *laricio* Maire) and Scots pine (*P. sylvestris* L.) resulting from planting largely between 1887 and the 1930s. Other species of pine are recorded by Payne (1982b), who records seven species on Ainsdale NNR, Edmondson *et al.* (1988/89, this volume) and Gray & Clitherow (1982). There is, however, no comprehensive list of all Pinopsida occurring coast-wide.

TABLE 10.24.
Garden Escapes Recorded in the 1988 NVC Survey

Species	Divisions of the Survey in Which Recorded	Number of Records
Aquilegia vulgaris	8	1
Aster sp.(novii-belgii type)	1,2,5,8,9	7
Berberis candidula	8	1
Brassica oleracea (cvr.)	1	1
Buddleia davidii	4	1
Calendula officinalis	7	1
Campanula rapunculoides	3	1
Cerastium tomentosum	7,1	5
Convallaria majalis	4,3	2
Cotoneaster frigidus	8	1
Dianthus deltoides	7	1
Euphorbia cyparissias	8	1
Euphorbia esula	1	1
Fallopia baldschuanica	7	1
Forsythia x intermedia	8	1
Gaillardia aristata	3	1
Geranium pratense	7	1
Geranium sanguineum	7	1
Helianthus rigidus	9	1
Helianthus annua	8	1
Iris germanica	8	1
Iris sibirica	2	1
Kniphofia x uvaria	2,4,8	3
Lamium maculatum	1	1
Leucanthemum maximum	1,3,8	3
Ligustrum ovalifolium	3	3
Lobularia maritima	1,8	2
Lychnis coronaria	8	1
Lycopersicon esculentum	1,8	2
Malus (cvrs.)	3,4,6,7,8	5
Nymphaea sp.	6	1
Papaver orientale	8	1
Papaver somniferum	7	1
Parthenocissus quinquefolia	3	1
Polygonatum sp.	1	1
Potentilla recta	1	1
Pyrus (cvr.)	3	1
Ribes sanguineum	1	1
Rosa (cvrs.)	7	1
Rosa rugosa	3	3
Rubus idaeus	8	1
Sedum album	7	1
Solidago sp.	1,8,9	6
Spinacia oleracea	1	1
Syringa vulgaris	5,8	2
Tritonia x crocosmiflora	1,4	2
Veronica spicata	8	1

Note - taxa deliberately planted are not listed here, and some widely and long established naturalised species are discussed in the text. Aster and *Solidago* spp., although widely naturalised, are also listed here as they are still being introduced with garden rubbish. NVC divisions - 1 Seaforth to Hightown. 2 Altcar Firing Ranges. 3 Cabin Hill N.N.R., Ravenmeols Hills L.N.R., Lifeboat Road, St. Joseph's Hospital and associated land. 4 National Trust and associated fields 5 Formby Golf Club to Woodvale Airfield. 6 Ainsdale Sand Dunes N.N.R. 7 Ainsdale L.N.R. and outlying dunes 8 Birkdale Hills L.N.R., Royal Birkdale, Hillside and Southport and Ainsdale Golf Clubs. 9 Southport Dunes and northern outliers.

Planting has introduced further species on golf courses. For example, Norway spruce (*Picea abies* (L.) Karsten) and a golden form of Leyland cypress (x *Cupressocyparis leylandii* (A.B.Jacks. & Dallim.) Dallim.) were recorded as newly planted in the NVC survey (Edmondson *et al.* 1988/89)

FERNS AND FERN ALLIES (PTERIDOPHYTES)
A. S. Gunn

Twenty-two species and hybrids of fern and fern ally have been recorded from the dune system. None of these is nationally rare although two species are nationally scarce (i.e. occur in less than 100, 10 km squares). The first of these, variegated horsetail (*Equisetum variegatum* Schleich ex Web. & Mohr) occurs in wet slacks. The second, marsh clubmoss (*Lycopodiella inundatum* (L.) Holub.) is a plant of open, wet, strongly acidic habitats. There is only a single record of this species from the "Formby sandhills" (Fisher l872). The loss of dune heath is probably responsible for the loss of this species from the coast although the national pattern of decline would also implicate air pollution as a cause (Page l982). Another species of interest is lesser clubmoss (*Selaginella selaginoides* (L.) Link) which is at the southern boundary of its distribution. Also, both common polypody (*Polypodium vulgare* L. sensu stricto) and western polypody (*P. interjectum* Shivas) occur on the dune system. It would be interesting to investigate the ecological separation of these species on the dunes and to search for the hybrid, *P.* x *mantoniae* Rothm., between these closely related species.

MOSSES AND LIVERWORTS (BRYOPHYTES).
A. S. Gunn

The sand dunes of the Sefton coast have been renowned since the 19th century as a rich habitat for bryophytes. A succession of bryologists, including Marrat (1855, 1860, 1864), Wheldon (1898, 1899, 1903), Wilson (1912) and Turner (1934) explored the dunes. The first British record for several species were from this area and one species new to science, *Bryum marratii* Wils. was based on material from these dunes. Much of the area studied by these early bryologists has been lost to development or substantially modified by golf course construction but the remaining areas, especially the Ainsdale NNR, are still a very important area for bryophytes (Savidge, Heywood & Gordon 1963). In the 1960s and 1970s several surveys on Ainsdale NNR added new records for the dunes (Musgrave 1975). However, by the late 1970s the area was still classified as under-recorded, that is, with less than 75% of the species that could be reasonably expected to occur recorded (A.J.E Smith 1978) and few new records have been added since. In all, 151 mosses and 31 liverworts have been recorded for the area and a list of these with up-to-date nomenclature has been compiled (Gunn 1991a).

Atmospheric pollution has probably been responsible for the extinction of several mosses in the coastal area, particularly epiphytic species such as *Tortula laevipila* (Brid.) Schwaegr. and *Orthotrichum* spp. which are especially sensitive.

Additions to the bryophyte list have appeared as part of a general invasion by alien species, for example *Orthodontium lineare* Schwaegr and *Campylopus introflexus* (Hedw.) Brid. or by the creation of new habitat, namely the pinewoods, which has allowed species such as *Plagiothecium curvifolium* Schliep. to colonise. Other additions to the flora are taxonomic, for example *Bryum gemmiferum* Wilcz. & Dem. now distinguished from *Bryum bicolor* Dicks. (Smith & Whitehouse 1978). Lastly some of the more recent additions such as *Trichostomum crispulum* Bruch are probably species long overlooked and, as mentioned above, it is likely that several more species remain to be found.

TABLE 10.25.
Rare, Endangered and Vulnerable Bryophytes on the Sefton Coast.

Name (synonym)	Status	
	GB	EEC
a) Red Data Book species: Main List.		
Liverworts		
Petalophyllum ralfsii (Wils.) Nees & Gottsche	V	E
Mosses		
Bryum calophyllum R. Brown	V	E
B. knowltonii Barnes	V	NT
(*B. lacustre* (Web. & Mohr.) Bland.)		
B. mamillatum Lindb.	E	NT
B. marratii Hook.f. & Wils.	V	NT
B. neodamense Itzig. ex C. Mull.	V	NT
B. uliginosum (Brid.) B. & S.	E	NT
B. warneum (Rohl.) Bland. ex Brid.	V	NT
b) Species threatened in Europe as a whole but not in Britain		
Mosses		
Amblyodon dealbatus (Hedw.) B. & S.	NT	V
Campylium elodes (Lindb.) Kindb.	NT	V
Drepanocladus lycopodiodes (Brid.) Warnst.	NT	V
Meesia uliginosa Hedw.	NT	V
c) Red Data Book species: Appendix 4. Species not threatened but requiring monitoring.		
Liverworts		
Cephaloziella rubella (Nees) Warnst.		
Reboulia hemisphaerica (L.) Raddi		
Mosses		
Catoscopium nigritum (Hedw.) Brid.		
Rhodobryum roseum (Hedw.) Limpr.		

E - endangered, V - vulnerable, NT - not threatened

Table 10.25 summarises the records from the dune system of species rare and scarce species listed in the Red Data Book for lower plants (Stewart 1991). It shows eight species under threat in Great Britain and a further four under threat in the EEC as a whole (Schumaker 1990). No bryophytes are included in the schedules of the Wildlife and Countryside Act but one of the Red Data book species, *Petalophyllum ralfsii* (Wils.) Nees & Gott. ex Lehm., is now included in the International Convention on Conservation (Bern Convention).

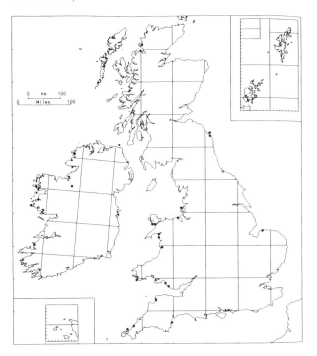

Figure 10.11 *Petalophyllum ralfsii*. A coastal species of calcareous sand-dunes where it may be locally frequent in and along the margins of slacks. Most conspicuous in winter and spring, it disappears almost completely during periods of drought. © British Bryological Society 1991, reprinted with kind permission. The symbols used are; o record made before 1950, or undated, ● record made in or after 1950.

Taken as a group, therefore, the bryophytes represent one of the most significant assets of the dune system and the impact on these plants by any management and conservation activity should be considered. Moreover many bryophytes are an important ecological component of the dune system and several species occur constantly in several of the National Vegetation Classification duneland categories (see Edmondson *et al.*, this volume). Apart from *Cephaloziella rubella* (Nees) Warnst which is found on the acidic parts of the dune system, all the species listed in Table 10.25 are found in the dune slacks. Although the ecology of these wet slacks has been described (Smith 1978), the factors influencing the bryophyte community in these areas has received little attention.

On dune systems as a whole, work done elsewhere (Birse, Landsberg & Gimingham 1957; Gimingham 1948) has shown the importance of bryophytes in the stabilisation of sand dunes. Similarly, the overall changes in the bryophyte community in the dune succession has been well established (Birse & Gimingham 1955; Gimingham & Robertson 1950; During 1973). The effect of grazing by rabbits on the balance between lichens, bryophytes and flowering plants, with its importance in maintaining diversity, has also been studied (Northfield 1968; Zeevalking & Fresco 1977) as has the effect of afforestation (Hill & Wallace 1989), and salt spray (Boerner & Forman 1975).

ALGAE
A. S. Gunn

DIATOMS (BACILLARIOPHYTA).

Diatoms are the most important of the microscopic algae of the dune slacks (Round 1958). High pH and the abundance of silica suit these algae and, in contrast to other planktonic (free-floating) algae, they are able to recover rapidly after periods of drought.

The diatoms are chiefly concentrated in the slack sediment with other epiphytic species (i.e. physically supported by the slack surface). Any kind of free-floating alga of open water is rare. The species found in slacks are typical of those found in ponds and lakes on calcareous substrates. Despite the close proximity to the sea, marine and brackish water forms were absent. Wider surveys of the diatoms of the coastal area were undertaken by W. Waddington in the late 1930s and early 1940s (Waddington 1938, 1939). Waddington's notes and voucher specimens of diatoms, many from the dune slacks, are housed in Liverpool Museum.

CHAROPHYTES (CHLOROPHTYA)

Twelve of the 38 British taxa of these large algae, sometimes called stoneworts, have been found in the Sefton coast area (Savidge, Heywood & Gordon 1963, Moore 1986). Their ecological preference is for waterbodies with a high pH and some species tolerate, or even prefer, brackish water. They can be the dominant vegetation in freshly dug waterbodies but they may eventually be out-competed by other water plants.

Several of the species have not been recorded recently but the reasons for their decline is not known. No studies have come to hand on managing water bodies to conserve these plants.

LICHENS
A. S. Gunn

Apart from some early, poorly localised, records by Marrat (1860), studies on the dunes began with Wheldon 1910 and Wheldon & Travis 1915. They described several new species from this area but few of these have stood the test of taxonomic time

(Hawksworth, James & Coppins 1980). As in the rest of Britain, lichen studies were few and far between in the period 1918 to 1945. But after the second world war their study was revived (Hawksworth & Seaward 1977). *Polyblastia wheldonii* Travis described from the Hightown area (Travis 1947), is included in Appendix 1 of the British Red Data List, i.e. species likely to be included in the main list when more is known of their distribution and ecology (Table 10.26). Salisbury (1950) also described several species in the genus *Thelocarpon* from the dunes which were new to science or new to Britain. All of these species are included in Appendix 2 of the British Red Data list as they occur in fewer than fifteen, 10km squares but are probably under-recorded and not threatened. Another of Salisbury's discoveries, but unpublished at the time, was the record for *Verrucaria psammophila* Erichs. from Hillside (Swinscow 1965) which is also in Appendix 2 of the Red Data list. Swinscow (1965) also recorded *Polyblastia agraria* Th.Fr. from Ainsdale for the first time in Britain; this is the only Sefton lichen on the main British Red Data Book list (Stewart 1991). The most recent studies of the lichens on the dunes have been by Greenwood (1979) on Ainsdale NNR. In all, 92 species have been recorded from the Sefton coast by different workers and a composite list of these, with the nomenclature updated according to Hawksworth, James & Coppins (1980) has been compiled (Gunn 1991b).

TABLE 10.26
Rare, Endangered and Vulnerable Lichens on the Sefton Coast.

a) British Red Data Book species: Main List. Status R.

   Polyblastia agraria Th.Fr.

b) British Red Data Book species: Appendix 1. Species likely to be included in the main list when more is known of their distribution and ecology.

   Polyblastia wheldonii Travis

c) British Red Data Book species: Appendix 2. Species occurring in less than 15, 10km squares but probably under-recorded and not threatened.

   Verrucaria psammophila Erichs.
   Thelocarpon impressellum Nyl.
   T. intermediellum Nyl.
        (*T. intermixtulum* Nyl.)
   T. laureri (Flotow) Nyl.
   T. magnussonii G. Salisb.
   T. olivaceum B. de Lesd.
   T. pallidum G. Salisb.

Like the bryophytes, several of the lichen species are an important component of the ground layer of the fixed dunes (Ranwell 1972a) but very few studies have been devoted to them (Alvin 1960) in Britain although their ecology and management have received attention as part of wider studies (Magnusson 1983). However, few, if any, lichens are restricted to sand dunes (James, Hawksworth & Rose 1977) and this has probably contributed to the lack of study of this habitat.

The effect of air pollution on lichens has been known for at least 150 years (see Ferry, Baddeley & Hawksworth (1973) for a review of this subject) and from the earliest days it was realised that the lichen flora was depauperate. Optimism that the problem would be soon resolved in the early years of this century (Wheldon & Travis 1915) proved unfounded by the 1960s (Savidge, Heywood & Gordon 1963) although the recent discovery of *Usnea* on Ainsdale NNR (Greenwood 1979) may herald future improvements. The largest impact on the dune lichen flora in recent years has probably been the development of the pinewoods as a new habitat. Many of the newer records have been from this habitat (Greenwood 1979). Other changes have probably been due to the loss of ephemeral habitats. One of these was old shoe leather where several of the rarest lichens, particularly *Bacidea* and *Thelocarpon* species occurred! Some of the more inconspicuous species are probably under-recorded.

FUNGI
A. S. Gunn

As with the lichens, the study of the fungi of the sand dunes began in the mid 19th century (Higgins 1858, 1859; Mcleod 1866), reached its zenith in the early years of the century (Travis 1922b; J.A. Wheldon 1911, 1912, 1918) and thereafter relatively little has been published.

However, in recent years the fungi have probably been the most intensively surveyed of all the lower plants and there have been several additions to the Ainsdale NNR species list (Aldridge 1975b) by the Merseyside Naturalists' Association (Poole & Jordan 1986; Poole 1987) and the British Mycological Society (Jordan 1988). A review of British sand dunes (Watling & Rotheroe 1989) also included information collected from the Sefton coast. A composite species list (Jordan 1991), based on over 30 fungal forays in the period 1980 to 1991, contains over 550 species (Jordan 1991). Most of these species are associated with the pinewoods but the coast retains many species typical of dunes such as *Agaricus devoniensis* Orton, *Conocybe dunensis* T.J.Wallace, *Psathyrella ammophila* (Dur. & Lév.) Orton and the dune stinkhorn (*Phallus hadriani* Vent. ex. Pers.). Amongst the national rarities (Ing 1992), the Sefton coast contains the only British site for *Bovista limosa* and only the second site for *Russula perscicina*.

The ecological role of soil fungi in the pinewoods has been studied by Indraratne (1964), Parkinson & Balasooriya (1967, 1969), Balasooriya & Parkinson (1967) and Parkinson & Crouch (1969), (see James, this volume) but no work appears to have been done on the ecology of the duneland species.

FUTURE RESEARCH

Coast protection and sand stabilisation by marram planting is now well developed and has been much studied (e.g. Johnson 1979; Ranwell & Boar 1986; Alexander, Ravault & Munslow 1988). But other aspects of dune management, especially nature conservation and education, could benefit greatly from studies of individual animal and plant groups. Particular studies have already been suggested for fish, sand lizards, birds, red squirrels, rabbits, dragonflies, bryophytes and ferns. This concluding section provides an overview of research needs.

Groups or species critical to the conservation of whole biological communities include introduced species such as the rabbit, the myxoma virus, sea buckthorn and the New Zealand water stonecrop, as well as the native creeping willow. Given the potential use of rabbit grazing as a management tool, and the small amount of work done so far, further study of population changes, distribution and feeding would be valuable, especially in relation to the restoration of dune vegetation following removal of pine woodland, and to the introduction of other grazing stock (Wheeler *et al.*, this volume). Knowledge of the precise conditions favouring or restricting the spread of sea buckthorn and the New Zealand stonecrop may assist in the control of these invasive plants. Creeping willow is involved in both dune building and dune slack succession and has both erect and prostrate forms (Edmondson *et al.*, this volume). As it becomes dominant in dune slacks, and especially co-dominant with the moss *Calliergon cuspidatum* (Hedw.) Kindb., a very species-poor community usually develops (P.S. Jones, pers. comm.). Detailed studies of these phenomena may help the managers maintain or enhance both species and structural diversity.

The monitoring of species that are especially sensitive to climate change, to grazing, or to air pollution may provide an early warning of the biological effects of these kinds of environmental change. Species near the northern edge of their geographical ranges (e.g. southern marsh orchid, lesser centaury, sharp club rush, sand lizard, the plant-hopper *Agallia laevis*), those near the southern edge (e.g. northern marsh orchid, baltic rush, lesser clubmoss), and species sensitive to the height of the water table (see Jones, this volume) should be sensitive to the effects of climatic change. As full a list of such species as possible should be available for the design of an efficient monitoring programme.

Species of high conservation value may have been overlooked, especially in under-recorded invertebrate and lower plant groups, and on most sites outside Ainsdale NNR. Conversely, rare species recorded in about 1960 (e.g. many flies, Table 10.10) and in the 1970s (e.g. some bees and wasps, Table 10.14) may have become extinct on the Coast without our knowledge. New surveys would help rectify some of these problems, preferably with the production of detailed distribution maps.

Species with special protection under the Wildlife and Countryside Act (1981) will need particular attention; these include bats, natterjack toad, sand lizard (also protected under the Bern Convention), great crested newt and red squirrel.

Moreover, despite our ignorance of the status of many species, and the difficulty in comparing rarity amongst very different animal and plant groups, it can be argued from the number of species in Red Data Books that more research and conservation effort should be directed towards rare moss and liverwort species (bryophytes: eight Red Data Book species, including *Petalophyllum ralfsii* protected under the Bern Convention, plus four threatened in the European Community though not in Great Britain), fly species (Diptera: sixteen Red Data Book species) and beetle species (Coleoptera: eight Red Data Book species). However, if species conservation is to be an adjunct to the conservation of natural dune processes, then especial attention should be paid to species which are dune-habitat specialists and indicators of site quality, particularly those that are also rare. The Red Data Book beetles of mobile dunes, *Aegialia rufa* and the tiger beetle *Cicindela hybrida*, would be two such species.

The educational potential of particular animal and plant groups or species could also be investigated. Monitoring and other data collection programmes could be set up for schools which may be of direct educational value as well as assisting management. Exercises in which the rate of spread of creeping willow dieback disease, or the changes in numbers of a conspicuous plant species in a fixed area, were monitored by successive school groups (each of which would receive a copy of the data accumulated prior to their visit) are just two possible projects.

Future collaboration between researchers and managers should help tackle these challenges of nature conservation and education.

ACKNOWLEDGEMENTS

We wish to thank our families and friends for tolerating our frenetic anti-social behaviour during the preparation of this chapter. Particular thanks go to: Hazel Baines and Hayley Callan for bravely coping with the haphazard submission of material for typing, to Rachael Lindsey for help in the survey of the N. W. Biological Field Data Bank; to Mick Brummage and Tony Duckels for helpful information; and to the managers of the data banks held at Liverpool Museum, Ainsdale NNR and the J.C.A.S. office for their help and tolerance of frequent invasion.

David Atkinson (Review co-ordinator)

Population Biology Research Group
Department of Environmental and Evolutionary Biology
University of Liverpool
PO Box 147
Liverpool L69 3BX

A full list of contributors is given in Appendix 2

CHAPTER ELEVEN

The Habitat of Sand Lizards *Lacerta agilis* L. on the Sefton Coast

A.S.Cooke

INTRODUCTION

The sand lizard *Lacerta agilis* L. is endangered in Britain and is fully protected on Schedule 5 of the Wildlife and Countryside Act, 1981. Most British sand lizards occur on the heathlands of southern England, but a small isolated population survives on dunes on the Sefton Coast (NCC 1983; Corbett 1988a). Since 1980, I have extended previous ecological studies (Jackson 1978a, 1979; Jackson & Yalden 1979) by investigating in more detail the habitat requirements of the species on the dunes. This chapter summarises some of the findings. A full account is given by Cooke (1991).

METHODS

Jackson (1979) described the habitat occupied by sand lizards on the Sefton Coast as being mobile dune, fixed dune and the transitional zone between mobile and fixed dune. I studied habitat preferences at eight sites. Five were 150-1300 m from the sea and were clearly of the fixed dune type, while another was eroded fixed dune, that is parts had reverted to a mobile state because of erosion. The remaining two sites were close to high water mark; although dominated by mobile and transitional dune, both of these sites had substantial fixed areas on the third dune ridge back from the sea and lizards could be found occupying any of these habitat types. In this study, these last two sites are referred to as being 'frontal' dune habitat.

Detailed information on sand lizard habitat on the southern heathlands has been gathered by means of quadrat analysis (House & Spellerberg 1983). I decided to adopt the same approach, choosing 5 x 5 m quadrats in order to record an area that was large enough to be representative of a lizard's home range (probably at least several hundred square metres), but not so large that much of the quadrat might be outside the home range. The centre of each quadrat coincided with where a lizard had been seen. Each quadrat was oriented squarely with two sides across the slope and two sides up the slope.

The following was recorded: area and nature of bare ground, structure of the vegetation, plant species composition, aspect and slope. The last two could be readily recorded by eye for the main part of the slope where the lizard was seen. Dominant (i.e. the most abundant) and other conspicuous plant species were noted. A technique was developed to record habitat structure. This had to be simple, rapid and reproducible. A three-stage process was adopted.

i) The total area of bare ground (usually sand, but sometimes including plant litter) was estimated by eye including all patches down to $0.1m^2$ and was expressed as percentage cover of the quadrat (note that $1m^2$ is equivalent to 4%).

ii) The number of square metres dominated by vegetation in the height ranges up to 5cm ('low' vegetation), 5-30 cm('medium'), 30-100 cm ('tall') and more than 100 cm (usually scrub) were estimated separately and expressed as percentages.

iii) These percentages were then summed to see if they totalled 100%(or more if scrub or trees over-hung lower vegetation). If there was a discrepancy, the process was repeated until it was internally consistent.

The method for recording vegetation cover was very rapid, but care was essential to ensure there was not a significant trade-off in reproducibility. Differences between observers were minimised by restricting the recording to only a handful of observers and ensuring that each was first trained and 'tested' in the field. Anyone wishing to use this technique should first contact English Nature for further advice.

RESULTS

The following analysis is based on 153 quadrats recorded at the eight sites.

ASPECT AND SLOPE

The median aspect of quadrats on all fixed dune sites was due south, whereas for frontal dune quadrats it was south east. For all quadrats, 92% faced E-SW, including 57% in the arc SE-S.

There were no significant differences between the mean slopes for quadrats in the different types of site. Overall mean slope was 36°. Only four quadrats (3%) were on flat ground.

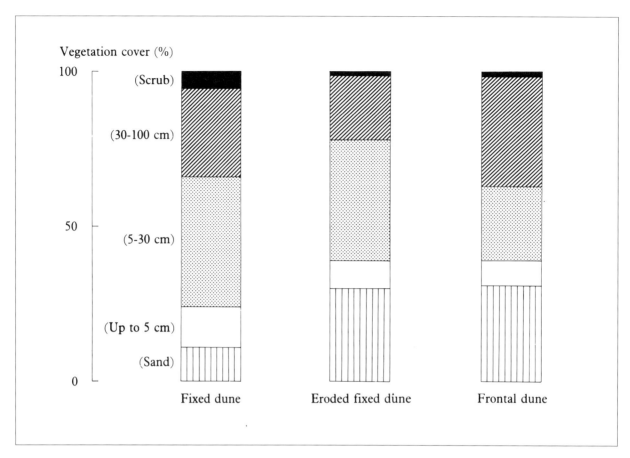

Figure 11.1 Mean cover for fixed dune (83 quadrats), eroded fixed dune (20) and frontal dune (50) quadrats.

VEGETATION COVER AND BARE GROUND

Mean data on vegetation cover and bare ground (sand) for quadrats of different types are presented in Figure 11.1. Quadrats in the fixed dune sites differed from those in the frontals by having:

i) Significantly less bare ground (P<0.001) and tall vegetation (P<0.05);

ii) Significantly more low vegetation (P<0.01), medium vegetation (P<0.001) and scrub (P<0.01).

Eroded fixed dune had similarities with both types. Sand cover and scrub were similar to frontal dune but differed significantly from fixed dune quadrats (P<0.05), whereas the reverse was true for medium and tall vegetation (P<0.001). All four vegetation classes showed decreases in cover when compared with fixed dune quadrats, although the difference was significant only for scrub. Eroded fixed dune showed the same trend as fixed dune for medium vegetation to have greater cover than tall vegetation (P<0.001), while the reverse held for frontal dunes (P<0.001).

DOMINANT SPECIES OF VEGETATION

For frontal dunes, marram (*Ammophila arenaria* Link) was dominant or co-dominant in 98% of quadrats. Red fescue grass (*Festuca rubra* L.) and dewberry (*Rubus*

caesius L.) were (co-)dominant in 20% and 10% of quadrats respectively. Six other species were recorded as (co-)dominant in fewer than 10% of quadrats.

On fixed dunes, marram, red fescue and dewberry again headed the list, being (co-)dominant in 66%, 36% and 22% of quadrats respectively. Creeping willow (*Salix repens* L.), sand sedge (*Carex arenaria* L.) and cocksfoot grass (*Dactylis glomerata* L.) were each (co-)dominant in 11-12% of quadrats. At least eight other species were recorded as (co-) dominant reflecting the more mature development stage of fixed dune.

On eroded fixed dune the only species recorded as (co-)dominant were marram (80% of quadrats), red fescue (45%), dewberry (15%) and creeping willow (5%).

CONSERVATION APPLICATIONS

The quadrat technique has many conservation applications which are dealt with in detail by Cooke (1991), including:

i) Determining the suitability of habitat where lizards occur or might be introduced;

ii) Re-recording quadrats to monitor the effectiveness of management or the impact of events such as fire or disturbance;

124

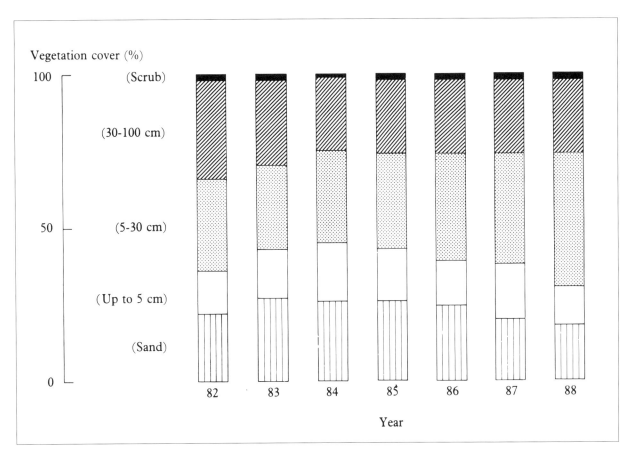

Figure 11.2 Mean cover in 32 re-recorded quadrats, 1982-1988.

iii) Using plant species as indicators of dune vigour (marram), fixing (woody species) or fire (rose-bay willowherb *Chamerion angustifolium* (L.) Holub.).

In this chapter, two such applications will be mentioned.

DEFINING OPTIMAL HABITAT

Although there are differences between frontal and fixed dune habitat, it can be argued that optimal habitat could be viewed as a single continuous entity with good frontal and fixed dune habitat occupying separate parts of the continuum. Eroded fixed dune habitat would then occupy an intermediate position. In attempting to define optimal habitat, information from all quadrats has therefore been pooled.

Where lizards are seen will not always represent optimal breeding habitat. For instance, habitat of lesser quality might allow a lizard to pass through it or even live in it without being able to breed. An attempt is therefore made to examine habitat features in turn and discard those parts of each data set that appear to offer the least suitable habitat.

For each feature, a decision has been made, based on a qualitative knowledge of sand lizards' requirements, whether to eliminate data from one or both ends of the set. The extent of elimination has been set arbitrarily at up to but not exceeding the quartile values. The

technique can be illustrated by examining the example of aspect, for which data were more or less normally distributed, centred on SSE. It is likely that quadrats inclined more towards the west or north (east) do not reflect optimal habitat and these have been eliminated leaving S-SE (57% of quadrats) as optimal habitat. Other features of optimal habitat are described in Table 11.1

TABLE 11.1.
Optimal habitat for sand lizards.

Aspect	SE-S
Slope of ground	30-49°
Cover of sand	5-34%
Vegetation cover:	
up to 5 cm in height	up to 19%
5-30 cm in height	at least 20%
30-100 cm in height	at least 15%
more than 100 cm in height	up to 9%

MONITORING HABITAT CHANGE

In order to be able to quantify changes in habitat at a scale and for features meaningful to lizards, 32 quadrats at three sites (one of each type) were re-recorded annually from 1982 to 1988. As the different sites showed similar trends, all quadrats have been amalgamated into one data set to follow overall trends (Figure 11.2). The increase in sand cover from 1982 to 1983 was statistically significant (P<0.001), but the

125

decrease in tall vegetation (30-100 cm) was not. After that, sand cover was reduced, low vegetation increased then declined, medium vegetation increased progressively, while tall vegetation decreased further before stabilising. From 1982 to 1988 there was a significant increase in medium vegetation ($P<0.001$) and a significant decrease in tall vegetation ($P<0.05$). In the early 1980s, the mean quadrat represented in Figure 11.2 had roughly equal proportions of medium and tall vegetation with a slightly lesser amount of sand. This would be expected from a mixture of quadrats from the three habitat types (see Figure 11.1). However, by 1988 the mean quadrat in Figure 11.2 was dominated by medium vegetation, a feature of fixed dune quadrats (Figure 11.1). It appears therefore that the two main modifying influences on the composition of the quadrats were the gales of 1982/3 and the dune fixing process itself, the latter being helped especially by the good growing years of 1987 and 1988.

SUMMARY

The habitat of sand lizards on the Sefton Coast has been described quantitatively for 153 quadrats, each measuring 5 x 5 m. The quadrat technique has many conservation applications. For instance it enables 'optimal habitat' to be defined. By re-recording fixed point quadrats at annual intervals, habitat changes can be monitored in localities occupied by lizards.

Arnie Cooke

English Nature
Northminster House
Peterborough PE1 1UA

SECTION 6

DUNE USE AND

MANAGEMENT

CHAPTER TWELVE

Dune Use and Management

D. J. Wheeler, D. E. Simpson and J. A. Houston

THE MANAGEMENT FRAMEWORK

The Sefton Coast is one of the largest dune systems in the UK and is a good example of a west-coast calcareous dune type. It is important on an international (European) and national scale and locally forms part of a complex of dune sites on the east Irish Sea. The Sefton dunes extend for 17 km and have an average depth of 1.5 km. Over 35% of the original dune area has been lost to development (Jackson 1979) and some habitats are badly fragmented but the remaining area still forms a large contiguous unit. Importantly, no one site can claim to be totally representative of the Sefton coast and it is the unified whole which makes the Sefton coast such an important dune area.

The three main management agencies on the Sefton coast are Sefton Council, English Nature and the National Trust (Figure 12.1). Other areas of land are managed by the Territorial Army, five Golf Clubs, and the Ministry of Defence (Woodvale). Only one area of unmanaged private land remains between Ravenmeols and Cabin Hill at Formby. The main agencies form a partnership on the Sefton Coast and co-ordinate their management through the Sefton Coast Management Scheme. The Coast Management Officer is the only permanent member of staff employed to specifically serve and overview the scheme; other coastal staff are primarily responsible for site management. The Coast Management Officer also maintains contact with the other land owners, particularly the several Golf Clubs, to promote the aims of the management scheme.

The business of co-ordination is carried out by a Working Party comprising Sefton Council officers, statutory agencies and the main landowners. The Working Party has a number of specialist sub-groups and reports to a Steering Group which includes the most senior local politicians and which advises the main committees of Sefton Council on matters relating to the Management Scheme. The Scheme is guided by a Management Plan (SMBC 1989a), prepared by the Borough Planning Officer, and updated at intervals by the Working Party.

THE COAST MANAGEMENT PLAN

The Coast Management Plan (1989) co-ordinates and reviews the policies for the whole of the coast. It is an important document and a foundation stone for the philosophy of land management practised on the coast. The plan gives a broad outline of how the potentially conflicting functions should be handled. The plan does not tell landowners what to do (it is a voluntary plan) but it lays out the rules for decision making. So, for example, if there was a conflict between a proposal to extend tree planting and high nature conservation interest the plan would recommend that the interests of nature conservation take priority.

The basic principles which have been endorsed by the various agencies working in Sefton are summarised as the plan's aims.

i)   The dune coast should be managed as an amenity area, with the emphasis on nature conservation while making provision where necessary for low-intensity recreational uses compatible with the carrying capacity of the area.

ii)   The natural dune coastline, its habitats and wildlife should be maintained and enhanced in a way compatible with sea defence and coast protection considerations.

iii) The landscape quality of the area should be improved where necessary and visitor pressure managed so that the environment is protected and people's enjoyment and understanding of it enhanced.

iv)   The role of the dune coast as an educational resource should be developed and enhanced.

The plan goes on to discuss the approach to management under seven headings: Dune Conservation, Land Management, Woodland Management, Nature Conservation, Recreation, Interpretation and Education and Monitoring and Research. The plan has been adopted by Sefton Council, English Nature and the National Trust as the basis for co-ordinated management.

SITE MANAGEMENT PLANS

Each of the main managing agencies (Sefton Council, English Nature and National Trust) either have written or have started work on site management plans (see

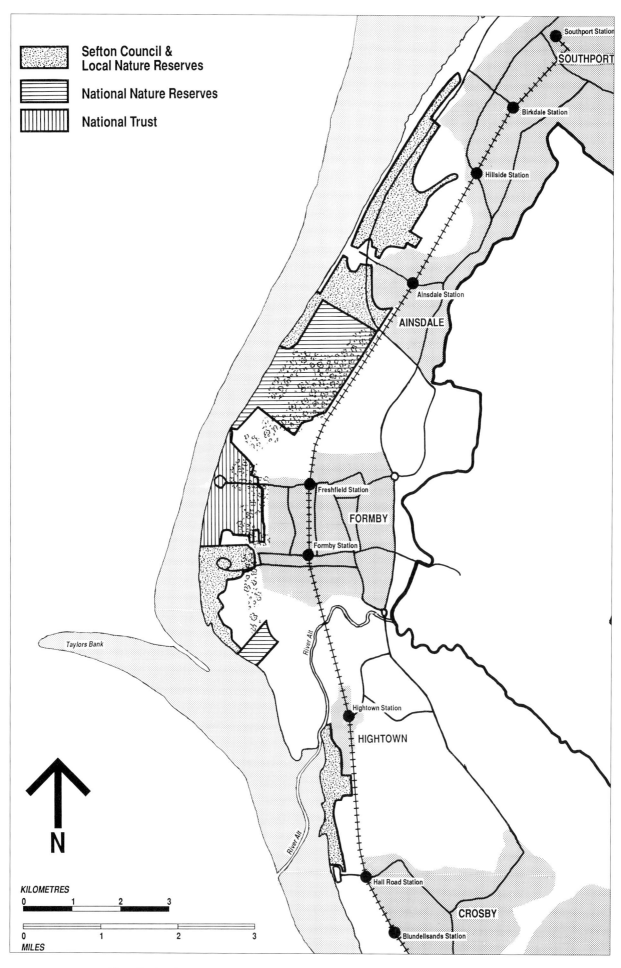

Figure 12.1: Duneland on the Sefton Coast managed by Sefton Council, English Nature and the National Trust.

Simpson 1990g; Wheeler 1986a, 1986c; Rolfe 1989; Sefton MBC undated). The suite of management plans will include those for,

Ainsdale Sand Dunes National Nature Reserve
Cabin Hill National Nature Reserve
National Trust property at Freshfield
Ainsdale and Birkdale Hills Local Nature Reserve
Ravenmeols Hills Local Nature Reserve
Hightown Dunes and Meadows (proposed Local Nature Reserve)
Lifeboat Road (Formby Point)

The plans will generally follow the format devised by the Nature Conservancy Council and the standard project recording system is to be adopted coastwide.

SUBJECT MANAGEMENT PLANS

One of the positive outcomes of the co-ordinated management scheme is the ability to look at the dunes as a single management unit and to prepare coastwide subject plans which have the support of the main landowners. The subject plans and coastwide reports that have been prepared include:

i) The Sefton Coast Data Base which collates the information on physical coastal processes along the coast. The report was the result of a 3 year secondment to Liverpool University from the Borough Engineer's Department. (Turner 1984)

ii) The Sefton Coast National Vegetation Classification survey. The Sefton Coast was surveyed by the Nature Conservancy Council in 1988/89 as one contract, but the results can also be divided according to the main land ownership boundaries. Nine main divisions are identified (Edmondson et al. 1988/89).

iii) Natterjack Toad Conservation. Coastwide annual reports have been produced since 1988. A conservation strategy is in preparation based on earlier work by Smith (1984a).

iv) A Working Plan for coastal woodlands complements similar plans prepared by English Nature and the National Trust to give an overview of the woodland resource on the Sefton Coast. (JCAS 1990)

v) The survey of Wetland Habitats of the Sefton Coast by Smith (1978) forms the basis for coastwide identification and monitoring of wet slacks.

Other coastwide surveys and subject plans are under consideration.

COASTAL PLANNING

The management of the dune area through the Coast Management Scheme is linked to wider issues of coastal zone management and to the planning system in general. The management framework which operates on the dune coast is, from 1991, to take on an expanded role to consider all aspects of coastal management in Sefton including the urban-fringe areas in the south of the borough, the beaches and part of the Ribble estuary marshes and associated wetlands. An integrated plan for the whole coastal area will be prepared by 1995. The 1989 Coast Management Plan review has been adopted by Sefton Council as a basis for development control in the dune area and its aims are incorporated as a policy statement in the draft Unitary Development Plan (the strategic statutory land-use plan for Sefton) which will come into force in 1993 (Cox 1991)

DUNE MANAGEMENT

The history of dune management up to the start of the Coast Management Scheme has been described by Jones et al. this volume. More recently, dune erosion linked to increasing and uncontrolled visitor pressure was one of the main problems which the coast management scheme was set up to tackle. In the first ten years of the scheme, from 1977 to 1987 a considerable amount of effort was put into dune management, including shoreline fencing, dune building, recontouring, revegetation and stabilisation. Techniques have improved with experience and attitudes have changed over time. There is now less emphasis on stabilisation, the stopping of the dynamic processes, and greater interest in dune conservation where management work attempts to work with the natural mobility of the dune system, whilst reducing the erosion caused by trampling. Only recently have attitudes almost come full circle with talk of actively encouraging destabilisation, along with the creation of new areas of yellow dune and blowouts (Houston 1991).

MANAGEMENT OF FRONTAL DUNES

The dramatic erosion witnessed at Formby Point has tended to overshadow a steady accretion along much of the coast. To the south of Formby Point, the accretion of the Altcar salient was at first achieved by sand-trapping but present dune growth is unaided and unaffected by light recreation pressure. At Ainsdale and Birkdale natural dune accretion has been disrupted by the compound effects of car parking, damage by trampling and mechanical beach cleansing. Dune management work at Ainsdale from 1986 to 1991 has demonstrated that rapid dune accretion can be achieved when these pressures are alleviated, and the natural strandline and foredune communities re-established.

Figure 12.2: Chestnut paling fencing being used at Ainsdale in June 1990 to trap wind-blown sand to encourage the regrowth of foredunes.

The management aim for accreting shores is to encourage natural dune growth coupled with low maintenance. Recreational impacts can be reduced without restricting the current level of public access to the beach or dunes. The ideal management aim for the accreting shorelines is to interfere as little as possible with natural processes. Inevitably where recreation pressure is high some form of access control will be necessary. For 1 km either side of the beach entrance at Shore Road, Ainsdale, and south of Weld Road, Southport, chestnut paling fencing is used to build out the dunes and control access and so limit damage to the vegetation (Figure 12.2). Elsewhere a simple line of posts, re-set seaward or landward when necessary, delimits the vegetated dune area from the recreation beach. Car parking, mechanical cleansing and horse riding are restricted to the seaward side of this line. In time it might be desirable to substitute the use of chestnut paling (which traps sand) with post and wire fencing (which does not) if permanent access control is necessary.

Coast erosion predominates both at Formby Point (from Alexandra Road to the north of Fishermans Path) and also at Hightown. The Hall Road to Hightown foreshore is mainly reinforced with tipped stone and only has a small remnant of eroding dunes. This shoreline is subject to proposals for major coast protection works and as a consequence little interim work has been carried out. At Formby Point coastal erosion was first tackled in 1978/79 with some success but only since 1983 (following a storm event) has a consistent approach been adopted.

The techniques for sand-trapping fencing along the eroding coast at Formby Point have been refined over the years but the whole approach is under review following the storm events of February 1990 and January 1993. The rationale behind the fencing work on the eroding coast is that it is better to trap sand at the foot of the dunes in the summer months to act as a first line of defence against the high tides of winter and also to keep as much sand as possible within the beach system rather than adding to the reservoir in the dunes. Fencing is now erected only in the summer months and is therefore designed to catch the sand blown on the predominantly south-westerly summer winds. The fencing at Lifeboat Road and Ravenmeols is supplemented by brushwood fences, now of waste christmas trees, and a risk is taken to put these out in January (storm damaged in 1990 but used successfully in 1991 and 1992). The regular monitoring work carried out by Sefton's engineers lends support to the effort put in to this fencing. The rate of erosion at Formby Point has reduced during the period of management, but, so has the rate of accretion recorded at Albert Road (on the accreting coast), so the management work may be affecting the adjacent stretch of coast. The relationship between dune management and changing beach levels is also unclear. English Nature and the National Trust, in particular, are finding it difficult to justify the continuation of this type of work. A programme of coastal research to be co-ordinated by the Director of Engineering and Surveying, should help to answer some of these concerns and review the management aims.

The division between accreting and eroding foreshores is somewhat arbitrary since the very nature of the coastline is one of constant change. An understanding of the coast as a whole is a pre-requisite to planning a co-ordinated approach to shoreline management. By trying to work with, and not against nature much can be done to alleviate the impacts of recreation pressure, to recognise and encourage natural accretion and to accept but ameliorate the effects of natural erosion.

DUNE RESTORATION

At numerous locations throughout the coast sand dunes have become badly eroded and unstable with the result that the prevailing westerly winds move sand inland, often causing problems to property and roads, amenities and wildlife habitats. Erosion is a natural phenomenon and it is certainly not true that all bare sand is unwelcome but there is a strong correlation between trampling on the vegetated dunes and subsequent erosion. Dune restoration, therefore, should not seek to harness nature but should identify those areas suffering from over-use and act to re-establish the dune vegetation. This can usually be achieved by controlling the existing pressure rather than closing off large areas of dunes.

Two major dune restoration projects were started at Formby Point in 1977 (Victoria Road) and 1978 (Lifeboat Road) and the initial works have been completed. These early projects were labour intensive, expensive in materials and, at first, poorly maintained. Techniques have now been improved producing lower cost solutions with simpler maintenance. From 1983 to 1988 the number of projects tackled increased but this level of activity has now reduced. During this period projects were carried out at Fisherman's Path (Nature Conservancy Council), Big Balls Hill, Ainsdale (Sefton Council), Birkdale frontal dunes (Sefton Council), former Pinetree Caravan Site (National Trust) and Lifeboat Road (Sefton Council). Management work at Ainsdale NNR is recorded by Payne (1983b) and Wheeler (1984b, 1988).

Areas of bare sand (usually of 0.25 ha or more) have been mapped and incorporated into a coastwide survey of dune condition. In this way a check can be kept on each area, deciding if a blowout should be conserved as a natural feature or whether a restoration project should be implemented and monitored. The rolling programme will enable the management history of each area to be accurately recorded. Generally it can be assumed that

dune restoration projects have a five year establishment period followed by maintenance. Over-stabilisation of the dunes is not to be desired; sand-dunes are dynamic by nature and in some areas blowouts may need active encouragement to allow the formation of new habitats and to conserve a range of animals and plants which depend directly on the presence of bare sand. More research effort could be directed at the development and subsequent natural stabilisation of small blowouts to assess whether climatic factors can maintain an adequate diversity of dune habitats. The Coast Management Plan recommends that the dunes should be conserved in large enough units to allow for natural mobility. The fragmentation of the Sefton dunes by roads, houses and golf courses has reduced the areas where natural mobility can be safely encouraged. Blowout systems are to be conserved on the Ainsdale NNR, Ravenmeols LNR and Ainsdale LNR as important geomorphological features.

DUNE RESTORATION TECHNIQUES

The techniques used on the Sefton Coast are similar to those used on other sites in the UK and successful projects usually involve access control, sand trapping, stabilisation and revegetation. The main techniques used are thatching, brushwood fencing, marram planting and mechanical recontouring.

i) Thatching

Small blowouts, where there is no fresh supply of sand, can be treated by laying a thatch of brushwood over the surface of the sand and planting marram grass or sowing grass seed in the gaps. Generally the thatching is dug into the sand to keep it in place and in the case of willow and poplar species also to encourage growth from the cut stem. Thatching, the oldest known technique for dune stabilisation is more effective than modern synthetic stabilisers. (Beach Protection Authority 1982). The large inland blowout known as 'Big Balls Hill' (SD 305115) was stabilised by thatching.

ii) Brushwood fencing

Traditional 'Dutch fencing' is an upright hedge of stacked brushwood which can be used to trap sand to rebuild dunes, or as a windbreak to protect areas of new planting. Traditional, biodegradable materials such as pine, birch and sea buckthorn brushwood are preferred with sea buckthorn used mainly on the nature reserves. Providing any fence is porous to the wind (50% porosity is desirable) it will be an effective sand-trapping or shelter fence. Sand carried in the wind will be deposited in the lee of the fence and generally it takes one year for a 1m high fence to become buried.

Figure 12.3: Recontouring of badly eroded dunes, Lifeboat Road, March 1987. The project was completed in phases over a two-year period. In the background is a phase of recontouring and planting completed in March 1986. Lifeboat Road, buried by blowing sand, is on the right of the photograph.

iii) Marram planting

Dune stabilisation projects are not usually possible without the replanting of the dune building marram grass (*Ammophila arenaria* L.). Marram grass spreads mainly by vegetative growth rather than from seedlings. The technique is to collect marram from healthy dune areas and to replant a dense matrix of shoots throughout the restoration area. Marram planting reintroduces the vegetation into bare areas but also provides an immediate protection from further wind erosion. From initial planting it takes five years for the grass to develop a thick cover and on larger schemes fertilizer has been used to promote growth. The colonisation of sand dunes after stabilisation with marram grass is discussed by Hewett (1970).

iv) Recontouring

Mechanical recontouring has been used where the dunes were so uneven as to make other techniques impossible or where the work was of a sufficiently large scale. Recontouring followed by marram planting is initially more expensive but has the advantage that there are no brushwood fences to be maintained over several years and there is more control over the final contours. The single largest recontouring operation, at Lifeboat Road (SD 272065) (Figure 12.3), involved the replanting of over 2 hectares of bare sand with some 300,000 marram plants over a 2 year period.

MONITORING

Beach levels, the extent of coast erosion and the condition of the dunes themselves can change quite dramatically over a relatively short period of time and regular and consistent monitoring is necessary to record the changes and detect trends. A variety of monitoring techniques have been established by the National Rivers Authority (responsible for sea defence matters) and Sefton's Director of Engineering and Surveying (responsible for coast protection matters). These include a biennial aerial survey, the production of contour maps of the dunes, beach profile measurements and the direct measurement of erosion and accretion. The mapping of areas of bare sand provides a basis for determining the policies for dune management.

WOODLAND MANAGEMENT

In the nineteenth century the Sefton coast dune system was sparsely vegetated with little to no woodland and large areas of blowing sand. The high degree of sand mobility caused a variety of problems for landowners adjacent to the dunes; agricultural smallholdings, tracks and the Liverpool to Southport railway line were continually subject to blown sand accumulating in significant quantities, destroying crops and disrupting transport. Backshore reclamation schemes involving the planting of large areas of marram grass were carried out in an attempt to stabilise the dunes. Although these were successful in areas close to the shore, they were less effective inland. The two principal landowners in the late nineteenth century, Charles Weld Blundell and Jonathan Formby, were responsible for the implementation of a conifer planting policy on their estates to address the sand mobility problem in these inland areas. The Sefton coast was the first area on the west coast of Britain where afforestation was practised as a means of dune stabilisation.

In the period 1887 to 1920, many thousands of young pines were planted on the coast. The principal species were Corsican pine (*Pinus nigra* ssp. *laricio* Maire) and Austrian pine (*Pinus nigra* ssp. *nigra* Arnold) with smaller numbers of Scots pine (*Pinus sylvestris* L.), maritime pine (*Pinus pinaster* Ait.) and mountain pine (*Pinus uncinata* Mill. ex Mirb.). The main planted areas were in the central part of the coast between Ainsdale dunes in the north and Ravenmeols dunes in the south.

A considerable amount of felling took place during the second world war. A policy of leaving shelterbelts of trees around felled areas was adopted to reduce the risk of remobilisation of sand in these areas. Although some restocking of felled areas took place after the end of the war, this and other forestry management generally declined until the Blundell estate was sold between 1965 and 1967 with the Nature Conservancy purchasing the northern area, later declared as Ainsdale Sand Dunes NNR, and the National Trust the southern section at Formby Point. The Formby estate plantations came into the ownership of the Formby Land Company who subsequently leased areas to private landowners and Sefton Borough Council. There are also a number of smaller areas of older plantations remaining in private ownership, the most significant of which is the Firwood plantation, thought to be the oldest on the coast (Jones *et al.,* this volume).

The total area of woodland on the coast in 1991 was approximately 289 hectares. This represents 69% of woodland in the Borough and 14% of all the woodland in the former County of Merseyside. On the coast, English Nature own and manage 130 hectares, the National Trust own and manage 65 hectares and the remaining 94 hectares are mainly under the management of Sefton Borough Council, Formby Golf Club and Formby Land Company.

Since the original period of conifer planting, a variety of deciduous species have become established within, or on the edges of the plantations. These include sycamore (*Acer pseudoplatanus* L.), various types of willows (*Salix* spp.), white poplar (*Populus alba* L.), balsam poplar (*P. trichocarpa* Hook.), black poplar (*P. nigra* L.), alder (*Alnus glutinosa* L.), silver birch (*Betula pendula* Roth), downy birch (*B. pubescens* Ehrh.), hawthorn (*Crataegus monogyna* Jacq.), oak (*Quercus robur* L.), and rowan (*Sorbus aucuparia* L.). The deciduous component of the coastal woodlands is still relatively small, forming less than 5% by area of the total, the remaining area now being mainly conifer high forest.

Conditions for tree growth on the coast are harsh. The soils are poorly developed and free draining. Strong salt-laden winds blow onshore throughout much of the winter period. Slow growing trees of stunted form with distorted crowns are characteristic of the most seaward woodland (Figure 12.4). In sheltered areas further inland, tree form is more normal and for certain exposure tolerant species, i.e. Corsican pine, growth rates approach those expected on non-coastal sites.

Figure 12.4: Stunted and salt-damaged pine trees at Freshfield.

Mammals too can have a significant affect on woodland development. Rabbits (*Oryctolagus cuniculus* L.) graze on deciduous and coniferous natural regeneration and planted saplings. In the southern coastal area where the dunes are contiguous with farmland, hares (*Lepus europaeus* L.) can also damage young plantations. The red squirrel (*Sciurus vulgaris* L.) reduces the seeding potential of the conifers by feeding on pine cones. Honey fungus (*Armillaria mellea* Vahl ex Fr.) and conifer heart rot (*Fomes annosus* Fr.) are both present in the woodlands, causing a limited amount of damage to the conifers.

Fires, deliberately started by vandals, occur throughout the coast every spring and summer. The pine needle layer of the conifer plantations is particularly flammable and although most fires are controlled by the efforts of the fire service and coastal agency staff, there is nevertheless, the potential for large-scale incidents to destroy significant areas of plantation.

The value of the woodlands as a shelterbelt to the residential areas of Freshfield and Formby is high.

Figure 12.5: Woodland Management at Formby, 1987. Thinning of Scots pine plantation and underplanting with beech at the National Trust squirrel reserve, Formby. Woodland work carried out in 1978.

Much of the housing is located close to the coast and the woodlands reduce the exposure factor.

The woodlands have a limited nature conservation interest. The red squirrel population is thriving and mainly associated with the conifer plantations. The nationally rare dune helleborine (*Epipactis leptochila* var *dunensis* Stephenson & T.A. Stephenson) is found throughout the conifer woodland, although this is equally well distributed in the dune system. Many of the fungi occurring on the coast are specifically associated with the woodland. The deciduous woodlands have a diverse invertebrate community. A notable spider community has been recorded in the conifer woodlands.

The landscape and recreational value of the woodlands is high. They form a major part of the total woodland cover in the borough and are a dramatic feature of the relatively flat landscape. There is a network of pedestrian footpaths throughout the woodlands of the coast and these are used by many thousands of people every year. The Sefton coastal woodlands are a significant feature of the Mersey Forest initiative and form the northern 'anchor point' of a proposed crescent of woodland around Merseyside linking to Delamere forest in Cheshire.

The woodlands are managed in different ways by different land owners. Taken together this adds to the overall interest whilst the different approaches are all compatible with the objectives and policies of the Coast Management Plan. The overall objective is "to maintain the continuity of woodland cover, improve its quality and wildlife value and extend it where cover is poor or for amenity reasons."

The plan recognises the protective function of the rear woodlands, their landscape and amenity value and their potential for habitat diversification. This active promotion and management of the woodlands is tempered by the wider interests of nature conservation and it is accepted that some frontal woodlands should be removed and that scrub development should be controlled on the open dunes. Specific woodland management operations are detailed in the management plans for Ainsdale NNR (Wheeler 1986c) and Cabin Hill NNR (Gateley 1987b), the National Trust Woodland Plan of Operations (National Trust 1988), the Working Plan for Woodlands on the Sefton Coast (JCAS 1990) and in the set of site management plans for Sefton Council (in preparation). A further, more detailed plan of woodland management is to be prepared for Ainsdale Sand Dunes NNR in 1992/1993.

The woodlands are managed by a variety of techniques. Clear-felling of large areas has only been carried out on the Ainsdale Sand Dunes NNR to create fire-breaks in the late 1970s or for the removal of frontal woodlands. Group-felling, the felling and re-planting of small pockets within the main woodlands, is more commonly employed. This approach is being used by the National Trust to regenerate the pinewoods at Formby. At Lifeboat Road the woodlands have been reinforced by new planting on the exposed western face and regenerated by cutting wedges in from the rear and replanting with a 80% pine, 20% broad-leaved mix. Thinning can allow either natural regeneration or the replanting with more shade tolerant species such as beech (*Fagus sylvatica* L). Underplanting of the pinewoods with beech was carried out in the National Trust's squirrel reserve in the late 1970s (Figure 12.5), and at Ainsdale the selective removal of pine, combined with the planting of oak has totally transformed a conifer wood to a deciduous wood. A fourth technique is coppicing, where areas of alder, sycamore and birch can be cut on a rotation to produce multi-stemmed trees yielding timber for brushwood or poles. It is unknown whether any of the coastal woodlands were originally planted as coppice, although some woods have certainly been coppiced in the past and the technique has been re-introduced by the National Trust at Formby. The recent management of woodlands on the coast is balanced by a few sites, on private land, where no management is taking place. In these areas the main plantations are dying back from their exposed windward edges but are being replaced by natural regeneration of pine and other species. Most concern is expressed about the centres of these woods where trees are ageing with no sign of replacement. The overall prediction is for the continuity of woodland cover on the coast, with a greater diversity of woodland species, types and habitats (pools, glades, rides and coppices) and a forest structure rather than a plantation structure.

VEGETATION MANAGEMENT

The ideal objective for vegetation management is to maintain all communities and associated species represented in the stages of semi-natural habitat succession through natural dynamic processes. These communities and species are described in brief in the SSSI citation documents. However, in determining the actual or operational management plan objectives, various factors influencing management have to be taken into account. The process of natural seral succession is producing increased vegetation cover over the entire dune system and within areas of fixed older dunes there is a trend towards scrub and woodland development (Figure 12.6) with evidence of decreased species diversity (Edmondson *et al.*, this volume) and changes in soil type and structure (James, this volume).

Figure 12.6: Evidence of vegetation succession from Ainsdale NNR based on fixed-point photographic monitoring, showing the transformation from fixed-dune grassland to dune scrub over a period of twenty years.

Figure 12.6(a): Slack 13 (long slack) in 1968 (ASD/68/NAR:L1)

Figure 12.6(b): The exact same viewpoint in 1988 (ASD/88/NAR:L1)

The reduction in grazing pressure in recent decades following the decline of the rabbit population post-myxomatosis has accelerated the rate at which these changes are occurring, as has the presence of conifer plantations through local shelterbelt and lowered water table effects.

On the eroding coast around Formby Point, strandline and foredune communities are not represented and as the mobile dunes roll back inland the fixed dune areas are being reduced in area and subject to higher recreation pressure.

Without management intervention, the processes described above will produce a system of dune scrub and woodland habitats of low species diversity with the earlier stages of succession being poorly represented. The relevant management objectives of the various site plans are designed to encourage the development of early stages of succession by promoting coastal accretion and by controlling scrub and woodland in the fixed dunes.

The techniques used on the coast to control certain vigorous scrub species and to recreate earlier stages of succession are summarised below.

SILVER BIRCH (*Betula pendula* L.)

Silver birch is widespread on the coast. Newlands, Thompson and Robinson (1987) describe an increasing abundance of this species, particularly at sites where distance from the sea, topography or the presence of pine plantations result in reduced exposure to salt-laden winds. Soil development and hydrology are also factors affecting distribution.

The majority of management work to control this species has been carried out on Ainsdale Sand Dunes NNR, using hand tools, chain saws and clearing saws. Cut material is usually burnt on site. The regrowth from stumps is treated in the following spring with herbicide applied by knapsack sprayer. The following herbicides have been used: *Roundup* (N-(phosphonomethyl) glycine), *Krenite* (ammonium ethyl carbamoyl-phosphonate), and *Garlon* ([(3, 5, 6 trichloro-2-pyridinyl) oxy] acetic acid).

Garlon has been found to be most effective. Single applications of herbicide are sometimes not adequate to kill trees. A second application to the regrowth in the second summer after cutting is required in these incidences. For further reading on the problems of scrub growth and the use of herbicides on nature reserves see, in particular, Marrs (1985) and Cooke (1986a).

SEA BUCKTHORN (*Hippophae rhamnoides* L.)

Sea buckthorn is well known as an invasive species on sand dune systems, capable of fixing dunes and reducing species diversity. So significant is this species in terms of its potential to influence plant communities, that the Nature Conservancy formed the Hippophae Study Group in 1969 to collect information on this plant, make management recommendations for its control and propose national policies in relation to sea buckthorn on sand dune National Nature Reserves (Nature Conservancy 1971). '*The Management of Sea Buckthorn* Hippophae rhamnoides *L. on selected sites in Britain*', edited by Ranwell (1972b), still remains the most complete text on the subject. The eradication programme, at one of the sites, Braunton Burrows in North Devon is recorded by Venner (1977).

Palaeobotanical studies have shown that sea buckthorn was present in the Sefton area in the early Flandrian period, 10,200 to c. 7,100 BP. (Innes 1983). Sea buckthorn is now native only to the east coast of Britain. Introduced to the Sefton Coast in the 1890s, sea buckthorn spread to become established throughout the fixed dunes of the coast and was planted to shelter young pine plantations. The history of this spread is not recorded, but ground and aerial photographs from the 1950 to 1970 period (Nesbitt 1981) show extensive stands of sea buckthorn in the Ainsdale and Birkdale Hills, many of which are more than 0.5 ha in extent. Simpson (1990a) records an "explosive spread" of sea buckthorn in the slacks of Ainsdale NNR, based on the analysis of data from surveys in the period 1960 to 1976. The National Sand Dune Vegetation Survey of the Sefton Coast (Edmondson, Gateley & Nissenbaum 1988/9) records the area and distribution of the SD17 (now SD18) *Hippophae rhamnoides* dune scrub community.

In the Ainsdale and Birkdale Hills LNR, priority is given to sea buckthorn clearance from slacks and the frontal dune area. Sefton Council and English Nature have expended considerable resources in control programmes, the Nature Conservancy starting in the late 1960s. Three main methods of control have been employed:

i) Physical removal by hand/power tools.

Stands of sea buckthorn are cut to ground level using bow saws, chain saws or clearing saws. Cut vegetation is either burnt on site or taken elsewhere to be used as sand trap fencing. Hand clearance is necessarily costly in terms of man/hours; it has however, been the most widely applied, particularly on the Ainsdale and Birkdale Hills LNR and the Ainsdale NNR. It may be used on dune ridges as well as in slacks and in the case of hand tools only, on grounds of safety, it is the only technique where voluntary labour may be involved.

ii) Mechanical uprooting.

Large stands of sea buckthorn are cleared using tracked bulldozers (Figure 12.7). A Massey Ferguson CAT 931 with a 3 in 1 bucket was used to clear 3 ha of dense sea buckthorn thicket on the Birkdale Hills LNR in 1984 and 1985 (Nissenbaum 1986). These machines are able to uproot vegetation by either pushing at ground level or grabbing and lifting. This may result in the removal of parts of sea buckthorn root systems. Although more cost effective than hand clearance it involves considerations of access for large machines and significant disturbance to the ground surface. In 1992/93 this technique was also used on the Ainsdale Hills LNR to clear scrub from slacks and dune ridges.

iii) Herbicide application.

The application of herbicides has been used only on Ainsdale NNR to control both young short stands of sea buckthorn and regrowth from large stands after manual or mechanical clearance. Application has been by knapsack sprayer. The following products have been used: *Econal*[245T] (1970s only), *Roundup* and *Garlon*. *Garlon* is generally more effective than *Roundup* and will continue to be used by English Nature in control programmes on the two NNRs.

Figure 12.7: Buckthorn clearance on the Birkdale Hills LNR 1984 using a tracked bulldozer. The cleared scrub was left to dry out and then burnt on site.

Sea buckthorn can propagate by vegetative reproduction and the physical removal of the aerial component of a stand is not always totally effective. Nissenbaum (1986) records regeneration after 2 years, in 13 out of 18 slacks in the Birkdale Hills where sea buckthorn had been cleared by bulldozer. However, Simpson (1990a), evaluating a 5 year monitoring programme of clearance on Ainsdale NNR, recorded only one site out of four where sea buckthorn had regenerated. Simpson also records re-establishment of typical dune communities in slacks cleared by bulldozer and on ridges where sea buckthorn was hand cut and regrowth treated with herbicide.

Although the majority of larger stands of sea buckthorn have now been controlled, many smaller stands still remain and will require management in the future. The value of stands of sea buckthorn to breeding and overwintering birds has been surveyed on the Birkdale Hills (Carty 1981) and some stands will be retained for their wildlife, amenity and screening value.

CORSICAN PINE (*Pinus nigra* ssp. *laricio* Maire)

The Corsican pine plantations along the coast are a source for seedling invasion into adjacent dune areas. The extent of seedling establishment is greatest in sheltered areas, the shelter often being provided by the older plantations. Control entails hand-pulling of young trees (up to 30 cm in height) and felling larger trees by hand saw or chain saw. As conifers do not generally coppice, further control of regrowth is not required. After felling an aqueous solution of urea is applied to

any stumps exceeding approximately 5 cm. in diameter to prevent infection by conifer butt rot.

Several studies have looked at the impacts of pine plantations on dune forming processes (see, for example Atkinson 1990; Leach & Kinnear 1985; Martyr 1968; Payne 1979c; Rothwell 1985; Simpson 1990l, 1990m and Sturgess 1989a, 1990) and the effects of subsequent removal are discussed by Sturgess (this volume).

CREEPING WILLOW (*Salix repens* L.)

Creeping willow is the dominant species in many of the ridge and slack communities of the coast. It occurs across the successional range from mobile to fixed dune and in both wet and dry habitats. It occurs both in a prostrate form and an erect form, sometimes up to 1 metre in height. Although an increase in creeping willow cover is a natural part of the successional process, a general increase in height and dominance in a number of communities is thought to have occurred since the decline in rabbit grazing post-myxomatosis (Payne 1980a).

Management to reduce the dominance of creeping willow began in 1976 on Ainsdale NNR, in the form of an experimental slack mowing programme. Originally, the mowing operation was carried out once a year in the autumn, using an 'Allen autoscythe' and cut material was left on site. The operation has been substantially modified since that period. Two slacks, one of which is approximately 1 ha. in size, are mown once a year in the spring using a tractor driven rotary swipe (Figure 12.8).

The cut material is raked up by hand and removed off site. Simpson (1990c), assessing the programme, reports that this management has resulted in a reduction in height and cover of creeping willow, with a corresponding increase in species diversity.

Although mowing appears to be a successful technique in reducing dominance, it has limited potential as a large scale management technique due to various problems associated with the actual mowing operation. The timing of mowing is dependent on prevailing hydrological conditions and a high spring water table may delay the operation until early summer. The collection of cut material is labour intensive and there does not appear to be any suitable machinery to mechanise the raking/collection process. The use of heavy machinery produces damage to the slack floor and soil compaction. The operation is only applicable to flat areas and may not be used to manage dune ridge creeping willow communities.

Figure 12.8: Slack mowing on Ainsdale NNR.

MANAGEMENT OF NEUTRAL GRASSLAND

Fixed point photographic monitoring on Ainsdale NNR illustrates the development of scrub on areas of neutral grassland. In order to maintain grassland, management is required. At Hightown, Cabin Hill NNR (Simpson 1989b) and Ainsdale NNR, mowing using tractor driven rotary mowers or flail mowers is undertaken to control scrub development on grassland. Mowing is carried out once a year and cut material removed from site.

GRAZING BY STOCK

The dominant grazing animal in British sand dunes is still the rabbit (Boorman 1986, 1989a), despite the widespread decline due to myxomatosis. The effects of grazing are generally regarded as beneficial and domestic stock are now used on many European dune sites as a management tool to control invasive scrub species. Different types of grazing animals e.g. cattle, sheep, ponies and goats, graze in different ways, have specific preferences for types of vegetation and therefore produce a variety of effects on vegetation

communities (Boorman 1989b). For a general background to the subject of grazing on dune systems see, in particular, Bullock and Kinnear (1988), Doody (1985c), Garson (1985), Gibson (1988), Glyn (1975), Hewett (1981), Oosterveld (1985) and Payne (1980a).

On the Sefton coast there are currently two management projects involving grazing stock.

i) Cattle grazing at Cabin Hill NNR

Grazing by cattle and horses of an area of dune pasture, slacks and fixed dune at this site began in the 1960s. Horses remained only for a limited period but cattle grazing continued as an all year round agricultural operation up to 1984 when the Nature Conservancy Council began managing the site as an NNR. The grazing regime has been altered twice during the period of NCC's management in order to maintain the botanical interest of the site and to take account of other management objectives. The rationale for the current regime of summer grazing only is described by Simpson (1991a). A maximum of 20 Friesian heifers are used to graze the site between April and November, with no supplementary feed supplied. Monitoring is ongoing and adjustments to the regime may be required in future. The effect of grazing on creeping willow have been studied by Danbury (1987).

ii) Sheep grazing at Ainsdale NNR

An experimental grazing programme began in February 1990 with the introduction of 30 Herdwick sheep to a 10 hectare enclosure of fixed dune ridges and slacks (Wheeler 1989). After two winter periods of grazing, monitoring determined that the sheep were reducing the density of creeping willow and also grazing birch, sea buckthorn and Corsican pine (Simpson 1990e, 1991b). Rank grass and herb vegetation were being reduced to a short sward and trampling was increasing the areas of bare sand. In July 1991, a flock of various rare breeds of sheep replaced the Herdwicks. These included primitive sheep, such as Hebridean, which are better adapted to feeding on coarser vegetation than modern commercial breeds (Figure 12.9). A small number of cattle were also introduced to the enclosure in summer 1991 and these animals were observed grazing and trampling creeping willow and other scrub. Following the success of the first phase of this project, an extension to the enclosure was constructed. The total enclosed area is now 55 hectares and a grazing regime using sheep in the winter and sheep and cattle in the summer is planned from autumn 1991.

TURF-STRIPPING

In the 1970s a series of excavations were created on the coast to provide breeding habitat for the natterjack toad, (*Bufo calamita* L.) during an extended period of low water tables. The excavations were dug mainly

Figure 12.9: Hebridean sheep grazing on creeping willow, Ainsdale NNR, 1991.

within fixed dune habitat in existing slacks and were shallow in profile with gently sloping sides.

Marginal areas of the excavations are wet or partially submerged during the winter/spring period but dry out during the summer. The excavation margins function as examples of the effect of turf stripping, the removal of the original vegetation and soil leaving a sand substrate, more typical of an incipient slack. On Ainsdale NNR vegetation development in the margins has been similar to that expected in a natural young slack (Simpson 1990f) with the establishment of species such as jointed rush (*Juncus articulatus* L.), toad rush (*J. bufonius* L.), few-flowered spike rush (*Eleocharis quinqueflora* (F.Hartmann) O.Schwarz), marsh horsetail (*Equisetum palustre* L.), brookweed (*Samolus valerandi* L.) and grass of Parnassus (*Parnassia palustris* L.)

As a large scale operation, turf-stripping presents various problems (see Jones, this volume). It is limited in application to slack areas. Peripheral vegetation on ridges may invade the stripped areas, modifying the process of succession. It produces large quantities of turf and soil which are difficult and expensive to remove from site but which if left as spoil heaps develop ruderal communities, which may later invade stripped areas.

The techniques of dune management described above are all attempts to ameliorate the effects of succession and scrub invasion. Vegetation management can perhaps go further to meet management objectives by more active intervention. Two such proposals are being considered.

WOODLAND REMOVAL

An opportunity exists on Ainsdale NNR to clear-fell a block of mature Corsican pine, approximately 40 ha. in size, adjacent to the frontal dunes. Removal of this block, known as the frontal woodlands, would provide an opportunity to recreate sand dune vegetation at an early successional stage through further management. The frontal woodlands currently act as a shelter belt for a 50 ha. area of fixed dunes to the east. This area is subject to rapid scrub encroachment due to the shelterbelt effect. Removal of the frontal woodland would result in a reduction in the rate of that encroachment. The programme of clear-felling, is further described by Wheeler (1990). The first phase of the operation was completed in 1992.

This project has considerable research potential. Few similar projects, where re-establishment of dune vegetation is the primary objective, are recorded. Sturgess (this volume) describes the ecological and pedological processes that follow clear-felling.

141

Figure 12.10: A typical natterjack 'scrape', an excavated pool, at Hightown 1985. The scrape is designed to have shallow margins and a gentle slope to a central area of deeper water. The pool is protected by fencing and information signs are used. Unfortunately the natterjack population at Hightown has remained at low levels despite the creation of this suitable pool.

CONVERSION OF OLD ASPARAGUS FIELDS TO DUNE HEATH

Edmondson, Gateley and Nissenbaum (1988/89) record the present distribution of dune heath on the coast. This is not extensive, and may have been reduced in area through past development, although this is not well documented. Small areas of ling (*Calluna vulgaris* (L.) Hull), consisting of a few plants only in each area, exist along the eastern edge of Ainsdale NNR. No monitoring of these areas has been carried out and so it is not possible to determine whether the species is developing or declining in these areas. Opportunities exist on the adjacent neutral grassland of the NNR, formerly asparagus fields and now of low nature conservation value, to create dune heath through management.

There is a research requirement to ascertain the suitability of these grassland areas for such management and to determine the form that management should take. An experimental technique has been proposed by Sturgess (1989b).

SPECIES CONSERVATION

Species conservation is a relatively recent practice on the Sefton coast. Around 1970, naturalists became concerned about the status of the natterjack toad and sand lizard on the Sefton coast. Much work has been done to improve the fortunes of these two species. Conservation management for other species has been minimal.

NATTERJACK TOAD

The natterjack toad has, perhaps, had the greatest amount of work expended on its conservation. Dry summers caused poor breeding seasons in 1970 and 1971. As a result, the Nature Conservancy attempted an artificial breeding scheme near the reserve office (ASD NNR file 2/6/2/3/5). Plastic sheeting was laid over sleepers and filled with water. Spawn was introduced from desiccating slacks and the tadpoles fed with meat. The scheme was very successful, with many toadlets emerging. Similar work was undertaken by a local resident, Mr S. H. Smith (Southport Visiter 1972) with much success. These toadlets were liberated in the Birkdale and Ainsdale dunes (Smith 1974a). At around the same time, several pools were excavated on the Ainsdale Sand Dunes NNR, which would hold water long enough to allow metamorphosis to occur (ASD NNR file 2/6/2/3/4). These were gradually colonised by natterjacks, in some cases by those from the artificial breeding scheme, and were quite productive in their first ten years. Systematic monitoring of breeding activity was also initiated at this time and has since developed to cover almost all sites on the coast.

In the early 1970s habitat management, by excavation of suitable breeding pools, became the main objective of conservation work by the Lancashire Naturalists' Trust (LNT) and the British Herpetological Society (BHS) (LNT 1972). A Working Party on natterjack toad conservation was set up to consider this in detail (BHS/NC/LNT 1973; BHS 1976, 1978). The exceptionally dry years, with low water tables, of the mid 1970s seemed to underline the need for such work. A large number of pools were excavated right across the dune system in the late 1970s (ASD NNR file 2/6/2/3/2; Beebee 1989). Pools were excavated in such a way that shallow water would be available to natterjacks for spawning in the spring and deeper water would be available to tadpoles for development and metamorphosis (Figure 12.10). Design of natterjack breeding pools is discussed in the British Trust for Conservation Volunteers (BTCV) handbook on coastal conservation, 'Coastlands' (BTCV 1987). Much of this information was provided by Sefton coast staff, in particular NCC wardens at Ainsdale NNR (Payne & Singleton 1978). As part of a national study (Beebee 1985), a survey was made of all artificial pools created for natterjacks on Ainsdale NNR (Wheeler 1984a). This provided information on pool conditions best suited to natterjacks. Further work on this subject has been undertaken at Ainsdale NNR (Aitcheson 1987). A NCC commissioned study (Banks & Beebee 1988) in Cumbria and Hampshire has studied the breeding biology in detail and provided valuable conservation information. These studies underlined the problems of deep, permanent water bodies in fixed dunes, which are soon colonised by large populations of common amphibians and aquatic invertebrates, causing the demise of the resident natterjack colony. Many of the pools created in the mid 1970s were deeply excavated, due to the exceptionally low water table at the time, and only became permanent when the dune water-table rose to a more normal level in the 1980s. Further excavations have been undertaken in recent years and these are reported in the annual reports.

This increase in commoner amphibians, common toad (*Bufo bufo* L.) and common frog (*Rana temporaria* L.), and decline of natterjacks was first noted in survey work in the early 1980s. It was suspected that the common amphibian tadpoles were out-competing the natterjack tadpoles in pools where both were present. This was assumed to be due to direct predation, which had been observed, and competition for food. As an experiment, the NCC warden removed common toad spawn and frog spawn from selected natterjack breeding pools on Ainsdale NNR to see whether this would benefit natterjacks. Unfortunately, those pools dried out and the success of this management technique could not be judged.

Research undertaken on the coast in the mid 1980s (Nicolle 1988), showed that the presence of larger common toad tadpoles, in sufficient numbers, inhibited the growth of natterjack tadpoles. This appears to be caused by an unpigmented algae passed in tadpole excreta and often results in the predation or desiccation of the smaller natterjack tadpoles. Studies elsewhere (Banks & Beebee 1987b) have shown a similar effect by both common toad and common frog tadpoles on natterjack tadpoles. The inhibition effect is not species-related, but merely that caused by larger on smaller tadpoles. In addition, common anuran tadpoles were shown to be significant predators of natterjack spawn in certain situations. Further studies (Banks & Beebee 1987a) have shown that natterjacks tend to avoid spawning in pools with high densities of other anuran tadpoles. Conservation work on the coast has responded to these findings. Initially, common toad spawn was removed at selected pools on Ainsdale and Cabin Hill NNRs in 1986. However, this proved to be an inefficient way of dealing with the problem and now adults are removed together with any spawn laid. This management technique has been adopted at all key natterjack pools as necessary and is recorded in the annual survey reports. Frog populations have generally not been interfered with due to their much lower levels.

A recent NCC-commissioned study of the terrestrial ecology of the natterjack (Beebee & Denton 1988-89, 1989-90, 1990-91), part of which was undertaken on the coast, highlighted the importance of the mobile dunes, short turf and strand line habitats to animals outside the breeding season. This emphasises the need for the conservation of such habitats.

A study of adult size differences at several colonies along the coast, over a number of years, has been undertaken (Smith 1990). This suggests that size of adults is a useful guide to the age structure of the population and could be a valuable conservation tool. Since the mid 1980s, sample measurements have been a part of the annual monitoring programme.

In 1984, a strategy for the conservation of natterjacks on the Sefton coast, was produced (Smith 1984a). This provided a co-ordinated approach and aimed at providing a chain of breeding sites along the coast, precluding the isolation of populations. It is suggested that future excavations should be primarily in the frontal dunes, being the area most favoured by natterjacks and least favoured by common toads. In addition, the clearance of sea buckthorn, removal of common toad and frog spawn, and fencing of pools along with explanatory signs in areas of high public pressure, were the main forms of management proposed. These prescriptions have been generally adopted by agencies on the coast. A revised strategy is in preparation.

Detailed sections on natterjack conservation are included in the Ainsdale NNR management plan (Wheeler 1986a). This involves maintaining key natterjack pools in the frontal dunes free of common toads and rank vegetation. In addition, scrub encroachment and monitoring is addressed. Plans for Cabin Hill NNR (Simpson 1990g) contain similar prescriptions but include the provision of pools in the embryo dune area.

The National Trust natterjack scrapes at Formby Point are, at present, suffering from a lowered water table. To counter this in 1991, the Trust experimented with an artificial liner for one scrape. This pool was topped up as necessary through the season and in an exceptionally dry year was successful in raising many toadlets. In 1992 two artificial pools were used.

The history of natterjack conservation at Altcar Rifle Ranges has been reported (Smith 1989; Simpson 1990n).

Much of the information required for the conservation of natterjacks on the coast has now been gained. Breeding pools will continue to be monitored as part of routine management. This in turn will assist the fine tuning of scrape/slack management. Research into status and management requirements on peripheral sites (eg, golf courses) is required.

SAND LIZARD

Sand lizards have not received the same degree of attention as natterjacks, despite being a rarer species. The Merseyside population, which appears to be a separate race from the southern heathland lizards, probably numbers less that 500 individuals (R Hall pers. comm.).

TABLE 12.1.
Sand Lizard Survey References

Boston	1970e
Aldridge	1972
Bruce	1973
Corbett	1974
Jackson	1978a,b
Cooke	1980
Corbett	1985
Dent	1986
Hall & Nissenbaum	1987
Nissenbaum	1988b
Cooke	1989b* (1980-86)
Nissenbaum	1989
Nissenbaum	1990

Nb Reference years are recording years except * where recording years are shown in brackets.

Conservation work began in 1970 and initially revolved around surveys to assess the status of lizards on the coast (Boston 1970e). A full survey of the coast (Corbett 1974) identified a series of sites from Southport to Altcar, including a number of golf courses. Surveys of known sites have continued to the present day (Table 12.1).

It was soon realised that many sites were under threat of development. A conservation meeting was held early in the 1970s to assess the status and consider future management work for the species (BHS/NC/LNT 1973). Further proposals were made later in the decade (BHS 1976,1978). Around this time two vivaria were created at Ainsdale NNR to take rescued animals from stricken sites. One vivarium was the island in the centre of the lake created by Ainsdale NNR office in 1971 (ASD NNR file 2/6/2/2/3). Unfortunately, it was not realised that sand lizards were such good swimmers and animals placed there escaped! A second vivarium was created by the Ainsdale NNR office. This was of glass sided construction and more successful. (ASD NNR file 2/6/2/2/4). This has been superseded by a plastic sided vivarium with a net roof. Although initially a haven for rescued lizards, the vivarium has been used for ecological studies, and today is part of a captive breeding and release scheme (ASD NNR file 2/6/2/2/1 & 2) undertaken in conjunction with the BHS. At first, the release scheme covered sites on the Ainsdale NNR dunes, including several large vivaria. It was hoped that these natural vivaria would provide better ecological information and give an indication of the success of the breeding and release scheme. However, after their introduction, few lizards were seen and the project was abandoned. In recent years, improved knowledge of habitat requirements (see below), and the need to strengthen local populations, has led to other release sites along the coast being identified and used. Details of sand lizard conservation techniques are given in a coastal conservation handbook (BTCV 1986). This was mainly compiled from notes by Ainsdale NCC wardens (Payne & Singleton 1978).

During the 1970s, NCC commissioned a study of the habitat requirements of sand lizards (Jackson & Yalden 1979). This work and similar studies in the 1980s by A.S. Cooke (see Table 10.4 for references), analysing detailed vegetation quadrat data, of known lizard sites, has provided valuable information for habitat management and the release scheme (see Cooke, this volume). These studies showed that generally south facing slopes with a mixture of bare sand and dense, tall ground vegetation, provided the most suitable conditions. As a result of improved knowledge of habitat requirements, known colony sites are actively managed where required. Encroaching scrub and rank vegetation has been removed on many sites and bare sand patches created. At one site, hibernacula burrows have been created. In areas of greatest public pressure, known colony sites are fenced off. More recently, management plans for Ainsdale NNR (Wheeler 1986a) and Cabin Hill NNR (Simpson 1990g) have detailed prescriptions for the conservation of sand lizards.

A sand lizard strategy for the Merseyside Coast (Lunn & Wheeler 1989), discussed the present status and reviewed past literature, habitat management and the captive breeding project. The need for a research project was highlighted. This has provided detailed information on present status and proposed a co-ordinated approach to management on the coast, including habitat management and the future of the captive breeding/release scheme. Studies of home range, dispersion and predation by domestic cats (*Felis catus* L.) and magpies (*Pica pica* L.) would be valuable.

OTHER SPECIES

Few other species have received special conservation attention. Research and conservation requirements for the red squirrel (*Sciurus Vulgaris* L.) are discussed by Atkinson *et al.,* this volume.

The great-crested newt (*Triturus cristatus* (Laurenti) Dunn) population is annually monitored at Ainsdale NNR (see amphibian section in Atkinson *et al.* this volume). The species was introduced to the reserve in the early 1970s after a number of pools were created, though it has spread little. Wardens at this reserve assisted a national NCC commissioned inquiry into the status and ecology of the species to aid conservation management (Wheeler 1986b). In recent years some scrub clearance has been undertaken around the main breeding pools.

Several plant species have been translocated within the coast when their habitats have come under threat. Sharp club-rush (*Schoenoplectus pungens* (Vahl) Palla), various-leaved pondweed (*Potamogeton gramineus* L.) and Baltic rush (*Juncus balticus* Willd.), including its hybrids with soft rush (*J. effusus* L.) and hard rush (*J. inflexus* L.), were all threatened due to their slack habitat drying-out and invasion by scrub (ASD NNR file 2/6/1/8). *J. balticus* x *J. effusus* located in a slack at Hightown was in danger of being lost to marine erosion (Smith 1977). Sharp club rush was further translocated in 1990 as a result of its decline at its first transplanted site. A project plan and first monitoring report have been produced (Simpson 1990h, 1990i). The distribution, status and conservation of Baltic rush in England, including the Sefton coast, has been reported (Smith 1984b).

Green-winged orchid (*Orchis morio* L.) and cowslip (*Primula veris* L.) populations at Altcar Rifle Ranges have been monitored in response to mowing operations since 1985 (Carty 1986c; Gateley 1987a; Hall 1988c; Simpson 1989a, 1990k). Monitoring of 'I' Range, including the green-winged orchid population, has been detailed in a project plan (Simpson 1990j). There are no specific requirements for research to assist the conservation of these 'other species'.

RECREATION USE & MANAGEMENT

The Sefton Coast is undoubtedly of regional importance as a destination for recreation, attracting a traditional sea-side day-trip market but increasingly becoming all all-season all-weather attraction. Many of the problems inherited by the Coast Management Scheme in the late 1970s could be attributed to the pressures of access to the beach (at Formby) and access from the beach (Ainsdale). Most of these visitors arrived by car and consequently much of the Scheme's effort has been aimed at better controlling the direct and indirect effects of vehicular access. Car parking has been better contained at Formby Point (Lifeboat Road and Victoria Road), informal car-parking discouraged at Ravenmeols (Albert and Alexandra Roads), beach car parking restricted adjacent to the Ainsdale Hills and proposals put forward for further zoning of access on the northern beaches. Intensive recreational use has not been positively encouraged (although Ainsdale beach is identified as a site for promotion) but facilities for the more extensive use of the coast, more in keeping with countryside management, have been improved and promoted.

Car parks giving access to the dune nature reserves, (eg at Hall Road (Crosby) and Sands Lake (Ainsdale)) have been upgraded, the footpath network has been waymarked and promoted, a permissive horse-riding route established, and an interpretive programme put into action.

CURRENT USE

The pattern of recreational use on the coast is well established but monitoring is necessary to detect changes and assess the likely impacts. Ainsdale NNR, for example, has maintained a consistent access policy for over twenty-five years and by its remoteness has remained fairly immune from changes affecting other parts of the coast. Over the same period of time the dune areas at Formby and Hightown have come under greater pressure from increasing local populations, and, conversely, pressures on the frontal dunes at Ainsdale and Birkdale have been reduced by a decline in visitors to the beach. For various reasons there has never been a comprehensive survey of the dune area and the many individual surveys and records have yet to be compiled in summary form. Some sources of information such as parking statistics for Ainsdale beach go back many years and give a good record of beach use whereas there is almost no information on the use of the adjacent sandhills. A list of known sources of information is given in Table 12.3.

TABLE 12.3
Summary of Visitor Survey Information 1966-1990

Lancashire Coastal Survey, Formby Area Report (1966). Survey carried out on Sunday 25th July 1965. Report also contains monthly car parking statistics (May-August) for Victoria Road 1960-1965.

Edmund Kirby & Sons (1974). Formby Coastal Area Report 1974. No new survey but a record of car-parking figures for Victoria Road and Lifeboat Road 1968-1973 and monthly car-parking figures for Lifeboat Road (April-September) 1973.

Merseyside County Council (1975). Analysis of the Formby Survey. A full survey was carried out on Sunday 10th August 1975.

Sefton Borough Council (1980). Visitor Survey: Formby Point. The 1975 survey was repeated on Sunday 31st August 1980.

Merseyside County Council and Sefton Borough Council. Formby Point Surveys. In addition to the two major surveys (1975 & 1980) 33 visitor counts were taken on Sundays from 1978-1988 (during the months of June-September). Summary sheets are available for each survey. Reports are also available for the surveys carried out on 5th July 1981 (H. Trees), 26th July 1987, 12th June 1988.

Sefton Borough Council. Ainsdale Beach Surveys. The Tourism and Attractions Department maintain daily and monthly records of beach car-parking at Ainsdale and Southport. Information on the distribution of vehicles has been obtained from ground and aerial survey. Surveys were carried out in 1984, 1986 and 1988. On 7th August 1988 an aerial survey counted 2,312 vehicles on the main beaches.

Sefton Borough Council, Beach User Survey (1990). An attitude survey was carried out at four main beach areas; Crosby, Formby, Ainsdale and Southport. A summary report is available.

Note: None of the reports are published. All are held by the Coast Management Scheme, Formby Council Offices, Freshfield Road, Formby.

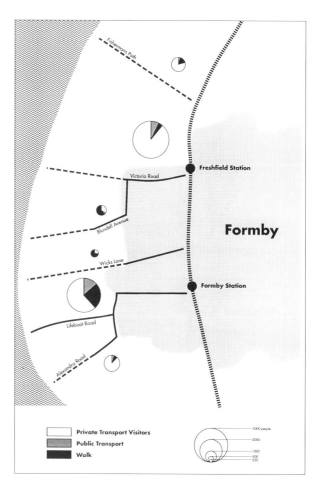

Figure 12.11: Distribution of visitors at Formby Point. Data taken from the analysis of the Formby Survey 1975 (Merseyside County Council).

The very nature of the coast as a fine-weather destination means that there will inevitably be times when very large numbers arrive on a single day. These 'peaks' have probably not increased over the years. In 1965 Lancashire County Council counted people at Formby Point on a fine day and estimated that the area could attract 15,000 people. Out of 35 surveys, carried out between 1977 and 1989 only one has recorded a similar high figure of 13,790 people. The average number of visitors to Formby Point on Sundays in the summer is 3,700 people. Formby Point is managed as an all-year amenity and the inevitable chaos on a few days is accepted. Ainsdale beach on the other hand is popular in its own right but also acts as a valve to accommodate almost unlimited numbers of visitors on fine days. Some problems could perhaps be solved by the better management and marketing of Ainsdale beach rather than the upgrading of Formby.

Formby Point is an interlinked unit of countryside virtually isolated from the southern unit centred on Hightown and the northern unit centred on Ainsdale.

Surveys of Formby show a fairly consistent distribution of visitors and the relationship between vehicular access and pedestrian access (Figure 12.11). Public transport is an important means of access and the spinal coastal footpath is designed to link with the Liverpool to Southport railway.

PRINCIPLES OF ZONATION

The pattern of land ownership on the Sefton Coast forms a basis for recreation management. There is a good balance between areas of extremely limited access (e.g. Altcar Rifle Range) and areas where visitor pressure must be managed to prevent damage to habitats. The problems that could be attributed to uncontrolled access at Formby (Lifeboat Road and Victoria Road) and at Ainsdale in the early 1970s have been tackled and these areas should be able to absorb a similar number of visitors as before but with much less damage. Problems could arise, however, if visitor numbers rose substantially, hence the need for monitoring.

With increased access to and interest in the 'wilder' parts of the Sefton Coast there is a danger that wildlife will be disturbed and habitats damaged by even the most considerate of visitor. There is a need to know whether the most important natural areas are well

146

enough protected from recreational disturbance and, if there is doubt, the precautionary principle should be applied. The Alt estuary, for example, has become an important sanctuary area for waders displaced from the Dee estuary by disturbance (see, for example, Mitchell *et al.* 1988). As a result the situation at the Alt must be studied and if necessary changes made to access policies on the beaches. Further north, the zoning of the beach area between the northern boundary of Ainsdale National Nature Reserve and Southport Pier has been proposed to reduce the area available to motorists and so indirectly improve the conditions for the large wintering flocks of waders.

On the dunes the main area of uncertainty lies in the future of the private land between the Ravenmeols Local Nature Reserve and Cabin Hill National Nature Reserve at Formby. Long standing proposals for the establishment of a golf course on part of this land are still an option and it could be argued that such a development would be a limited access use more in keeping with the nature reserves than, say, a large caravan park. On the other hand light recreational use combined with rabbit grazing maintains the area at present with little need for intervention.

The present mosaic of land ownerships and access levels works well to create a range of sanctuary areas and recreation areas. Even on the more intensively used sites, such as Lifeboat Road, a great deal of habitat management work is possible and the image of the coast as a continuous nature reserve is one which is often portrayed by the management scheme.

ACCESS CONTROL

The association between excessive trampling of dune vegetation and subsequent erosion is well researched and reviewed (see, for example, Boorman 1977; Ranwell & Boar 1986). On the Sefton Coast the impact of this recreation pressure from 1945 onwards can be followed on the series of available aerial photographs. At Ainsdale where car parking has traditionally been permitted on the foreshore, the amount of bare sand was found to correlate with the incidence of parking along the dune frontage (Handley 1980). Dune erosion at Formby Point, Fisherman's Path and near the beach access points at Ainsdale and Birkdale was initiated and/or exacerbated by recreational use.

The techniques for dune management and access control are also well documented and are broadly similar throughout the UK (BTCV 1986; CCS 1984; Ranwell & Boar 1986). The BTCV handbook '*Sand Dunes*' uses several examples of access management work on the Sefton Coast to illustrate the techniques developed and used by Sefton Council, the National Trust and English Nature.

Only on areas with extremely low use is the evidence of paths difficult to discern. On any moderately used area a network of informal paths will develop. There are some good examples at Formby of the 'natural' networks that form on disused fields once the fencing has become redundant. On heavily used dune areas path surfaces are reinforced using gravel, woodchip mulches and boardwalks to counter erosion (Figure 12.12).

A number of areas on the Sefton Coast (Altcar Rifle Ranges, Cabin Hill NNR, and the five golf courses) have no general access. The remaining areas are linked by a footpath network giving extensive access and including a 24km waymarked Coastal Footpath. English Nature restricts access to defined footpaths on the Ainsdale NNR, and some other areas are fenced for management reasons but elsewhere the public enjoy free access.

Prior to 1978 the only well defined footpaths on the coast were those on Ainsdale NNR. In the early years of the Management Scheme, Merseyside County Council rationalised the footpath network at Formby Point, and Sefton Council laid out a series of paths on the Ainsdale Local Nature Reserve to complement and complete the network based on the National Nature Reserve. The subsequent development of the Formby network would make an interesting study in recreation management. The network of 14km of gravel or boardwalk paths, (1.5m wide,) that was established largely remains today (Wood 1985). Some paths were heavily used and have since been repaired and widened whilst others were little used and have been returned to grass. In some places paths were buried by blown sand or they resulted in more erosion and were taken out, and new paths have been added to the network as features of interest, for safety, or to better control pressures.

A number of studies have been carried out on the use of paths on the Sefton Coast (Slatter 1978; Rooney 1987; Marshall 1988) and these have helped to guide the development and management of the footpath network.

RECREATION IMPACT RESEARCH

The Sefton Coast is one of the most heavily used dune systems in the UK, yet very little is known about the overall impact of recreation. Information on visitor numbers, distribution and attitudes is collected on a fairly *ad-hoc* basis and only a few studies have looked at the impact of recreation on dune vegetation (e.g. the ongoing work by Slatter at Hightown).

The impact of outdoor recreation on dunes has been reviewed by Van der Zande (1989). All too often recommendations for management are based on best professional judgements and not on recreation impact analysis. The recreation impact processes that are

Figure 12.12: Recreation Management at Lifeboat Road, Formby. A formal car parking layout channels visitors along several wide surfaced paths (woodchips in this example) to the beach.

relevant to the Sefton Coast, as defined by Van der Zande (1989) are :

i)   Loss of habitat by the establishment of recreation sites or recreation facilities

ii) Trampling effects on soil and vegetation by walking and riding

iii) Disturbance of fauna by the presence of visitors

iv) Pollution of soil, water and air by visitors and visitor facilities

Recreation pressure has an ecological impact but also a social impact and management must aim to reduce conflict between users. Some activities, such as the use of off-road recreation vehicles (ORRVs), especially motor-cycles, are incompatible with the Coast Management Plan. Others, such as horse riding, orienteering, cycling and jogging are acceptable at low intensities and in certain areas but require monitoring. Informal pedestrian access is by far the most extensive recreational use on the dunes and the impacts include trampling, disturbance and pollution. Dog ownership is high in the local area; surveys at Formby Point on Sundays in the summer have regularly counted over 400 dogs entering the dune area over an 8 hour period.

A considerable amount of data, from vehicle counts, visitor surveys and questionnaires has been collected since 1965 but no attempt has yet been made to assess and collate the data or to establish a strategy for recreational and social research that could be integrated with other fields of study.

Van der Zande (1989) dismisses two types of recreation management, the concepts of zoning and deflecting facilities ('honey-pots'). He argues that they are used as convenient solutions for decision makers in difficult situations with conflicting interests. Zoning is often employed as a means to justify an increase in visitor numbers but on the Sefton Coast the proposals for zoning are to give greater protection to important wildlife areas where uncontrolled visitor access is either unnecessary or undesirable. The only conscious use of the 'honey-pot' concept on the coast was the creation of the Wicks Lane recreation lake as a counter attraction to the beach at Lifeboat Road to reduce visitor pressure on the frontal dunes. There is no evidence that this worked and the lake probably attracted extra visitors and was later transformed into a wetland habitat. A single large visitor centre on the Sefton Coast could become an attraction in its own right and lead to the over-use of the adjacent area. The Coast Management Scheme, for this reason, favours the development of a series of smaller information points. Huddart (this volume), however, puts the case for a single visitor centre.

Figure 12.13. Ainsdale Nature Trail, 1968. Until 1991 the Nature Trail at Ainsdale National Nature Reserve was the only formal provision for schools on the Sefton coast. Photograph by Technical Service Section, Nature Conservancy H.Q.: English Nature archive, Ainsdale NNR.

EDUCATIONAL USE

The beaches, dunes and woods of the Sefton Coast are a rich education resource. Huddart (this volume) reviews the educational use and opportunities of the coast and makes a recommendation for a co-ordinated coastwide education project. Sefton Council and English Nature, launched the Sefton Coast Education Project in 1991 with a Project Officer appointed to a three-year post. The aims of the Education Project are; i) to develop curriculum based resource material for schools, ii) to provide in-service training for teachers, and iii) to work with the coastal agencies to identify sites for fieldwork and set up a central booking system. The project will prepare its long-term management plan in 1993.

David Wheeler (Review co-ordinator)

English Nature
Ainsdale NNR
2 West End Lodge
Pinfold Lane
Ainsdale PR8 3QW

A full list of contributors is given in Appendix 2

APPENDIX: CURRENT RESEARCH IN DUNE MANAGEMENT

THREATS POSED BY SUCCESSIONAL CHANGES AND DUNE FIXATION TO THE RARE HERPETOFAUNA

T.J.C. Beebee and J.S. Denton

The Merseyside dunes constitute an important habitat for two of Britain's three species of endangered herpetofauna: the sand lizard and the natterjack toad. For the lizard it is a unique northern outpost; for the toad, the largest area of habitat in the country. Both species have declined substantially on Merseyside over the past few decades. Direct habitat destruction by urbanisation, afforestation and golf course creation has taken a major toll; more recently, scrub (sea buckthorn and creeping willow) encroachment has rendered much of the undeveloped dune area unsuitable for both of the endangered species. Extensive overgrowth and dune stabilisation have removed egg-laying, and possibly basking sites for sand lizards; the same processes have facilitated invasion by competitively superior anurans (common toads and frogs). These early-breeding species' larvae prevent successful natterjack reproduction by predation and growth inhibition of natterjack spawn and tadpoles, ultimately depriving the rare amphibian of breeding ponds. As succession progresses, the terrestrial habitat also becomes too dense to support adult natterjacks which are thus driven out of such areas. Sand lizards and natterjacks are now absent from large parts of the Merseyside dune system upon which they were common twenty or more years ago. This progression towards ever more fixed dunes poses threats to the remaining populations of both species, forcing them into narrowing areas of unstable dunes close to the sea. Drastic action to destabilise recently fixed dune areas is recommended.

A more detailed discussion of the threats to the natterjack toad from competition and habitat change is given by Beebee (1992).

T J C Beebee   J S Denton

School of Biology
University of Sussex
Falmer
Brighton BN1 9QG

IMPACT OF VISITORS ON DUNE COMMUNITIES AT HIGHTOWN

R. J. Slatter

There is evidence from studies of dune slacks at Ainsdale that limited use by ramblers need not have a detrimental effect. Among the lower lying wet slacks diversity within the slack community may increase as a result of path production. Mild trampling appears to disrupt the competitive balance to favour plants with a high degree of productivity, including annuals and short-lived perennials with a capacity for rapid seed establishment and vegetative spread. Where this reserve pool of resistant species is small or non-existent one might expect path erosion to be more severe.

This idea seems to be borne out at Hightown where the dune system has been disrupted by human activity and where there is a greater habitat diversity. The Hightown dunes and meadows encompass in a small area a variety of plant communities perhaps unrivalled along the Sefton coast. Analysis of these communities has shown that there is a negative correlation between plant diversity within the habitat and the degree to which path surfaces are eroded. The most resistant areas are the grassland sites adjoining the dry slacks, where a variety of monocotyledons provides a useful reserve of species tolerant to treading. Showing least resistance are the fringing saltmarsh, reedbeds and mobile dunes.

As housing developments take place and the dune system responds to changing use, it should be possible to monitor these effects. Beneficial changes can be expected as a result of sealing the dunes from vehicular traffic. The prevention of rubbish dumping and the control of unauthorised horse-riding and motor cycling leaves the dunes free from drastic intrusion. On the other hand adverse effects could well occur due to increased recreational use by pedestrians of the limited area of dune systems that remains.

Robert J Slatter

Science Department
Edge Hill College of Higher Education
Ormskirk
Lancs L39 4QP

CHAPTER THIRTEEN

The Use of the Sefton Coast as an Educational Resource

D. Huddart

INTRODUCTION

To manage an environmental resource effectively requires accurate information at an early stage of the management process before strategies are developed to influence the management plan. The initial aim of this work, commissioned by the Sefton Planning Department in 1988, was to provide such data, to constructively influence future educational provision and fuel debate on educational management strategies for the Sefton coast (Huddart 1988).

In 1987 the author believed that this coast had not been developed to its full potential for education and that whilst the coast was well managed in terms of nature conservation, recreation and coastal protection the Sefton Coast Management Scheme needed to consider in detail its plans for developing environmental education. The educational provision that was available seemed to be low-key and uncoordinated and education did not appear to be a high priority in the early work of the Scheme, when other perhaps more important considerations were to the forefront.

However, by the late 1980s there had been a change of emphasis, partly stimulated by the report of Derbyshire, Frost and Mincher (1985), towards the realisation that education in the widest sense will eventually pay dividends in terms of environmental conservation (SMBC 1989a). Since 1988 the English educational framework has been revolutionised and there may be implications for this coast as an educational resource.

The educational value of the Sefton coast has been recognised for many years (Jones 1985) because it is an area where it is possible to study the complete succession of habitats from sandy nearshore to dune heath. As well as geographical, geological and biological fieldwork, there is conservation, land management, tourism and recreation interest which can be developed for specialist educational use. The Sefton Coast is extremely valuable scientifically (Ratcliffe 1977; Smith 1978) but it is the multiple use of the coast that gives it wider educational value.

This review attempts to answer four questions which will benefit the implementation of future management plans.

These are:

i) What is the demand for educational use of the coast?

ii) What provision is made to meet this demand?

iii) How will recent educational changes shape this demand in the future?

iv) What future educational provision is needed on the Sefton coast to maximise the educational benefits of the available resources?

REVIEW

1. WHAT IS THE DEMAND FOR EDUCATIONAL USE OF THE COAST?

The educational potential is a combination of the educational audience size and the relative scale of environmental interest that the coast might generate compared with other major ecosystems. There are two broad audience categories: the formal education sector and the general public. Information about these groups, their size and educational needs is sparse but an attempt was made to quantify data for the formal education sector by the analysis of questionnaire surveys; the Merseyside Environmental Education Review Survey (MEER) 1985 (Brummage 1990) and the Coastal Environmental Education Planning Review Survey (CEEPR) organised by Huddart (1988). Demand figures were supplemented by analysis of data supplied by the educational providers on the coast.

Higher Education
In undergraduate teaching over 1200 students visit the coast per year and there appear to be 30-35 undergraduate dissertations per year across a wide range of subjects in both cases. In terms of staff research there appear to be about twenty-five active workers, across a diverse range of specialisms, who have inspired approximately forty research students over the preceding ten years. This undergraduate and postgraduate research is estimated to take 1650 field days per year.

Primary Education

The MEER survey did not collect data on the number of children visiting sites or the visit frequency and it was difficult to interpret the exact locations accurately (Huddart 1988). However, it did show there was extensive interest in environmental education on Merseyside, that 75% of 302 schools carried out fieldwork in the Merseyside area and 62% outside the area and that the coast was of over-riding importance for this fieldwork in Sefton, Liverpool and Wirral(the coast accounting for 47% of all fieldwork visits). An attempt was made to quantify these data by assuming that each school only visits the coast once with forty in the party. This likely underestimate means that 5160 primary pupils visit the coast per year.

Secondary Education

Fifty-seven schools responded to the MEER survey and 70 to the CEEPR survey (a response rate of 27%). From the CEEPR the total number of pupils using the coast is a minimum 4381. Only 13 responses came from 24 Sefton Local Education Authority (LEA) schools and some of the non-response schools are known to use the coast. However, the figures in Figure 13.1 can be used as an indicator of the use of the coast. From the MEER, 73.9% of all secondary schools use the coast for fieldwork and again assuming only one visit this gives an estimate of 6610 pupils per year.

Adult Education

The potential audience for environmental education on the coast is immense and it is estimated that the dune coast alone is visited by over half a million visitors each year (Houston & Jones 1987) and that the coast is within an hour's access for five million people. However, it is not known with any certainty what the expectations of visitors are, although surveys like that of Trees (1981) provide a limited amount of information, such as 15% came to observe nature. There is only sparse data on the many specialist groups who carry out 'leisure time learning for adults' using the coast.

2. WHAT PROVISION IS MADE TO MEET THIS DEMAND?

The Seaforth Nature Reserve

About 1000 children visit the reserve each year, with steady growth since 1986. In terms of potential this site has been under-used due to factors such as difficult access, uncertainty over job provision under temporary employment schemes and particularly the short term lease with the Mersey Docks and Harbour Company.

The Ranger Service

This service provides a valuable informal educational provision, summarised in Huddart (1988). But education comes after site and visitor management and there has never been a specific budget line for education or specific responsibility for education in job descriptions. There have also been few links with the LEA and no staff have any specific educational training. In 1987 44 field trips led by the Rangers catered for about 1000 people and 785 people took part in 35 guided walks. Talks and slide shows per year number 30 and 75 respectively and the latter were attended by about 3000 people.

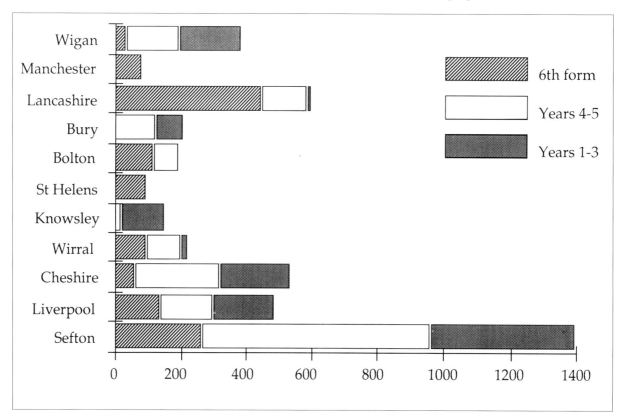

Figure 13.1: Secondary school pupils using the Sefton coast

The National Trust

The policy at present seems to be that education is absorbed into the wardens' work programme as and when it can be. There is caution about their role due to time and money factors and there is no definite local Trust policy with regard to educational provision (Huddart 1988). The following number estimates relate to educational visits to the property per year: 6300 by coach, 1680 by rail, 840 who have also been to the Ainsdale National Nature Reserve, guided walks catering for 830 which gives a total of 9650.

The Ainsdale National Nature Reserve

The Nature Conservancy Council (now English Nature) has operated since 1964 the extremely important and pioneering Ainsdale Educational Project, including the Educational Nature Trail (Greenwood 1970) and wardens, a field base, a Museum Gallery, In-Service and Sixth-Form courses and education zone. A review of the work and the problems associated with its operation are summarised in Huddart (1988). There was a period of sustained growth between 1969-1978 with a peak of almost 10,000 in 1974 (Figure 13.2). The period 1979-1981 was the nadir of the provision as severe financial cut-backs did not allow a trail warden and in 1980-81 it was closed completely as an educational provision. At the same time between one third and one quarter of all schools visiting the reserve had also visited the museum. The break in provision resulted in a 70% reduction in the number using the gallery and teachers' courses were no longer held with the consequent demise of a unique educational initiative. The period from 1982 when it reopened again has resulted in numbers up to about 6000 per year, although the number of party visits per year is higher than the mid 1970s. The number of sixth form and higher education users gradually increased to a significant percentage by the mid-1980s (Figure 13.3).

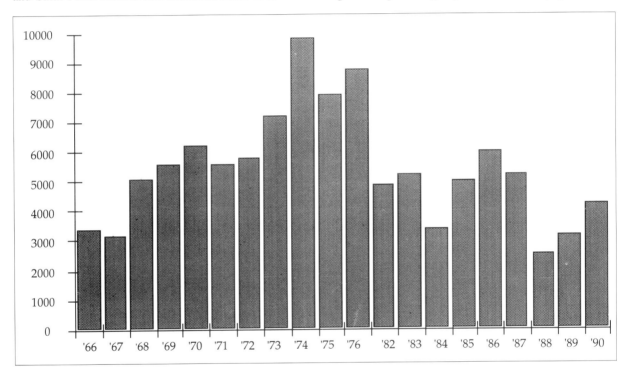

Figure 13.2: Use of Ainsdale NNR nature trail and educational zone by educational parties (booked in groups and non-permit holders). Data for years 1966-76 and 1982-90 derived from NCC figures.

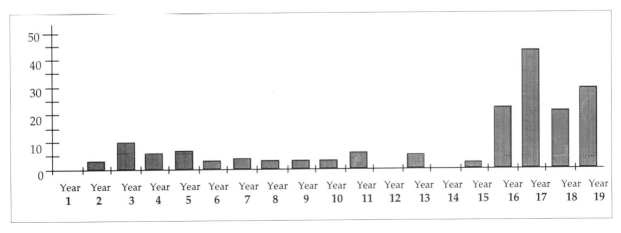

Figure 13.3: Use by sixth form and Higher education (% of total)

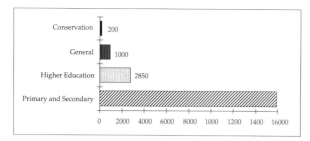

Figure 13.4: Best estimates of person days per year for the use of the coast for educational purposes

There are now no teachers' in-service courses and no sixth-form ecology courses. Schools visiting in 1987 came from Merseyside 57%, Greater Manchester 21%, Lancashire 17% and Cheshire 9%.

There is a serious commitment by English Nature to a future education facility on this coast but their Education Officer feels that National Nature Reserves should not be used for general educational use and that there should be a bias towards older groups.

Summary of Numbers Using the Coast for Educational Purposes

From the providers survey primary and secondary school users spend around 15,980 person days per year in the field on the coast. In addition there are guided walks for the general public and BTCV conservation days to be added. From the users survey higher education, primary and secondary users spend around 14,620 person days per year so the data from both surveys would appear to be compatible. The sub-totals and the grand total best estimates for the late 1980s educational use of the coast are given in Figure 13.4.

3. HOW WILL RECENT EDUCATIONAL CHANGES SHAPE THIS DEMAND IN THE FUTURE ?

The introduction of the General Certificate in Secondary Education (GCSE) has meant a major revision of the 14-16 age curriculum and a significant change in the methods and organisation of many examination courses.

Personal field investigation on environmental topics (a Geographical Enquiry) forms an essential part of most geography courses and usually accounts for 20-25% of the assessment marks which must mean an increasing use of local coastal resources. To meet the National Criteria in Science and Geography (DES 1985a, b) teaching methods have to be much more practical and pupil-centred, with a specified minimum amount of investigative work in the field undertaken by all pupils. In all the Northern Examination Association (NEA) GCSE Geography syllabuses the local coast can provide a rich source of topics and examples. Databases, like that provided by Bradley (1990) will prove a stimulating resource. In Biology it is disappointing to find no compulsory fieldwork in the

assessment schedule but the aims of the NEA syllabus do not preclude field investigation. The Sefton coast can be used extensively in many sections of this syllabus. This is also true for NEA A-level geography, biology and geology where the coast is an important resource providing examples, case studies and fieldwork locations.

The Sefton coast can be used extensively to teach the Science and Geography National Curricula (DES & WO 1989, 1991). Primary schools now formally have to study aspects of geography and science which can only mean an increased use of local fieldwork sites and the trend to balanced science 11-16 will generate more outdoor environmental science in the curriculum (ASE & NCC 1990). This is even more likely when it is realised that all children will have to experience the cross-curricular theme environmental education which will be part of the National Curriculum in the future (Bradley 1989; DES 1989; NCC 1990).

Regrettably two other features of the Educational Reform Act of 1988 suggest that perhaps there may be a lessening of resources for fieldwork: the local financial management of schools (LMS) and the changes in the field visit legislation (DES 1988; Thomas 1989). However, first surveys suggest that prognostications have been too negative, that worst hit have been inner-city primary schools (NFER 1991) and that local fieldwork may well be the beneficiary of such legislation at the expense of more exotic, costly locations. However, staff attitudes were felt to have adversely affected the number of pupils taking part in trips rather than LMS which it is believed has had little effect on pupil involvement in visits and activities (NFER 1991; Fallon 1991).

In summary it is suggested that the educational changes of the last five years must mean an increasing demand for educational use of the Sefton coast but that it is difficult to predict if there will be a major increase. This seems doubtful.

4. WHAT FUTURE EDUCATIONAL PROVISION IS NEEDED ON THE SEFTON COAST TO MAXIMISE THE EDUCATIONAL BENEFITS OF THE AVAILABLE RESOURCES ?

An evaluation of other coastal educational provision case studies like Gower and Ynyslas in Wales suggest a summary of points in Figure 13.5, which the Sefton coast did not have in the late 1980s. A co-ordinated policy needs to be achieved, with co-operation between the site managers, capital investment and guaranteed running costs. The LEA should have a central role to play in planning the future provision. There has not been such close co-operation to date in Sefton between English Nature and the LEA which can be found on Gower in the organisation of the Gower Field Education Project. There are no seconded teachers on

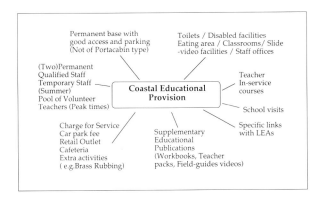

Figure 13.5: Summary of points related to Coastal Education Provision

this coast and in the past there have been few formal links between the LEA and other educational providers. The need for regular meetings with LEA advisers, visits to schools and in-service teacher training courses has now been re-initiated through the establishment of the Sefton Coast Education Project (SCEP) (see Wheeler *et al.*, this volume).

From the data in the MEER survey the additional needs of teachers are quite clear. Primary schools would like teacher packs (76.8%), followed by site staff, school visits and covered accommodation. Secondary schools require teacher courses (78.4%) and teacher packs (76.5%), followed by audio-visual aids, work-books and school visits. The CEEPR survey asked schools to select four from a list of extra facilities most useful on the coast. The ranked data, analysed by giving four points for every first place down to one point for every fourth place, are shown in Figure 13.6. Teacher's packs are most important, followed by in-service courses and then by a coast interpretive centre, with education facilities, classroom and education officer.

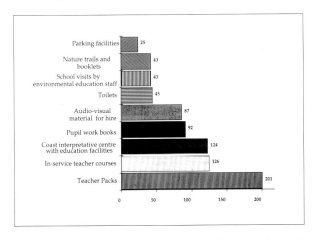

Figure 13.6: Ranking of extra facilities that would greatly improve educational provision (CEEPR survey)

There was a general feeling in the late 1980s from most of the providers of educational support on the coast, the LEA and Museum Service, that there was a need for the establishment of an independent coastal education officer. An officer was appointed in 1991 with the establishment of the SCEP and will provide an influential role in co-ordinating, evaluating and developing the educational provision. An educational base and interpretive centre should be established as suggested in the Coast Management Plan Review (SMBC 1989a) and in the Sefton Coast Interpretive plan (SMBC 1989b) and argued for by Huddart (1988). There may be problems of location, although Ainsdale is thought to be the best overall site. The essential requirements for such a centre and Ainsdale's positive attributes are given in Figures 13.7 and 13.8. However, discussion with the Centre for Environmental Interpretation (1989) revealed that they "would not like information, education and interpretation all to be accepted under one umbrella. Education in particular is quite different from interpretation and should be considered as a separate but parallel programme". Consequently, the need for a single centre was reappraised and plans postponed. The emphasis has

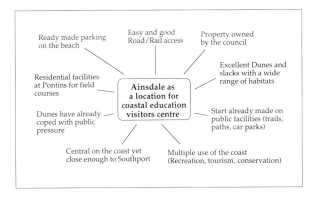

Figure 13.7: Positive attributes of Ainsdale as a location for coastal education visitors centre

moved to the establishment of a series of smaller centres providing visitor information. Yet it is recognised that there will be considerable overlap between interpretation and education and the work that will develop educational material is likely to have a positive spin-off for interpretive ideas. The educational and interpretive use of nature reserves will be developed and integrated within an overall programme for the coast (SMBC 1991a).

To give the education officer an appropriate measure of operational independence Huddart (1988) recommended that a scheme be established that might be called the Sefton Coast Education Project (SCEP). A version of this is now in place (SMBC/SCEP 1991).

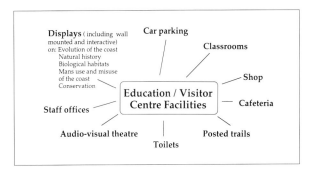

Figure 13.8: Facilities required at an Education/Visitor centre

The aim of the SCEP is to improve environmental education on the coast through co-operation between the LEA, English Nature, the National Trust, departments of Sefton Council, the Museum Education Service and other interested groups such as departments providing teacher training courses and teacher in-service provision. The project's responsibility should be to co-ordinate and liaise with other groups in relation to educational provision and to co-ordinate, implement and promote the educational use of the coast.

There seem to be few locations on the coast that could not be used for education because of conservation interests, although parts of the Ainsdale and Cabin Hill NNRs and parts of the Birkdale Hills might fall into this category. It is best that teachers develop their own fieldwork sites which suit their own needs wherever these may be. However, it seems that there could be an obvious general zonation of educational use. Ainsdale and Birkdale Hills LNR for secondary up to GCSE, the Ainsdale NNR would be the best location for sixth form ecology and conservation, the National Trust and Formby Point in general for infants/primary, Ravenmeols for GCSE and Hightown for sixth form. However, a base for primary visits in the National Trust/Formby Point area with access to woodlands would be desirable. At all costs a balance needs to be maintained between zonation and rigid control, haphazard development and individual teacher freedom.

Higher education users of the coast would benefit from easy access to centralised resources in one base similar to those provided by the Joint Countryside Advisory Service. The development of the Sefton Coast Research Forum, conferences, and a research publication series would be a stimulus to further research, would foster co-operation between researchers and would lead to more applied research with the land managers (Huddart 1988).

The needs of adult and continuing education are summarised in Huddart (1988) but, despite organisational difficulties, central is the need to use the locality: learning about it, its people and its environment. Smyth (1985) suggests a local learning centre, with structured learning about the locality, to develop local confidence and capability to participate. The whole process could be self-reinforcing and spiralling which would result in increased environmental awareness, a rising quality of citizen capability, professional sensitivity, local effective administration and a genuine participation by all concerned.

CONCLUSION

The Sefton coast is arguably Sefton's greatest landscape asset and educational resource. Lees (1976) has shown that the coast is of far greater importance ecologically on Merseyside than other ecosystems and it is of national scientific importance, both for its physiographic features and for a rich variety of wildlife supported by the complex of dune habitats (Houston & Jones 1987). When one adds the international significance of the Ribble estuary for wildlife one can see why it is used to the extent that it is in education. In the short term there must be continued commitment to coastal environmental education by the providers whilst the education officer develops the Education Project to co-ordinate educational policy and whilst interpretive/education centres are established. There is considerable overlap between education and interpretation and the links here must be maintained and strengthened. In the opinion of the author the dismissal of the concept of a central visitor interpretation/education centre should be reappraised as part of Sefton Council's tourism strategy. The development of smaller, site-specific centres should continue as valuable adjuncts to visitor information and education. The brief of the SCEP could be wider than envisaged in 1991 and could be structured in a similar way to that suggested by Huddart (1988). The coast could cope with considerably increased numbers for educational purposes but there is a need for co-ordination, co-operation, and augmentation of provision.

ACKNOWLEDGEMENTS

Thanks are due to many people who responded to questionnaires and informal discussions and have given generously of their time and information. Special thanks are due to Leo Bradley and Ruth Stronge whose comments have improved the original manuscript and to Ken Travis for drafting the figures.

David Huddart

Department of Science and Outdoor Education
Liverpool Polytechnic
IM Marsh Campus
Barkhill Road
Liverpool

CHAPTER FOURTEEN

Methods of Monitoring Land Use and Condition

J. M. Mackay

INTRODUCTION

To assess rate of change and the impact of management practices it is necessary to record regularly in some way a wide range of factors. The monitoring approach must vary according to the needs of the individual. For site managers, local recording may be most appropriate, such as land-based photographic coverage from fixed points (fixed-aspect still photography), along with key location measurements, faunal surveys, quadrat vegetation counts, soil analyses etc. To gain a more complete picture of the larger system, however, requires a different approach which lends itself to some form of remote sensing, such as analysis of aerial real or false-image photography.

Monitoring of any type can only be carried out satisfactorily if a consistent and objective method of classification is used, so that like is compared with like. The Merseyside Land Utilisation Surveys of 1976 and 1982 used virtually the same classification, and while the proposed Land Condition Survey will be more detailed and will have more sub-categories, it will be possible to derive the same classification. Earlier surveys, such as the 1965 Lancashire Land Use Map, however, did not use the same classification system and hence may not be directly comparable to later surveys.

The regularity of monitoring is also critical, but will depend on the rate of change of the site. Perhaps a 10 year interval would be most appropriate for assessing the health of the dunes, and a 5 year interval on areas such as the slacks where change is more rapid.

LAND UTILISATION SURVEYS

Numerous land utilisation surveys have been carried out on Merseyside, utilising different classifications. Most recently, the Sefton Coast was fully covered in the Land Utilisation Surveys of 1976 and 1982, using a classification developed from the methodology of the 1:25,000 Second Land Utilisation Survey of Britain (Coleman & Maggs 1968). In these surveys, a classification system utilising colours and letters in combination was used to specify land use on 1:10,000 base maps. These however were very broad-brush, and most of the coast is simply depicted on these maps as fixed dune or woodland (conifers) or woodland (conifers with scrub invasion). There are smaller areas indicated, such as areas of artichoke (*sic*) growing, less-

intensively managed grass used for horses, open space used for such activities as golf links, and idle land invaded with scrub or *Festuca/Agrostis*.

These Surveys were carried out relatively quickly, and hence relatively cheaply, on the ground, and mostly utilised existing boundaries of land parcels to demarcate areas of different land uses. They suffer from several constraints:

i) They are relatively small scale, and areas of different vegetation within larger parcels of land are not indicated.

ii) The fixed dune area is not sub-categorised in any way.

iii) The areas under different land uses have never been fully quantified. In the Land Use Statics, several sampling points were utilised to estimate overall areas under different land uses, but this is recognised as not being an accurate method.

However, these surveys do give an overall picture of the Coast at different periods and with regular updating might satisfy many management requirements.

The choice of land use classification system must depend on the use to which the information is to be put. Some classification systems are not specific enough to the area to be particularly useful, such as the ECE Standard Statistical Classification of Land Use (Economic and Social Council, Statistical Commission and Economic Commission for Europe 1989) which includes categories such as wet tundra, but nevertheless it may be useful for a classification scheme to be so designed that it can be incorporated within such a broader scheme.

Research needs and opportunities:

i) Determination of a suitable land use and condition classification scheme for the Sefton Coast

ii) Regular updating of detailed Land Utilisation / Condition Surveys

iii) By digitising past and future information and loading it into a GIS system, more reliable figures for summing areas of land use/condition, and changes in land use, could be obtained

iv) Determination of impact of factors on land use/condition

v) Determination of management or other changes necessary in light of trends detected from land use change

DETAILED VEGETATION SURVEYS

NATIONAL SAND DUNE VEGETATION SURVEY

At the opposite end of the spectrum is the detailed community and sub-community vegetation map as compiled in the 1988 National Sand Dune Vegetation Survey of the Sefton Coast. This was obtained by the surveyor dividing the vegetation by eye into homogeneous stands, and then drawing boundaries of those parcels of land on aerial photograph overlays, all in the field. The data are presented as parcels of land with detailed vegetation keys on 1:5,000 base maps. These parcels of land go down to an approximate width of only 5 m. They suffer from several constraints.

i) The smaller parcels of land have a large degree of error built into them. In some cases the combined width of the boundary lines is wider than the area contained within them.

ii) Such detail requires a lot of time in the field - each of the nine areas comprising the Sefton coast took approximately seven person days of fieldwork.

iii) Such detail would require a lot of time to enter into a GIS system, and the degree of error might prove unacceptably high.

Thus in this survey aerial photography and fieldwork were both used, to give far more information than could be obtained simply by analysis of the aerial photography. The combined area of the smallest parcels of land could not be obtained, but their position and distribution were recorded.

Research needs and opportunities:

i) The points relating to Land Utilisation Surveys (above) apply equally to more detailed vegetation surveys.

ii) The best approach to utilise these data more fully might be to enter the larger parcels of land into the GIS system, but valuable information relating to the smaller parcels of land would thus be lost. The smaller parcels could, however, be entered as points, or as linear features, so that their position and distribution could be analysed.

AERIAL PHOTOGRAPHY AND OTHER REMOTE SENSING METHODS

1. AERIAL PHOTOGRAPHY

Aerial photographic analysis provides a quick method of identifying parcels of land and, to some extent, vegetation, condition and level of maintenance, within these parcels of land. They can be used purely as desk-studies, as in the Ainsdale Hills and Birkdale Frontal Dunes site quality monitoring by air photo interpretation (Robinson 1989), or as an aid in field-studies, as in the Sefton Coast NCC National Sand Dune Vegetation Survey.

Good aerial photographic coverage of the coast exists (see Table 14.1), but this has not yet been subjected to detailed analysis to extract the maximum amount of useful information with respect to land use and condition. An important part of any such exercise has to be to derive the classification system that is most suitable for the purposes of the study.

Constraints include:

i) Inaccuracy associated with small mapping units - very small mapping units can be used, but what degree of error is entailed?

ii) Colour infrared photography may be more appropriate for vegetation analysis

iii) Aerial photographs have to be corrected to be map true

iv) Difficulty in deriving a reliable index of degree of use, and maintenance can complicate estimates of degree of use

v) Difficulty in establishing causes of land condition

vi) Difficulty in determining nature conservation value

The relative importance of some of these restraints will be identified in the Land Condition Survey pilot study to be carried out by Aston University for Sefton. In this, 1:10,000 1989 aerial colour stereoscopic photography (Figure 14.1) will be utilised to compile an open land/land condition survey of 25 km^2. The methodology utilises a video camera to capture 1 km^2 from aerial photography, and a national grid reference correction is then made. Features are digitised on screen, giving a co-ordinated position for each of the features down to pixel level, representing 2 m by 2 m. Areas of each classified use are calculated by number of pixels.

The maximum amount of detail that can be extracted from this photography will be recorded for categories in a classification system to be worked up between

Figure 14.1. 1:10,000 scale aerial photograph of Formby Point, 1989. Showing the Lifeboat Road dune area and car park (bottom right) and the National Trust dune area and Victoria Road car park (top right). Also shown is the pattern of asparagus fields and pinewoods. © Merseyside Information Service, 1989; reproduced with kind permission.

TABLE 14.1
Sources of Aerial Photography
All black and white vertical unless otherwise stated

Date	Scale	Coverage	Contractor	Holder	Notes
1945	6"-1 mile	Ainsdale NNR	RAF	EN	
1945-1948	6"-1 mile	Former Lancs CC	RAF	JCAS	
1951	6"-1 mile	Sefton Coast	RAF	SCDB	
1957	1:10,000	Ainsdale NNR	RAF	EN	
1957	1:5,000	Ainsdale NNR	RAF	EN	
1960	Oblique	Ainsdale NNR	Prof. Burges	EN	
1961	6"-1 mile	Former Lancs CC	Hunting Surveys	JCAS	
1962	Oblique	Ainsdale NNR	J.K. St. Joseph	EN	
1963	Oblique	Ainsdale NNR	J.K. St. Joseph	EN	
1965	1:2,500	Borough of Crosby	Hunting Surveys	SCDB	
1965	1:10,000	Ainsdale NNR	RAF	EN	
1966	6"-1 mile	Ainsdale NNR	Ordnance Survey	EN	
1968	Oblique	Ainsdale NNR	J.K. St. Joseph	EN	
1971	1:10,000	Ribble Estuary	Hunting Surveys	EN	
1971	1:10,000	Sefton Coast	Hunting Surveys	JCAS	
1972	1:5,000	Formby and Crosby	Hunting Surveys	SCDB	High & Low tides
1973	1:10,000	Former Lancs CC	Hunting Surveys	JCAS	
1974	1:5,000	Sefton Coast	Hunting Surveys	SCDB/EN	High & Low tides
1974	1:10,000	Former Lancs CC	B.K.S	JCAS	
1975	1:10,000	Merseyside	B.K.S	JCAS	False colour (infra-red)
1975	1:10,000	Merseyside	Meridian	JCAS	
1976	1:5,000	Sefton Coast	Fairey Surveys	JCAS/SCDB	High & Low tides
1977	1:5,000	Ainsdale NNR	-	EN	Colour
1977	1:10,000	Merseyside	B.K.S.	JCAS	
1978	1:5,000	Sefton Coast	Meridian	JCAS/SCDB	High & Low tides
1979	1:10,000	Merseyside	Meridian	JCAS/SCDB	
1979	1:10,000	Ribble Estuary	Meridian	EN	
1980	1:5,000	Sefton Coast	Meridian	JCAS/SCDB	High & Low tides
1982	1:5,000	Sefton Coast	Meridian	JCAS/SCDB	High & Low tides
1982	1:5,000	Ainsdale NNR	Meridian	EN	Colour
1983	1:5,000	Ainsdale NNR	Meridian	EN	
1984	1:5,000	Ainsdale NNR	Meridian	EN	
1984	1:10,000	Sefton Coast	Clyde	JCAS/SCDB	
1984	1:20,000	Ribble Estuary	Clyde	NRA/SCDB	High & Low tides
1985	1:5,000	Sefton Coast	Cartographical	NRA/SCDB	Low tide
1988	1:10,000	Sefton Coast	Hunting Aerofilms	NRA/SCDB	High & Low tides
1988	1:10,000	Ribble Estuary	Hunting Aerofilms	NRA/SCDB	Colour
1989	1:10,000	Merseyside	JAS air	JCAS	Colour
1992	1:10,000	Sefton Coast	Geonex	NRA/SCDB	Colour, Low tide

The main holders of aerial photography are the Joint Countryside Advisory Service (JCAS), the Sefton Coast Data Base (SCDB) maintained by the Director of Engineering and Surveying, Sefton Council and English Nature (EN) at Ainsdale NNR and the regional office at Blackwell, Cumbria. Other holders of relevant photography include the National Rivers Authority (NRA) and Sefton Planning Department (at the Formby and Bootle offices). For general studies the main reference library is held by the Joint Countryside Advisory Service, Bryant House, Maghull where there are facilities for viewing and working from aerial photographs.

Aston and Sefton. Each land unit will be identified, mapped and areally measured, and the data will be provided in a form suitable for incorporation into a GIS system. Selected ground checks will be carried out as necessary to assess accuracies and clarify interpretation queries. The smallest mapping unit used will be 0.1 ha (32 m by 32 m on the ground, or 3.2 mm by 3.2 mm on 1:10,000 photographs), and the degree of error associated with mapping land parcels of 0.1 ha, 1.0 ha and 10.0 ha will be ascertained. While only a small area of the coast falls into the pilot study area, this should prove a useful testing ground for a later all-Sefton, or wider, Land Condition Survey.

Obviously, by examination of the coast areas of exposed sand (distinguishing between sand and dune), areas of marram grass, established grassland, coastal woodland and so on could be identified, but other categories and sub-categories which could be incorporated must be determined in the near future. The classification of Robinson (1989) could perhaps be used as a basis. In this, land parcels for the following classes were identified, though not quantified, from 1:5,000 aerial photography of the Southport Sand Dunes and Foreshore SSSI: pools, bare sand, embryo dune, mobile dune, mobile/fixed dune transition, fixed dune, slack, scrub, blowout and scrape.

Research needs and opportunities:

i)   Derivation of multi-purpose coastal land use/condition classification scheme suitable for aerial interpretation.

ii) Determination of the limits of useful data that can be obtained from coastal aerial photography.

iii) Determination of error involved in not only delineation of land parcels but also categorisation of land use/condition within land parcels.

2. INFRARED FALSE COLOUR PHOTOGRAPHY

Handley (1980) has reviewed the use of infrared photography for environmental management on Merseyside. Generally, infrared photography is more useful in determining some vegetation characteristics (such as stressed areas within one community.) However, utilising both normal colour and false colour infrared photography taken at the same time is the most effective option, and hence it is hoped that both forms of photography will be carried out during the next Aerial Survey of Merseyside.

3. GROUND AND AERIAL OBLIQUE PHOTOGRAPHY AND PHOTO MOSAICS

Ground photography can be used to record dune condition and condition of vegetation, and can be a useful management and performance tool. Grimes (1975) used ground photography to record areas of stress, including those on the Sefton Coast, picked up on the false colour photography taken by B.K.S. Ltd. in June 1975. Fixed point photography has been used at Ainsdale Sand Dunes NNR since 1967 to record vegetation change (See Figure 12.6, Wheeler *et al.*, this volume).

While stereoscopic examination of vertical aerial photography gives good three-dimensional visualisation of the area of interest, oblique photography gives a more immediate three-dimensional effect. It is not so useful in quantifying areas but it could be useful for identifying and monitoring certain types of problem, e.g. erosion. English Nature hold important collections of oblique aerial photography by St. Joseph (1962 to 1968) and ground photography by Gresswell (see, for example, Figures 2.9, 1.3, 1.4, 1.6 & 1.8).

It has been suggested (Handley 1980) that photo mosaics can be useful in directly plotting distribution of visitors and their vehicles over an entire study area, as an aid to formulating a management scheme. They are also useful as a tool for easily monitoring large areas of coast.

4. VIDEO

The possibility of including video photography in the next Aerial Survey of Merseyside is being investigated. While video may not be suitable for obtaining accurate limits of land parcels, it may provide a quick and inexpensive method of monitoring change within land parcels previously delimited (W.G. Collins, personal communication, 1991).

5. SATELLITE IMAGERY

Space imagery has a resolving power at present of at best 10 m (SPOT- Systeme Probatoire de l'Observation de la Terre, a French satellite). Landsat Thematic Mapping (TM) gives a ground resolution of 30 m at most wavebands used. Satellite imagery has been used on Merseyside, the most recent example being Aston University Remote Sensing Unit's study for the National Rivers Authority on cloud free, 30 m resolution Landsat TM imagery captured in August 1990 (W.G. Collins, personal communication, 1991).

Realistically, however, for large scale mapping such imagery is not particularly useful at present. Further, weather conditions play an important role, for sensors operating in the optical and infrared regions of the spectrum cannot penetrate cloud cover. The usefulness of such imagery for monitoring land use/condition on the Sefton coast thus must be limited, although there may be more scope for it in obtaining environmental information on a wider geographical area. However, a number of microwave radar instruments have been developed that can penetrate cloud (and can operate at night). With a 25 m resolution, coastal images can be produced that reveal wave patterns and topographic detail that reflects sea-bed topography, which would be useful in coastal studies.

GEOGRAPHICAL INFORMATION SYSTEMS

At present Merseyside Information Services are evaluating three different GIS systems, and Sefton will obtain the system to be recommended.

GIS systems are often described as being 'raster' or 'vector' based, although a combination may be used in the most recent systems. In the raster technique the area is divided up into a matrix of picture elements (pixels) each of which is attributed with one or more values. The picture is built up from a set of horizontal parallel lines. In the totally different vector technique a cursor or light pen is drawn around parcels of land within the area, and these parcels of land are represented as points, lines or polygons.

Data are entered into the GIS system from various sources: source maps from different years, database information linked to grid references, data sets derived from manipulating existing data sets. The original data are incorporated into the GIS as a collection of data layers (or coverages), each layer containing data on one particular theme.

Fundamental questions need to be addressed at the beginning of any such exercise, such as who would use such a GIS, who would maintain it especially in the longer term, cost-effectiveness etc.

Data sets relating to communities already existed prior to the Sefton Coast NCC National Sand Dune Vegetation Survey, and where compatible with the classification system could be entered and utilised for analysis within specified areas. Descriptions of these can be found in the Survey.

Three research aspects in an as yet hypothetical coastal GIS system need consideration.

Research needs and opportunities:

i) What it would be useful for?

Assessing rate of change of coastal patterns - both physical and vegetational.

Determining impact of factors on rate of change.

ii) Which data sets might be loaded onto it?

Physical topography (sand dunes, sand banks, streams etc.) drift geology.

Parcels of land of communities, sub-communities and variants according to the National Vegetation Classification.

High and low water levels over time.

NNRs, SSSIs, LNRs etc.,ownership.

Built-up areas, etc.

iii) Constraints

Difficulty in reliably assessing the accuracy or errors of analysis using current GIS systems, particularly when multiple data layers are combined.

Digitising information without adding more error.

Staff training and staff time spent preparing, digitising, checking, editing and updating data.

Usefulness of GIS system will depend on quality of original data.

Finally, other areas of coast apart from the dune system must be considered for incorporation into any coastal database.

Jim Mackay

Joint Countryside Advisory Service
Bryant House
Liverpol Road North
Maghull L31 2PA

162

6/5/1/4.

Franks, P.
Sites 1 May

Gagen, P. (
Township in
Archaeologi
Liverpool.

Galliford, A
Ainsdale an
Naturalists'

SECTION 7

REFERENCES AND

GENERAL

APPENDICES

APPENDIX 1
GUIDE TO THE DATABASES

Joint Countryside Advisory Service

The Joint Countryside Advisory Service database is housed at Bryant House, Liverpool Road, Maghull. The computerised database gives access to publications, aerial photographs and maps of relevance to studies on the Sefton Coast. JCAS was set up in 1986 to serve the Boroughs of Sefton, Knowsley and St Helens following the abolition of Merseyside County Council. The database, therefore, contains many of the unpublished environmental studies commissioned by Merseyside County Council (1974-1986). Where known the JCAS database code is given after the references at the end of the volume. In general, material in the database is organised by subject. The database can be used by appointment only and assistance can be given to help with research topics. For more information telephone 051 934 4951.

The Sefton Coast Database

The Sefton Coast Database collates all known information on the physical processes affecting the Sefton Coast. The Guide to the Sefton Coast Database was compiled and is updated by the Coastal Engineering Group within the Department of Engineering and Surveying at Sefton Borough Council. Most of the source material is held within the Department of Engineering and Surveying, Balliol House, Bootle L20 3NJ.

Copies of the Guide to the Database may be inspected by prior arrangement at the Joint Countryside Advisory Service or Coast Management Scheme offices. The text and diagrams may be copied or quoted for academic purposes, provided acknowledgement is made of their source. If further information is needed after reference to the Guide enquiries should be addressed in writing to the Director of Engineering and Surveying.

North West Biological Field Data Bank

The North West Biological Field Data Bank is housed in Liverpool Museum. The Data Bank collates records on a site by site basis, and acts as a depository for information on the biological interest of known sites. Much of the material, in the form of notes and species lists, has been gathered by amateur naturalists. Voucher specimens for many records are held within the collections of Liverpool Museum.

The Data Bank is updated by the Museum and the records are to be computerised to facilitate access to the data. Enquiries should be addressed to The Department of Botany, National Museums and Galleries on Merseyside, Liverpool Museum, William Brown Street, Liverpool, Telephone 051 207 0001.

English Nature Archives

The English Nature files held at the Ainsdale National Nature Reserve contain detailed information on species and management at Ainsdale NNR (mainly covering the period 1960-1990), Cabin Hill NNR and other sites on the coast. Archive material is also held, including part of R. K. Gresswell's photographic collection and oblique aerial photography by J. K. St. Joseph. Information is also held at English Nature's Regional Headquarters at Blackwell, Cumbria. A list of material held by English Nature is available for inspection at the Reserve Office, Pinfold Lane, Ainsdale. General enquiries, however, should in the first instance be addressed to the JCAS or Coast Management Scheme offices.

Coast Management Scheme Offices, Formby

The Coast Management Officer, Education Officer and Coastal Ranger Service are based at the Formby Council Offices, Freshfield Road, Formby L37 6PQ. Students and researchers are welcome to visit the offices to make enquiries about sources of further information, suitability of sites for project work, or for a general introduction to the Sefton Coast. The data held includes information on dune sites owned or managed by Sefton Council, reports related to the Coast Management Scheme and a library of educational material. A limited stock of aerial photographs is also available for inspection. The Coast Management Scheme Offices are easily accessible and are centrally placed in relation to the dune coast. In the first instance enquiries should be made in writing or by telephone on 051 934 2960/2962.

Lancashire Record Office

Much of the historical archive material relating to the Sefton Coast is held in the Lancashire Record Office, Preston. All the material is available for inspection and includes maps, legal documents and books. The LRO also offers a consultation service. Enquiries should be made to the County Archivist, Lancashire Record Office, Bow Lane, Preston PR1 2RE.

APPENDIX 2
LIST OF CONTRIBUTORS

Dr David Atkinson
Department of Environmental and Evolutionary Biology
The University of Liverpool
PO Box 147
Liverpool L69 3BX

David Bateman
Flat 7
7 Gambia Terrace
Liverpool 18

Dr Trevor Beebee
School of Biology
University of Sussex
Falmer
Brighton BN1 8QG

Mick Bird
The Cottage
Hoghton Chambers
Hoghton Street
Southport PR9 0PA

Dr Derek Clarke
Institute of Irrigation Studies
Department of Civil Engineering
University of Southampton
Highfield
Southampton SO9 5NH

Dr Arnie Cooke
English Nature
Northminster House
Peterborough PE1 1UA

Dr Jonathan Denton
c/o T J C Beebee
School of Biology
University of Sussex
Falmer
Brighton BN1 9QG

Dr Pat Doody
Joint Nature Conservation Committee
Monkstone House
City Road
Peterborough PE1 1JY

Tom Eccles
59 Linkstor Road
Liverpool L25 6DH

Mike Edmondson
Widnes Sixth Form College
Cronton Lane
Widnes
Cheshire WA8 9WA

Sally Edmondson
Liverpool Institute of Higher Education
Environmental & Biological Studies
Stand Park Road
P.O. Box 6
Liverpool L16 9JD

Chris Felton
Zoology Department
Liverpool Museum
William Brown Street
Liverpool L3 8EN

Martyn Garbett
National Trust Office
Victoria Road
Formby L37 1LJ

Peter Gateley
21 Latham Avenue
Ormskirk
Lancashire L39 2EU

Dr Angus Gunn
Department of Botany
Liverpool Museum
William Brown Street
Liverpool L3 8EL

Richard Hall
English Nature
North West Regional Sub-Office
Blackrod Council Offices
Church Street
Blackrod
Bolton
Greater Manchester BL6 5ES

John Houston
Sefton Metropolitan Borough Council
Planning Department
Vermont House
375 Stanley Road
Bootle L20 3RY

Dr David Huddart
Department of Science and Outdoor Education
School of Education and Community Studies
I M Marsh Campus
John Moores University

Dr Mike Hull
Windcliffe
Alvanley Road
Helsby
Cheshire WA6 9PS

Dr Jim Innes
Department of Geography
Science Laboratories
University of Durham
South Road
Durham DH1 3LE

Peter James
Department of Geography
University of Liverpool
Roxby Building
PO Box 147
Liverpool L69 3BX

Ceri Jones
Sefton Metropolitan Borough Council
Planning Department
Vermont House
375 Stanley Road
Bootle L20 3RY

Peter Jones
Kenfig Dunes NNR
Ton-Kenfig
Pyle
Mid Glamorgan CF33 4PT

Steve Judd
Section of Entomology
Department of Zoology
Liverpool Museum
William Brown Street
Liverpool L3 8EL

Dr Jim MacKay
Joint Countryside Advisory Service
Bryant House
Liverpool Road North
Maghull L31 2PA

Adrian Neal
Postgraduate Research Institute for Sedimentology
University of Reading
Whiteknights
Reading RG6 2AB

Deborah Nissenbaum
Environmental Advisory Unit
Yorkshire House
Chapel Street
Liverpool L3 9AG

Dr Roy Pegg
Enterprise and Enrichment
14 Oxford Street
PO Box 147
The University
Liverpool L69 3BX

Dr Andy Plater
Department of Geography
University of Liverpool
Roxby Building
PO Box 147
Liverpool L69 3BX

Dr Kenneth Pye
Postgraduate Research Institute for Sedimentology
University of Reading
Whiteknights
Reading RG6 2AB

Paul Rooney
32 Ellaby Road
Rainhill
Prescot
Merseyside L35 4PP

David Simpson
English Nature
Ainsdale NNR
2 West End Lodge
Pinfold Lane
Ainsdale PR8 3QW

Robert Slatter
Science Department
Edge Hill College of Higher Education
Ormskirk
Lancashire L39 4QP

Tony Smith
Sefton Metropolitan Borough Council
Engineer and Surveyor's Department
Balliol House
Bootle

Dr Phil Smith
School of Natural Sciences
John Moores University
Byrom Street
Liverpool L3 3AF

Dr Peter Sturgess
Bristol Ecological Consultants
School of Biological Sciences
University of Bristol
Woodland Road
Bristol B58 1UG

Dr Mike Tooley
Department of Geography
University of Durham
Science Laboratories
South Road
Durham DH1 3LE

David Wheeler
English Nature
Ainsdale NNR
2 West End Lodge
Pinfold Lane
Ainsdale PR8 3QW

Ken Wood
37 Delph Common Road
Aughton
Nr Ormskirk L39 5DN

REFERENCES

Aitcheson, K. M. (1987). *A study of the factors determining the suitability of artificially constructed breeding sites for the natterjack toad* Bufo calamita *at the Ainsdale National Nature Reserve.* Unpublished thesis *ASD 6/5/3/2/2.*

Aldridge, A. C. (1971a). *Ainsdale Sand Dunes National Nature Reserve Bird Species List* Unpublished. *ASD.*

Aldridge, A. C. (1971b). *Ainsdale Sand Dunes National Nature Reserve, Comparison of Species Lists* 1968, 1969, 1971. Unpublished. *ASD.*

Aldridge, A. C. (1972a). *Ainsdale Sand Dunes National Nature Reserve Bird Species List* Unpublished. *ASD.*

Aldridge, A. C. (1972b). *Scirpus americanus,* Ainsdale Sand Dunes National Nature Reserve (two documents) *ASD 6/2/2.*

Aldridge, A. C. (1973a). *Ainsdale Sand Dunes National Nature Reserve, Mammals Recorded on the Reserve.* (Summary of a short paper read to the mammal society regional meeting, held at the University of Manchester, on Saturday 24 March 1973). *ASD 6/5/1/2.*

Aldridge, A. C. (1973b). *Ainsdale Sand Dunes National Nature Reserve. The Mapping of Mammal Observations. Report for the Period April to December 1972, inclusive.* Unpublished report. *ASD 6/5/1/3.*

Aldridge, A.C. (1974). *Ainsdale Sand Dunes National Nature Reserve. The Mapping of Mammal Observations. Report for 1973.* Unpublished report. *ASD 6/5/1/3.*

Aldridge, A. C. (1975a). *Ainsdale Sand Dunes National Nature Reserve Lepidoptera: Checklist, Moths* (Lepidoptera) *Recorded on the Reserve, Nov. 1975.* Unpublished list. *NWBFDB.*

Aldridge, A. C. (1975b). *Ainsdale National Nature Reserve Mycological Species List.* Unpublished report. *ASD NWBFDB.*

Aldridge, A. C. (1975c). *Ainsdale Sand Dunes National Nature Reserve. The Mapping of Mammal Observations. Report for 1974.* Unpublished report. *ASD 6/5/1/3.*

Aldridge, A. C. (1976a). *Ainsdale Sand Dunes National Nature Reserve, Bird Species List 1967 to 1975. ASD 6/5/2/2.*

Aldridge, A. C. (1976b). *Comments on the Effects of Fluctuations in the Rabbit Population on Dune Vegetation.* Unpublished. *ASD 6/5/1/2.*

Aldridge, A. C. (undated). *The Distribution and Autecology of the Tiger Beetle* Cicindela maritima *on the Ainsdale Sand Dunes National Nature Reserve.* Unpublished report. *ASD 6/6/1/5/7.*

Aldridge, A. C., Bruce, M. & Robinson, N. A. (1972). A survey of the sand lizard (*Lacerta agilis*) population in the Southport area 1972. Unpublished report to NCC. *ASD 6/5/3/3/2.*

Aldridge, A. C. & Musgrave, M. (undated). *Ainsdale Sand Dunes National Nature Reserve Bird Species List.* Unpublished. *ASD.*

Aldridge, A. C., Musgrave, M. & Twyman, M. (1973). *Amphibian Breeding Survey 1973. Ainsdale and Birkdale.* Unpublished NCC file note. *NWBFDB.*

Alexander, M., Ravault, F. & Munslow, R. (1988). *Improvements to Marram Planting.* NCC, Contract Surveys No. 30.

Allen, M. J. (1932). Recent changes in the sea-beach flora at Ainsdale, Lancashire. *North West Naturalist,* **7(2)**, 114-117.

Alt Drainage Act (1779). 19th GEO.III, Ch.339,1779.

Alvin, K. L. (1960). Observations on the lichen ecology of South Haven Peninsula, Studland Heath, Dorset. *Journal of Ecology,* **48**, 331-339.

Anon. (1920). Liverpool Botanical Society (1920) Report of Field Meeting. *Lancashire and Cheshire Naturalist,* **13**, 83-4.

Anon. (1948/49). Field meeting - Freshfield August 28th 1948. *Annual report and proceedings of the Lancashire and Cheshire Entomological Society,* **72**, 25.

Anon. (1950/51). Field meeting - Saturday 12th August at Formby, Lancashire. *Annual report and proceedings of the Lancashire and Cheshire Entomological Society,* **74**, 9-10.

Anon. (1953/54-1954/55). Field meetings 1953 - Saturday August 1st at Formby. *Annual report and proceedings of the Lancashire and Cheshire Entomological Society,* **77 & 78**, 13.

Anon. (1958/59-1960/61). Record of Lepidoptera captures at Formby Moss, 20th August 1960. *Annual report and proceedings of the Lancashire and Cheshire Entomological Society,* **82-84**, 39.

Anon. (1961/62-1963/64). Field meetings - Formby Moss, Lancs. 17th August 1963. *Annual report and proceedings of the Lancashire and Cheshire Entomological Society,* **85-87**, 58.

Anon. (1967/68-1969-70) Field meetings - Ainsdale, Lancs. 17th May 1969. *Annual report and proceedings of the Lancashire and Cheshire Entomological Society,* **91-93**, 52.

Anon. (1969a). *Bird and Mammal Study in Pinewoods 1968-1969.* Unpublished. *ASD.*

Anon. (1969b). *Bird Breeding Study (by habitats) 1969.* Unpublished. *ASD.*

Anon. (1970/71-1972/73) Field meetings - Formby, Lancs. 20th August 1972. *Annual report and proceedings of the Lancashire and Cheshire Entomological Society,* **94-96**, 55.

Anon. (1972a). *Large Mammal Observations, Stoat,* Mustela erminea, *and Weasel,* Mustela nivalis, *Ainsdale Sand Dunes National Nature Reserve. ASD 6/5/1/3.*

Anon. (1972b). *Large Mammal Observations, Brown Hare,* Lepus europeaus, *Ainsdale Sand Dunes National Nature Reserve. ASD 6/5/1/3.*

Anon. (1972c). *Large Mammal Observations, Hedgehog,* Erineus erineus, *Ainsdale Sand Dunes National Nature Reserve. ASD 6/5/1/3.*

Anon. (1972d). *Large Mammal Observations, Fox,* Vulpes vulpes, *28th March 1972 to 31st December 1972. Ainsdale Sand Dunes National Nature Reserve. ASD 6/5/1/3.*

Anon. (1972e). *Ainsdale Sand Dunes National Nature Reserve, February 1972. Report on Small Mammal Surveys Conducted on the Reserve to Date.* Unpublished. *ASD 6/5/1/4.*

Anon. (1973/74-1976/77a) Field meetings - Formby Point, Merseyside. 12th May 1973. *Annual report and proceedings of the Lancashire and Cheshire Entomological Society,* **97-100,** 22.

Anon. (1973/74-1976/77b) Field meetings - Formby Point, Merseyside. 17th May 1975. *Annual report and proceedings of the Lancashire and Cheshire Entomological Society* **97-100,** 40.

Anon. (1973/74-1976/77c) Field meetings - Formby Point, Merseyside. 22nd May 1976. *Annual report and proceedings of the Lancashire and Cheshire Entomological Society,* **97-100,** 47.

Anon. (1975a). *Ornithological Report 1968-1975.* Unpublished. *ASD.*

Anon. (1975b). *Ainsdale Sand Dunes National Nature Reserve, Bird Species List 1967-1975.* Unpublished. *ASD.*

Anon. (1975c). *Ainsdale Sand Dunes National Nature Reserve, Map of Rabbit Myxomatosis Sightings 1975.* Unpublished. *ASD 6/5/1/3.*

Anon. (1976). *Ainsdale Sand Dunes National Nature Reserve, Map of Rabbit Myxomatosis Sightings 1976.* Unpublished. *ASD 6/5/1/3.*

Anon. (1977). *Winter Atlas Records 1976-1977.* Unpublished. *ASD.*

Anon. (1979a). *Winter Bird Census Records 1978-1979.* Unpublished. *ASD.*

Anon. (1979b). *Common Bird Census Records April-June 1979.* Unpublished. *ASD.*

Anon. (1981-82). *Ainsdale Sand Dunes National Nature Reserve. Common Bird Census* (Records for 1981 and 1982). Unpublished. *ASD.*

Anon. (1985). *Natterjack Toads at Hightown 1985.* Unpublished. *ASD 6/5/3/2/2.*

Anon. (1986/87). Field meetings - Altcar, Merseyside SD20, Friday 14th August 1986. *Annual report and proceedings of the Lancashire and Cheshire Entomological Society,* **110,** 45-46.

Anon. (1988/89). Field meetings - Formby Point, Merseyside SD20, 13th May 1989. *Annual report and proceedings of the Lancashire and Cheshire Entomological Society,* **112,** 124-125.

Anon. (1989). *Ainsdale Sand Dunes National Nature Reserve. New Atlas Records, 1989.* Unpublished. *ASD.*

Anon. (1990). *Bats at Cabin Hill National Nature Reserve.* Unpublished note. *CH 6/5/1.*

Anon. (post-1970). *Ainsdale Sand Dunes National Nature Reserve, Lepidoptera: Butterflies.* Species recorded by R. N. Boston (Warden) 1966-70. Unpublished. *ASD 6/6/1/5/4.*

Anon. (post-1983). *Butterflies at Ainsdale Sand Dunes National Nature Reserve.* Unpublished. *ASD 6/6/1/5/4.*

Arak, A. (1982). *Mate Searching Behaviour of the Natterjack Toad.* Unpublished Ph.D. thesis, University of Cambridge. *ASD 6/5/3/2/2.*

Arak, A. (1988a). Female mate selection in the natterjack toad: active choice or passive attraction? *Behavioural Ecology and Sociobiology,* **22,** 317-327.

Arak, A. (1988b). Callers and satellites in the natterjack toad: evolutionary stable decision rules. *Animal Behaviour,* **36,** 416-432.

Arnold, H. R. ed. (1973). *Provisional Atlas of the Amphibians and Reptiles of the British Isles.* Biological Records Centre, Monks Wood Experimental Station, Huntingdon.

Ash, H. J. & Clitherow, J. (1983). *Merseyside Natural History Survey. Botany Section.* Unpublished Report on work undertaken 1982-1983. Merseyside County Museums *JCAS 75 Dc 25, NWBFDB.*

Ashton, W. (1909). *The Battle of Land and Sea on the Lancashire, Cheshire and North Wales Coast and the Origin of the Lancashire Sandhills,* W. Ashton and Sons, Southport.

Ashton, W. (1920). *The Evolution of a Coastline.* E. Stanford, London.

Askew, R. R. (1969). *Ainsdale National Nature Reserve. Gall Wasps* (Cynipidae) *and their parasites* (Chalcidoidea). Unpublished species list. *E N, Blackwell.*

Askew, R.R. (1981). Pompiloidea (Hymenoptera Aculeata) in Lancashire and Cheshire. *Lancashire and Cheshire Fauna Society,* **78,** 5-8.

Askew, R. R. (1988). *The Dragonflies of Europe.* Harley Books,

Association of Science Education and the Nature Conservancy Council. (1990). Opening Doors for Science: some aspects of environmental education and science in the National Curriculum 5-16, ASE/NCC.

Atkinson, D. (1985). *A Comparative Study of Life Histories in the Grasshoppers,* Chorthippus brunneus *and* Myrmeleotettix maculatus *in a Sand Dunes Habitat.* Unpublished Ph.D. thesis, University of Liverpool.

Atkinson, D. (1988). The effects of afforestation on a sand dune grassland. *British Ecological Society Bulletin,* **29:2,** 99-101.

Atkinson, D. (1990). *Restoration Techniques following Deforestation of Dunes: Interim Report for the NCC, January 1990.* [Contract HF3-03-432(28)]. Unpublished report. Dept. of Environmental and Evolutionary Biology, University of Liverpool.

Atkinson, D. & Begon, M. (1987a). Reproductive variation and adult size in two co-occurring grasshopper species. *Ecological Entomology,* **12,** 119-127.

Atkinson, D. & Begon, M. (1987b). Ecological correlates and heritability of reproductive variation in two co-occurring grasshopper species. *Ecological Entomology,* **12,** 129-138.

Atkinson, D. & Begon, M. (1988a). Adult size variation and its correlates in two co-occurring species of sand-dune grasshoppers. *Journal of Animal Ecology,* **57,** 185-200.

Atkinson, D. & Begon, M. (1988b). Changes in grasshopper distribution and abundance at sites in the north Merseyside sand dunes. *The Naturalist,* **113,** 3-19.

Atkinson, D. & Sturgess, P. W. (1991). Restoration of sand-dune communities following deforestation. *Perturbation and recovery of terrestrial and aquatic ecosystems.* (Ed. by O. Ravera). Ellis Horwood, London.

Aughton, P. (1988). *North Meols and Southport, a History.* Carnegie Press, Preston.

Balasooriya, I. & Parkinson, D. (1967). Studies on fungi in a pine-wood soil II. Substrate relationships of fungi in the mineral horizons of the soil. *Revue d'Ecologie et du Biologie du Sol*, **4**, 639-643.

Banks, B. & Beebee, T. J. C. (1987a). Factors influencing breeding site choice by the pioneering amphibian *Bufo calamita*. *Journal of Holarctic Ecology*, **10**, 14-21.

Banks, B. & Beebee, T. J. C. (1987b). Spawn predation and larval growth inhibition as mechanisms for niche separation in anurans. *Oecologica*, **72**, 569-573.

Banks, B. & Beebee, T. J. C. (1988). Reproductive success of natterjack toads *Bufo calamita* in two contrasting habitats. *Journal of Animal Ecology*, **57**, 475-492.

Barron, J. (1938). *A History of the Ribble Navigation from Preston to the Sea*, Preston Corporation and Guardian Press, Fishergate.

Barton, J. (1981). *The taxonomy of* Salix repens *agg. and related ecological aspects at Ainsdale Sand Dunes National Nature Reserve.* Unpublished B.Sc. dissertation, University of Liverpool.

Bateman, D. (1990). *The Formby Landscape: Its Geological, Ecological and Historical Basis.* Unpublished thesis, Diploma in Landscape Interpretation, University of Liverpool. *JCAS database.*

Baxby, P. (1967). *The microbial decomposition of chitin in a pinewood soil.* Unpublished Ph.D. thesis, University of Liverpool.

Beach Protection Authority, (1982). Report No D. 02. 8. Mulch Trial. Dune Management Research Papers, Beach Protection Authority, Brisbane, Australia.

Beard, G. R., Thompson, T. R. E. & Lea, J. W. (1987). *Soils of the Liverpool District.* Memoirs of the Soil Survey of England and Wales.

Beck, J. (1953). *Church brief for the inundation of the Lancashire coast in 1720.* Lancashire and Cheshire Historical Society.

Beebee, T. J. C. (1978a). Planners Rule, OK ? Commerce versus Conservation in the Lancashire Sand Dunes. *Wildlife*, April 1978, pp 174-179.

Beebee, T. J. C. (1978b). An attempt to explain the distributions of the rare herpetiles *Bufo calamita, Lacerta agilis* and *Coronella austriaca* in Britain. *British Journal of Herpetology*, **5**, 763-770.

Beebee, T. J. C. (1979). Historical aspects of British herpetofauna distribution. Letters to the editor, *British Journal of Herpetology*, **6**, 105.

Beebee, T.J.C. (1983). *The Natterjack Toad.* Oxford University Press, Oxford.

Beebee, T. J. C. (1985). *An analysis of the successes and failures of artificial ponds created for natterjack toads.* Unpublished report *ASD 6/5/3/2/2*

Beebee, T. J. C. (1989). Natterjack Toad. Site Register. Unpublished University of Sussex report to NCC *ASD 6/5/3/2/2*

Beebee, T. J. C. (1992). Trying to save the natterjack toad - a case study in amphibian conservation. *British Wildlife*, **3**, 137-145.

Beebee, T. J. C. & Denton, J. (1988-89). *The terrestrial ecology of the natterjack toad.* 1st yr. report to NCC, Unpublished. *ASD 6/5/3/2/2.*

Beebee, T. J. C. & Denton, J. (1989-90). *The terrestrial ecology of the natterjack toad.* 2nd yr. report to NCC, Unpublished. *ASD 6/5/3/2/2.*

Beebee, T. J. C. & Denton, J. (1990-91). *The terrestrial ecology of the natterjack toad.* 3rd yr. report to NCC, Unpublished. *ASD 6/5/3/2/2.*

Belderson, R. H. & Stride, A. H. (1969). Tidal currents and sand wave profiles in the north-eastern Irish Sea. *Nature*, **222**, 74-75.

Bell, M. N., Barber, P. C. & Smith, D. G. E. (1975). The Wallasey embankment. *Proceedings of the Institution of Civil Engineers*, **58**, 569-590.

Bennett, C. (1981). *Summary of Small Mammal Study in Ainsdale National Nature Reserve.* From unpublished thesis, Liverpool Polytechnic. *ASD 6/5/1/4.*

Berg, B. & Staaf, H. (1981). Leaching, accumulation and release of nitrogen in decomposing forest litter. *Terrestrial Nitrogen Cycles* (Ed. by F. E. Clarke & T. Rosswall), Ecology Bulletin, **33**, 163-178.

Best, R. (Ed.) (1972). *Out of sight, out of mind, Report of a working party on sludge disposal in Liverpool Bay,* HMSO, London, 2 Volumes.

Best, R., Ainsworth, G., Wood, P. C. & James, J. E. (1973). Effects of sewage sludge on the marine environment, a case study in Liverpool Bay. *Proceedings of the Institution of Civil Engineers*, **55**, 43-66; 755-765.

Bevercombe, A. M. (1969). *An Investigation of the Cladocera and Copepoda of Massam's Slack.* Unpublished M.Sc. thesis, University of Liverpool.

Bevercombe, A. M., Cox, N., Thomas, M. P., & Young, J. O. (1973). Studies of the invertebrate fauna of a wet slack in a sand dune system. *Archiv für Hydrobiologie*, **71**, 487-516.

BHS Conservation Committee (1973). Herpetological transloca-tions in Britain a policy. *British Journal of Herpetology*, **6**, 314-316.

BHS Conservation Committee (1976). Conversation Proposals. Unpublished report. *ASD 6/5/3/2/2*

BHS Conservation Committee (1978). *Conservation of the Merseyside dune coast, with special reference to the herpetofauna.* Unpublished report. *ASD 6/5/3/2/2*

BHS Conservation Committee. (undated). Correspondence with NCC concerning lizard management and status.

BHS/NC/LNT. (1973). *Natterjack toads, sand lizards - S. W Lancs.* Meeting between BHS conservation committee, Nature Conservancy and Lancashire Naturalists' Trust 20/5/73. Unpublished report. *NWBFDB.*

Binney, E. W. & Talbot, J. H. (1843). *On the Petroleum found in the Downholland Moss, near Ormskirk,* Paper read at the 5th annual general meeting of the Manchester Geological Society, 6th October, 1843.

Bird, M. (1986). *Odonata at Ainsdale National Nature Reserve, 1986.* Unpublished. *ASD.*

Bird, M. (1987). *Odonata at Ainsdale National Nature Reserve, 1987.* Unpublished. *ASD.*

Birse, E. L. & Gimingham, C. H. (1955). Changes in the structure of Bryophytic communities with the progress of succession on sand-dunes. *Transactions of the British Bryological Society*, **2(4)**, 523-531.

Birse, E. M., Landsberg, S. Y. & Gimingham, C. H. (1957). The effects of burial by sand on dune mosses. *Transactions of the British Bryological Society, 3,* 285-301.

Blair, J. (1984). The Anglo-Saxon period. *The Oxford illustrated history of Britain* (ed. K. O. Morgan) Oxford University Press, Oxford. Pp 52-103.

Blanchard, B. (1952). *An ecological survey of the sand dune system of the south west Lancashire coast, with special reference to an associated marsh flora.* Unpublished Ph.D. Thesis, University of Liverpool.

Blundell, N. (1702 - 1711). The Great Diurnal of Nicholas Blundell of Little Crosby, Lancashire. *The Record Society of Lancashire and Cheshire,* 110.

Boerner, R. E. & Forman, R. T. T. (1975). Salt spray and coastal dune mosses. *Bryologist, 78,* 57-63.

Boorman, L. A. (1977). Sand-dunes. *The Coastline* (Ed. by R.S.K. Barnes), pp. 161-197. John Wiley and Sons, Chichester.

Boorman, L. A. (1986). *A survey of sand dunes in relation to grazing interim report.* NCC Research Contract HF3/03/296. CSD report No. 632.

Boorman, L. A. (1989a). The Grazing of British Sand Dune Vegetation. *Proceedings of the Royal Society of Edinburgh, 96B,* 75-88.

Boorman, L. A. (1989b). The Influence of Grazing on British Sand Dunes. *Perspectives in Coastal Dune Management,* (Ed. by F. van der Meulen, P. D. Jungerius & J. H. Visser.) Pp 121-124.

Boorman, L. A. & Fuller, R. M. (1982). Effects of added nutrients on dune swards grazed by rabbits. *Journal of Ecology, 70,* 345-56.

Boston, R. N. (1968a). *Bird Breeding Census.* Unpublished Report. *ASD.*

Boston, R. N. (1968b). *Warden's Natural History Report 1968.* Unpublished. *ASD.*

Boston, R. N. (1969a). *Ainsdale Sand Dunes National Nature Reserve, Species List 1969.* Unpublished. *ASD.*

Boston, R. N. (1969b). *Bird Population Studies.* Unpublished Report. *ASD.*

Boston, R. N. (1970). *Ainsdale Sand Dunes National Nature Reserve sand lizard study, April-October 1970.* Unpublished NCC report *ASD 6/5/3/3/2.*

Boston, R. N. (1970a). *Ainsdale Sand Dunes National Nature Reserve, Bird Breeding Study (by habitats)* Unpublished. *ASD.*

Boston, R. N. (1970b). *Ainsdale National Nature Reserve Lepidoptera - Butterflies.* Unpublished species list. *E. N., Blackwell.*

Boston, R. N. (1970c). *Ainsdale National Nature Reserve Lepidoptera - Moths.* Unpublished species list. *E. N., Blackwell.*

Boston, R. N. (1970d). *Breeding Birds.* Unpublished Report. *ASD.*

Boston, R. N. (1970e). *Sand lizard study, Ainsdale Sand Dunes National Nature Reserve.* Unpublished files. *ASD.*

Bradley, L. (1989). *Environmental Education: towards a statement of entitlement 5-16,* Unpublished interim document. Sefton Local Education Authority.

Bradley, L. (1990). Environmental Education Database for Sefton, Sefton Local Education Authority.

Brewster, K. W. (1981). Letter re: Ainsdale birds. Unpublished. *ASD.*

Brindle, A. (1962). *Freshfield Entomological Survey.* Unpublished report. *ASD.*

BTCV (1979). *Coastlands* BTCV, Wallingford, Oxford.

BTCV (1986). *Sand Dunes, A Practical Handbook* BTCV, Wallingford, Oxford.

Britten, H. (1930). Hemiptera-Heteroptera. *A Checklist of the Fauna of Lancashire & Cheshire, 1,* 66-70.

Broderick, H. (undated). Copy of Notebook of Harold Broderick, F.G.S., on Martin Mere. Sefton Coast Data Base.

Bruce, M. (1972). *A Survey of the sand lizard population in the Southport Area 1972.* Unpublished report to NCC. *ASD.*

Bruce, M. (1973). *A survey of the sand lizard* (Lacerta agilis*) population in the Southport area 1973.* Unpublished report to NCC. *ASD 6/5/3/3/2.*

Brummage, M. K. (1990). Merseyside Environmental Education Review Schools Questionnaire 1985, *JCAS.*

Bullock, D. J. & Kinnear, P. K. (1988). The use of goats to control scrub in Tentsmuir Point National Nature Reserve, Fife: a Pilot Study. *Proceedings of the Botanical Society of Edinburgh, 45,* 131-139.

Bunn, D. S. (1968). *Grasshoppers and Groundhopper of the Reserve* [Ainsdale Sand Dunes]. Unpublished Report *E N, Blackwell.*

Burrows, H. L., Fielding, E. H., & Goodwin, D. (1966). *Entomological Survey (Lepidoptera, Diptera, Coleoptera).* Manchester Entomological Society. Unpublished report referring to Freshfield area. *E N, Blackwell.*

Butler, L. & Given-Wilson, C. (1979). *Medieval monasteries of Great Britain.* Michael Joseph, London.

Byerley, I. (1856). *Fauna of Liverpool.*

Calder, I. R. & Newson, D. (1979). Land use and upland water resources in Great Britain - a strategic look. *Water Research Bulletin, 15(6),* 1628-1639.

Campbell, B. (1954). Ornithological surveys of nature reserves. *Bird Study, 1(2),.*

Campbell, B. (1955). Ornithological surveys of nature reserves. *Bird Study 2(2)* 84-86.

Carty, P. (1981). *The value of sea buckthorn to wintering and breeding birds in the north Merseyside sand dunes.* Unpublished thesis. Liverpool Polytechnic.

Carty, P. (1985). *Ainsdale Sand Dunes National Nature Reserve - Odonata Report 1984.* Unpublished. *ASD.*

Carty, P. (1986a). *Butterfly Records, Cabin Hill National Nature Reserve* Unpublished list *ASD CH 6/6/1/5.*

Carty, P. (1986b). *Cabin Hill National Nature Reserve.* Unpublished list of moths. *ASD CH.*

Carty, P. (1986c). *Orchis morio* on Altcar Rifle Range. Ainsdale National Nature Reserve Files: CH 6/12/1.

Cashin, J. A. (1949). Engineering works for the improvement of the estuary of the Mersey. *Journal of the Institution of Civil Engineers,* **32,** 296-355.

Centre for Environmental Interpretation (1989). Sefton Coast Management Scheme Interpretive Plan: notes to accompany the draft interpretive plan, resulting from discussion with J. Houston and A. Birch, 17th November 1988, 5pp.

Chaster, G. W. & Burgess-Sopp, E. J. (1903). *Coleoptera of the Southport District.* (Reprinted from British Association Handbook 1903). Southport l903.

Chatwin, S. L. A. (1986). *Cabin Hill and Altcar Range, Freshwater Invertebrate Survey.* Unpublished. *NWBFDB, file SD/20/85 Cabin Hill.*

Cherrill, A. J. (1987). *The Development and Survival of the Eggs and Early Instars of the Grasshopper* Chorthippus brunneus (*Thunberg*) in North West England. Unpublished Ph.D. thesis. University of Liverpool.

Cherrill, A. J. & Begon, M. (1989a). Predation of grasshoppers by spiders in sand dune grasslands. *Entomologia experimentalis et applicata,* **50,** 225-231.

Cherrill, A. J. & Begon, M. (1989b). Timing of life cycles in a seasonal environment: the temperature-dependence of embryogenesis and diapause in a grasshopper (*Chorthipus brunneus* Thunberg). *Oecologia,* **78,** 237-241.

Cherrill, A. J. & Begon, M. (1991). Oviposition date and pattern of embryogenesis in the grasshopper *Chorthippus brunneus* (Orthoptera, Acrididae). *Holarctic Ecology,* **14,** 225-233.

Clapham, A. R., Tutin, T. G. & Moore, D M. (1987). *Flora of the British Isles.* Third Edition, Cambridge University Press, Cambridge.

Clarke, D. (1980). *The groundwater balance of a coastal sand dune system: a study of the water table conditions in Ainsdale Sand Dunes National Nature Reserve, Merseyside.* Unpublished. Ph.D. thesis, University of Liverpool.

Clements, D. & Lutley, W. (1987). *National Trust Biological Survey : Formby.* Report of the N.T. Biological Team. Unpublished report. The National Trust, Cirencester. *JCAS database, NWBFDB*

Coates, U. A. (1966). *Lancashire Coastal Survey, Formby Area Report.* Lancashire County Council 36. pp. *JCAS database. O55 Db 014.*

Coleman, A. & Maggs, K. R. A. (1968). Land Use Survey Handbook. An Explanation of the Second Land Utilisation Survey of Britain on the Scale of 1:25,000. JCAS database.

Cook, A. L. M. (1989). *Altcar - The Story of a Rifle Range.* Territorial, Auxiliary and Volunteer Reserve Association. JCAS database. 105 Gb 030.

Cook, M. A. (1976). *The Natterjack Toad* Bufo calamita *in North Merseyside 1976.* Unpublished report, Liverpool Polytechnic. *ASD 6/5/3/2/2.*

Cooke, A. S. (1980). *Report on Sand Lizard Survey of Birkdale Frontal Dunes.* Unpublished report, Chief Scientists' Directorate, NCC.

Cooke, A. S. (1981). Merseyside sand lizards. Analysis of habitat forms 1981. Unpublished NCC report *ASD 6/5/3/3/2.*

Cooke, A. S. (1982). Merseyside sand lizards. Analysis of habitat forms 1982. Unpublished NCC report *ASD 6/5/3/3/2.*

Cooke, A. S. (1986a). *The Use of Herbicides on Nature Reserves.* Focus on nature conservation No 14, NCC.

Cooke, A. S. (1986b). Merseyside sand lizards. Quadrat work, further Analysis 1986. Unpublished NCC report *ASD 6/5/3/3/2.*

Cooke, A. S. (1986c). Merseyside sand lizards. A summary 1986. Unpublished NCC report *ASD 6/5/3/3/2.*

Cooke, A. S. (1986d). Cabin Hill, release site, selected quadrats 1986. Unpublished NCC report *ASD 6/5/3/3/2.*

Cooke, A. S. (1987a). Merseyside sand lizards. Quadrat work. Repeat 1987 quadrat analysis and Ainsdale Frontals August. Unpublished NCC report *ASD 6/5/3/3/2.*

Cooke, A. S. (1987b). Merseyside sand lizard habitat 11-13 May. Unpublished NCC report *ASD 6/5/3/3/2.*

Cooke, A. S. (1987c). *Merseyside Sand Lizards, August 1987.* File note, NCC.

Cooke, A. S. (1988). Merseyside sand lizard quadrats, May. Unpublished NCC report *ASD 6/5/3/3/2.*

Cooke, A. S. (1989a). *Sand Lizard Conservation Strategy.* Unpublished note to file. NCC.

Cooke, A. S. (1989b). *A Summary of sightings information 1980-88.* Unpublished NCC report. *ASD 6/5/3/3/2.*

Cooke, A. S. (1991). *The habitat of sand lizards* Lacerta agilis *at Merseyside.* Research Survey No 41. NCC.

Cope, F. W. (1939). Oil occurrences in south-west Lancashire (with a biological report by K. B. Blackburn). *Bulletin of the Geological Survey of Great Britain, 2,* 18-25.

Corbett, K. F. (1974). Field survey to determine the status of the sand lizard (*Lacerta agilis*) in S. W Lancashire - Spring 1974. Unpublished NCC report *ASD 6/5/3/3/2.*

Corbett, K. F. (1985). The Merseyside sand lizard - changing status 1985. Unpublished report *ASD 6/5/3/3/2.*

Corbett, K. F. (1987). *Hesketh Golf Course Sand Lizard Conservation Proposals, Spring 1987,* Letter to file held with English Nature.

Corbett, K. F. (1988a). The distribution and status of the sand lizard, (*Lacerta agilis*) in Britain. *Mertensiella* **1,** 92-100.

Corbett, K. F. (1988b). Conservation strategy for the sand lizard, (*Lacerta agilis)* in Britain. *Mertensiella,* **1,** 101-l09.

Corbett, K. F. & Beebee, T. J. C. (1975). The disappearing natterjack. *Oryx,* **13,** 47-49.

Corbett, K. F. & Tamarind, D. L. (1979). Conservation of the sand lizard (*Lacerta agilis*) by habitat management. *British Journal of Herpetology,* **5,** 799-823.

Cotton, J. (1916/1917). The president's address. *Annual report and proceedings of the Lancashire and Cheshire Entomological Society,* **40 & 41,** 18-23.

Countryside Commission for Scotland (1984). Beach Recreation Management. Information Sheet Plants. 5. 1. 2.

Cox, N. (1970). *An Investigation of the Zoobenthic Fauna of Massam's Slack.* Unpublished M. Sc. thesis, University of Liverpool.

Cox, T. M. (1991). A Plan for Sefton. Sefton Metropolitan Borough Unitary Development Plan. Draft for Deposit, October 1991. Sefton Council.

Crawford, R. M. M. & Wishart, D. (1966). A multivariate analysis of the development of dune slack vegetation in relation to coastal accretion at Tentsmuir, Fife. *Journal of Ecology*, **54**, 729-743.

Cross, S. (1987). *Birds of Cabin Hill. 1981-1987*. Unpublished. *ASD*.

Cross, S. (1989). *The Insects of Altcar Rifle Range Estate, 1st Report*. Unpublished report *NWBFDB*.

Cunliffe-Shaw, R. (1965). *The Royal Forest of Lancashire*. Guardian Press, Preston.

Danbury, P. J. (1987). Grazing on sand dunes: a study of creeping willow *Salix repens* at Cabin Hill National Nature Reserve, Formby. Unpublished undergraduate thesis, Oxford Polytechnic. *Held at Ainsdale CH 6/2/1.*

Daniels, J. L. & Knights, P. J. (1985). Larkhill Lane Dune Heath Management. Unpublished letter; National Trust Field Office, Formby.

Darbyshire, M. (1958). Waves in the Irish Sea. *Dock and Harbour Authority*, **39**, 245-248.

Davies, F. L. (1967). *A synecological study of actinomycetes in a pine forest soil*. Unpublished. Ph. D. thesis, University of Liverpool, 167pp.

Davies, F. L. & Williams, S. T. (1970). Studies in the ecology of actinomycetes in soil I: The occurrence and distribution of actino-mycetes in a pine forest soil. *Soil Biology and Biochemistry*, **2**, 227-238.

Davies, N. B. & Watmough, B. R. (1966). *North Alder Grove. Account of the Population of Bird Life from 1964-66*. Unpublished Report. *E N, Blackwell*.

Davis, C. A. (1981). *Natterjack Toad Report, Cabin Hill and Altcar Rifle Range*. Unpublished report. *ASD 6/5/3/2//2.*

Davis, C. A. (1985). *The Population Dynamics of the Natterjack Toad* (Bufo calamita) *in the North Merseyside Sand-dune System*. Unpublished Ph.D. thesis, Liverpool Polytechnic. *ASD 6/5/3/2/2.*

Daws, J. (1990). *Woodlice of Lancashire and Cheshire*. Unpublished list of records. *NWBFDB*.

Dent, S. (1986). Merseyside sand lizard survey Unpublished NCC report *ASD 6/5/3/3/2.*

Denton, J. (1990). *Cabin Hill National Nature Reserve. Aquatic Coleoptera Recorded by J. Denton B. B. A. C.* Unpublished list. *NWBFDB*.

Department of Education and Science and the Welsh Office. (1989). Science in the National Curriculum, HMSO, London.

Department of Education and Science and the Welsh Office. (1991). Geography in the National Curriculum, HMSO, London.

Department of Education and Science. (1985a). GCSE, The National Criteria: Geography, HMSO, London.

Department of Education and Science. (1985b). GCSE, The National Criteria: Science, HMSO, London.

Department of Education and Science. (1988). Draft Circular on Charges for School Activities, HMSO, London.

Department of Education and Science. (1989). Environmental Education from 5-16, Curriculum Matters, HMSO, London.

Department of the Environment (1991). *The Potential Effects of Climate Change in the United Kingdom*, United Kingdom Climate Change Impacts Review Group, First Report, HMSO, London.

Derbyshire, R. J., Frost, S. & Mincher, L. J. (1985). *Environmental Awareness on the Sefton coast: a feasibility study*. Report by the University of Salford Environmental Institute, commis-sioned by the NCC, 83pp.

Doody, J. P. (1985a). *Focus on Nature No. 13. Sand Dunes and their Management*. NCC, Peterborough.

Doody, J. P. (1985b). The conservation of Sand Dunes in Great Britain - A review. *Focus on Nature Conservation No. 13. Sand Dunes and their Management*. (Ed. by J. P. Doody), pp. 43-50. NCC, Peterborough.

Doody, J. P. (1985c). A note of grazing on coastal habitats. CSD Note 38. Unpublished report NCC.

Doody, J. P. (1989). Management for nature conservation. *Proceedings of the Royal Society of Edinburgh*, **96**B, 247-265.

Doody, J. P. (1991). *Sand Dune Inventory of Europe*. Joint Nature Conservation Committee, UK.

Doornkamp, J. C. (Ed.) (1990). *The Greenhouse Effect and Rising Sea Levels in the U. K.* M1 Press. 161pp.

Draper, L. (1966). The analysis and presentation of wave data - a plea for uniformity. *Proceedings of the 10th Conference on Coastal Engineering, Tokyo*, **Volume 1**, 1-11.

Draper, L. & Blakey, A. (1969). Waves at the Mersey Bar light ves-sel. *N. I. O. Internal Report* **A37**, 1-4.

Duckels, A. S. (1973a). Ringing at the Alt Estuary. *S. W. Lancashire Ringing Group Annual Report*.

Duckels, A. S. (1973b). Breeding birds of the Alt Estuary. *S. W. Lancashire Ringing Group Annual Report*.

Duckels, A. S. (1974). *Breeding Birds of the Alt Estuary and Hightown Sand Dunes 1955-73*. Unpublished. *NWBFDB*.

Duckels, A. S. (1978). Information from ringing Stonechats & Whinchats in S. W. Lancashire. *S. W. Lancashire Ringing Group Annual Report*.

Duckels, A. S. (1989). Results from ringing Siskins. *S. W. Lancashire Ringing Group Annual Report*.

During, H. J. (1973). Some bryological aspects of pioneer vegetation in moist dune valleys in Denmark, the Netherland and France. *Linbergia*, **2**, 99-104.

Eccles, T. M. (1978). *A Survey of the Coleoptera of Ainsdale National Nature Reserve* Unpublished illustrated account. *ASD*.

Eccles, T. M. (1990). *A Survey of the Coleoptera of Cabin Hill National Nature Reserve* Unpublished report. *ASD*.

Economic and Social Council. Statistical Commission and Economic Commission for Europe. (1989). ECE Standard Statistical Classification of Land Use. CES/637, 7 April 1989.

Edmondson, J. R., Gunn, A. S. & Penney, D. (1984). Vegetation map of Ainsdale Sand Dunes N. N. R. . Report. Merseyside County Council, Merseyside County Museums, Botany Dept. *NWBFDB*.

Edmondson, S.E. (1976). *Hydrological Conditions on the Sand Dunes of the Merseyside Coast.* Environmental Rehabilitation Unit, Liverpool University. JCAS database, 50 Da 10.

Edmondson, S.E. (1987). *The Effect of Rabbit Grazing on Dune Slack Vegetation at Ainsdale Sand Dunes National Nature Reserve, Merseyside U.K.* Unpublished report, Liverpool Institute of Higher Education.

Edmondson, S. E. (1991). *Temporal and spatial variation in dune slack vegetation at Ainsdale, Merseyside.* Unpublished M.Sc thesis. University of Liverpool.

Edmondson, S. E., Gateley, P. S. & Nissenbaum, D. A. (1988/9). National Sand Dune Vegetation Survey: the Sefton Coast. *N.C.C. Report* No 917. JCAS database. 075 Da 116/118/120.

Edmund Kirby & Sons. (1974). *Formby Coastal Area Report.* Unpublished.

Edwards, K. & Hierons, K. (1984). Serial Pollen Grains in Pre-Elm decline deposits; implications for the earliest agriculture in Britain and Ireland. *Journal of Archaeological Science,* **11,** 71-80.

Ellis, J. W. (1889). *The Coleopterous Fauna of the Liverpool District* Liverpool 1889.

Ellis, J. W. (revised by Mansbridge, W. (1940)). *The Lepidopterous Fauna of Lancashire and Cheshire.* Lancashire and Cheshire Entomological Society.

Erdtman, G. (1928). Studies on the post-arctic history of the forests of North-west Europe. I. Investigations in the British Isles. *Geologiska Foreningens i Stockholm Forhandlingar,* **50** (2:373), 123-192.

Evans, C. (1980). *Dune slack systems. A study of the morphology and chemistry of slack soils in Ainsdale N. N. R.* Unpublished. B. Sc. thesis, University of Liverpool.

Evans, W. B. & Arthurton, R. S. (1973). North-west England. *A Correlation of Quaternary Deposits in the British Isles* (Ed. by G. F. Mitchell et al), Geological Society of London,

Fairhurst, C. (1977). Hightown saltmarsh *Spartina anglica* report. (quoted in Tuscon, 1989).

Fairhurst, C. P. (1976). *Assessment of Day Visitor Use in the Sefton Dune System at Formby Point August 1975.* Report to Merseyside County Council.

Falk, S. (1991). *A Review of the Scarce and Threatened Bees, Wasps and Ants of Great Britain. Research and Survey in Nature Conservation No. 35.* Nature Conservancy Council, Peterborough.

Fallon, M. (1991). Found not guilty as charged, Times Educational Supplement, 15th March.

Fearon, P. &. Duckels, A. S. (1966). *Causes of the decrease of the Nightjar at Freshfield.* Unpublished Report. *E.N. Blackwell.*

Felton, C. (1966). Check list of birds and their ecology on the S. W. Lancashire Dunes & Shore. *North Western Bird Report (1963-66).* pp. 54-6. Merseyside Naturalists' Association.

Felton, C. (1991). *Some Invertebrate Records from the Sefton Dunes.* Unpublished list *NWBFDB.*

Felton, C. & Jones, K. (1982). *Freshfield: Massam's Slack and Formby Golf Course. List of invertebrate species collected. 6 July 1982.* Unpublished report. *NWBFDB 34/21.*

Ferry, B. W., Baddeley, M. S. & Hawksworth, D. L. (1973). *Air Pollution and Lichens.* Athlone Press, London.

Fisher, H. S. (ed.) (1872). *The Flora of Liverpool.* Liverpool Naturalists' Field Club, Liverpool.

Fitter, R. & Fitter, M. (1967). *The Penguin Dictionary of British Natural History.* Allen Lane, London.

Fletcher, J. D. (1987). Woodvale Willow warblers. *S. W. Lancashire Ringing Group Annual Report.*

Flint, J. H. (1959-1962). *Freshfield Entomological Survey* (Coleoptera). Unpublished report.

Flint, J. H. (1964). *Unpublished Interim Report on Hemiptera at Freshfield. ASD.*

Ford, W. K. (1953). Lancashire and Cheshire Odonata (a preliminary List). *North Western Naturalist. New Series* **1(2),** 227-233.

Fowler, W.W. & Donisthorpe, H. (1887-1913). *The Coleoptera of the British Isles. 6 vols.* Reeve London. First five volumes written by Fowler (1887-1891), sixth is a supplement by Fowler and Donisthorpe (1913).

Fox, A. (1972). *Small Mammal Survey Results.* Unpublished. *ASD 6/5/1/4.*

Franks, P. (1990). *Species List, Hoverfly Records, Sefton Coast All Sites 1 May 1990.* Unpublished list *NWBFDB.*

Gagen, P. (1982). *The soil landscape history of Little Crosby Township in Sefton District, Merseyside.* Unpublished report, Archaeological Survey of Merseyside, Merseyside County Museum, Liverpool.

Galliford, A. L. (1952). Notes on the aquatic fauna of the Freshfield-Ainsdale and Hightown Sand Dunes. *Proceedings of the Liverpool Naturalists' Field Club.* 25-27.

Galliford, A. L. (1963). *Additions to the Fauna of the Freshfield-Ainsdale Sand Dunes.* Unpublished list *ASD 6/6/4.*

Galliford, A. L. (1979). *Notes on the Rotifera, Cladocera, Copepoda and Ostracoda recorded from the artificial ponds and other freshwater environments of the Ainsdale Sand Dunes Nature Reserve between April 1978 and March 1979.* Unpublished report. *ASD 6/6/4.*

Galliford, A. L. (1981). *Report on the Rotifera and Entomostraca recorded from the artificial ponds (scrapes) and other freshwater environments in the Ainsdale Dunes National Nature Reserve between April 1979 and April 1981.* Unpublished report. *ASD 6/6/4.*

Galliford, A. L. (1984). *Report on the Rotifera and Entomostraca recorded from the artificial ponds and other freshwater environments at Ainsdale Dunes National Nature Reserve Between May 1981 and July 1983.* Unpublished report. *ASD 6/6/4.*

Garbett, M. (1990). A short history of the pinewoods. *Coastlines: Sefton Coast Newsletter, Winter 1990 Edition.* Sefton Council.

Garson, P. (1985). Rabbit grazing and the dune slack flora of Holy Island, Lindisfarne National Nature Reserve. *Focus on Nature No. 13. Sand Dunes and their Management* (Ed. by P. Doody). pp. 205-16. NCC, Peterborough.

Gateley, P. S. (1987a). Count of green-winged orchid on Altcar Firing Range. Ainsdale National Nature Reserve files: CH 6/12/1.

Gateley, P. S. (1987b). Cabin Hill National Nature Reserve: Project plan for woodland management. Unpublished NCC Report. *ASD CH 2/2*.

Gateley, P. S. (1987c). *Cabin Hill NNR. Draft vascular plant list* Internal NCC file.

Gateley, P. S. (1990). *The status and distribution of* Epipactis dunensis *on the Sefton Coast*. Unpublished report to NCC.

Gibson, D. J. (1988). The relationship of sheep grazing and soil heterogeneity to plant spatial patterns in dune grassland. *Journal of Ecology,* **76**, 233-252.

Gimingham, C. H. (1948). The role of *Barbula fallax* Hedw. and *Bryum pendulum* Schp. in sand dune fixation. *Transactions of the British Bryological Society,* **1**, 70-2.

Gimingham, C. H. & Robertson, E. T. (1950). Preliminary investigations on the structure of bryophytic communities. *Transactions of the British Bryological Society,* 1, 330-40.

Glyn, P. J. (1975). *Effects of pony grazing on Whiteford National Nature Reserve*. NCC Research contract F3/03/16. CST Report No. 115.

Godfrey, A. (1989). *Annotated list of Diptera and some other insects collected at Ainsdale Dunes, 25 June 1989*. Unpublished. *NWBFDB, file 34/21*.

Godwin, H. (1959). Studies of the post-glacial history of British vegetation. XIV. Late-glacial deposits at Moss Lake, Liverpool. *Philosophical Transactions of the Royal Society, Series B* **242** (689), 127-149.

Goodfellow, M. (1966). *The classification of bacteria in a pine wood soil.* Unpublished. Ph.D. thesis, University of Liverpool, 146pp.

Goodfellow, M., Hill, I. R. & Gray, T. R. G. (1968). Bacteria in a pine forest soil. *The Ecology of Soil Bacteria* (Ed. by T. R. G. Gray & D. Parkinson), pp. 500-15. Liverpool University Press, Liverpool.

Gordon, V. and Savidge, J. P. (1963). Sand-dunes. *Travis's Flora of South Lancashire*. (Ed. J.P. Savidge, V. H. Heywood and V. Gordon), pp. 60-68. Liverpool Botanical Society, Liverpool.

Gosz, J. R., Likens, G. E. & Bormann, F. H. (1973). Nutrient release from decomposing leaf and branch litter in the Hubbard Brook Forest, New Hampshire. *Ecological Monographs,* **43**, 173-191.

Granstrom, A. (1987). Seed viability of fourteen species during five years of storage in a forest soil. *Journal of Ecology,* **75**, 321-331.

Gray, H. J. & Clitherow, J. H. (1982). *Sefton Woods Report, June-July 1982*. Sites:- Atherton Cottage Woods, Shorrocks Hill and Lifeboat Road Woods, Cabin Hill, Ravenmeols, Asparagus Cottage Wood, Firwood, Cambridge Road, Formby, Formby Golf Course. *NWBFDB*.

Gray, L.C. (1980). *Environmental Bibliography of North-West England (Vice-County 59, 60, 69 & 70) 1850-1979*. University of Lancashire Library Occasional Papers. No. 10.

Gray, T. R. G. & Baxby, P. (1968). Chitin decomposition in soil II: The ecology of chitinoclastic micro-organisms in forest soil. *Transactions British Mycological Society,* **53**, 293-309.

Green, C. (1933). *The Flora of the Liverpool District*. T. Buncle & Co., Arbroath.

Greeno, P. T. (1987). *The breeding sites of the Natterjack Toad* Bufo calamita *on the Sefton Coast*. Unpublished report. *ASD 6/5/3/2//2*.

Greenow, A. D. (1989). *A comparative study of seedbanks in Ainsdale Nature Reserve*. Unpublished B.Sc. Thesis. Department of Geography. University of Liverpool.

Greenwood, B. D. (1979). *Lichens recorded from Ainsdale National Nature Reserve*. Unpublished manuscript, *NWBFDB*.

Greenwood, E. F. (1970). *Ainsdale Wild Life*. City of Liverpool Museums, Liverpool.

Grensted, Rev. L. W. (1922). Mollusca: some notes on the mollusca of the sandhills about the mouth of the River Alt. *Lancashire & Cheshire Naturalist,* **14**, 167-172

Gresswell, R. K. (1937). The geomorphology of the south-west Lancashire coastline. *Geographical Journal,* **90**, 335-349.

Gresswell, R. K. (1953). *Sandy shores in South Lancashire; the geomorphology of South-West Lancashire*. Liverpool University Press, Liverpool.

Gresswell, R. K. (1957). Hillhouse coastal deposits in south Lancashire. *Liverpool and Manchester Geological Journal,* **2**, 60-78.

Gresswell, R. K. (1964). Western coast of Britain: Wales to the Lake District. *Field Studies in the British Isles* (Ed. by J. Steers). London and Edinburgh, Nelson.

Gresswell, R. K. (1966). *Report regarding an application to dig Sand from the Foreshore opposite Ainsdale and Birkdale, Southport*. Report to Southport BC. Sefton Coast Data Base.

Griffiths, B. S. (1979). *A study of the colonization of some freshwater ponds*. Unpublished B.Sc. Thesis, Liverpool Polytechnic.

Grimes, B. H. (1975). Report No. 1: Merseyside County Council ektachrome colour infra-red photography (false colour) survey. Report to Merseyside County Council.

Grootjans, A. P., Hendriksma, P., Engelmoer, M., & Westhoff, V. (1988). Vegetation dynamics in a wet dune slack I: rare species decline on the Waddenisland of Schiermonnikoog in The Netherlands. *Acta Botanica Neerlandica,* **37**, 265- 278.

Gunn, A. S. (1991a). *Bryophytes recorded from the Sefton coastal dunes*. Unpublished manuscript, *NWBFDB*.

Gunn, A. S. (1991b). *Lichens Recorded from the Sefton coastal dunes*. Unpublished manuscript. *NWBFDB*.

Guy, J. (1984). The Tudor Age, *The Oxford illustrated history of Britain* (ed. K.O. Morgan), pp. 223-285. Oxford University Press, Oxford.

Hall, B. R. (1954-55). Borehole Records from the mosses of south-west Lancashire, *Soil Survey of England and Wales*, MS65.

Hall, B. R. & Folland, C. J. (1967). Soils of the South-West Lancashire Coastal Plain. *Memoir Soil Survey Great Britain*, Harpenden.

Hall, B. R. & Folland, C. J. (1970). Soils of Lancashire. *Soil Survey Great Britain Bulletin* No 5, Harpenden.

Hall, R. A. (1986). *Birkdale Hills Local Nature Reserve Odonata Report 1986*. Sefton Metropolitan Borough Council Report.

Hall, R. A. (1987). *Sefton Ranger Service Odonata Report 1987.* Sefton Metropolitan Borough Council Report.

Hall, R. A. (1988a). *Butterflies of Ainsdale Sand Dunes, National Nature Reserve.* Unpublished list with status and relative abundance. *ASD 6/6/1/5/4.*

Hall, R. A. (1988b). *Sand Lizard Release - Ainsdale 1988.* Note to file. *ASD 6/5/3/3/1.*

Hall, R. A. (1988c). *Green-winged Orchid* (Orchis morio) *and Cowslip* (Primula veris) *on Altcar Firing Ranges. ASD 6/2/2.*

Hall, R. A. (1988d). *Yellow Bartsia* (Parentucellia viscosa) *on Ainsdale Sand Dunes NNR. 1988.* Note for file *ASD 6/2/2.*

Hall, R. A. (1988e). *Sefton Coast Dragonfly Report 1988.* NCC Report.

Hall, R. A. (1988f). *Status of Sand Lizards on Ainsdale Sand Dunes National Nature Reserve, 1988.* Note to file. *ASD 6/5/3/3/2.*

Hall, R. A. & Nissenbaum, D. A. (1987). Merseyside sand lizard survey 1987. Unpublished NCC report *ASD 6/5/3/3/2.*

Hall, R. A. & Smith, P. H. (1991). Dragonflies of the Sefton coast sand dune system, Merseyside. *Lancashire Wildlife Journal, (1),* 22-34.

Halliwell, A. R. (1973). Residual drift near the sea bed in Liverpool Bay; an observational study. *Geophysical Journal of the Royal Astronomical Society, 32,* 439-458.

Hammond, C. O. (1983). *The Dragonflies of Great Britain and Ireland.* Harley Books.

Hancock, E. G. (1972). *Observations on the Amphibia in the Hightown Area in 1972.* Unpublished report *NWBFDB.*

Hancock, S. (1970). List of Lepidoptera species recorded, Ainsdale National Nature Reserve, 2 June 1970. Unpublished. *NWBFDB.*

Handley, J. F. (1980). The application of remote sensing to environmental management. *International Journal of Remote Sensing, 1* (2), 181-195.

Handley, J. F. (1982). The Land of Merseyside. *The Resources of Merseyside* (Ed. W. T. S. Gould & A. G. Hodgkiss), pp. 83-100. Liverpool University Press, Liverpool.

Hardy, E. (1941). *The Birds of the Liverpool Area.* T. Buncle, Arbroath.

Hardy, E. (1959). Ornithology of the Liverpool and north-west area, 1958-59. *Bird Report of the Merseyside Naturalists' Association.* 2-40.

Hardy, E. (1979). *Birdwatching in Lancashire.* Dalesman.

Harper, P. (1988). Melanism in the Oak Eggar Moth (*Lasiocampa quercus* (L.)) on Ainsdale Sand Dunes National Nature Reserve. Unpublished report. *E N, Blackwell.*

Harris, L. & Nance, D.A. (1974). *A Study on some Aspects of the Ecology of Small Mammals in Three Different Habitats at Ainsdale Nature Reserve.* Unpublished thesis, LeedsUniversity. *ASD 6/5/1/4.*

Harrop, M. (1990). *Ainsdale National Nature Reserve 8/7/1989, moths collected at m. v. light with generator on a warm calm evening up to 11.15p.m.* Unpublished list. *ASD.*

Harrop, S. A. (1982). Fishing Stalls on the South West Lancashire Coast. *Transactions of the Historic Society of Lancashire and Cheshire, 131,* 161-164.

Harrop, S. A. (1985). *Old Birkdale and Ainsdale - Life on the South West Lancashire Coast 1600 - 1851.* The Birkdale and Ainsdale Historical Research Society, Southport.

Hawksworth, D. L., James, P. W. & Coppins, B. J. (1980). Checklist of British lichen-forming, lichenicolous and allied fungi. *Lichenologist, 12(1),* 1-115.

Hawksworth, D. L. & Seaward, M. R. D. (1977). *Lichenology in the British Isles l568-1975.* The Richmond Publishing Co. Ltd., Richmond.

Hewett, D. G. (1970). The colonisation of sand dunes after stabilisation with Marram Grass *Ammophila arenaria. Journal of Ecology, 58,* 653-668.

Hewett, D. G. (1981). Grazing studies on sand dunes. ITE Annual Report pp. 78-79.

Hibbert, F.A., Switsur, V.R. & West, R.G. (1971). Radiocarbon dating of Flandrian pollen zones at Red Moss, Lancashire. *Proc. R. Soc. Land. B., 177,* 161-176.

Higgins, H. H. (l858). The fungi of Liverpool and its vicinity, Part 1. Hymenomycetes. *Liverpool Literary and Philosophical Society Proceedings,* Session 47(12) Appendix pp. 55-106.

Higgins, H. H. (l859). The fungi of Liverpool and its vicinity, Part 2. Gasteromycetes. *Liverpool Literary and Philosophical Society Proceedings,* Session 47(12) Appendix pp. 123-38.

Hill, M. O. & Wallace, H. L. (1989). Vegetation and environment in afforested sand dunes at Newborough, Anglesey. *Forestry, 62,* 249-68.

Hodkinson, M. (1966). *Fungal decomposition of pine roots in a sandy soil.* Unpublished. Ph.D. thesis, University of Liverpool.

Holder, F. W. (1920). Bird notes from the South Lancs. dunes *Lancashire & Cheshire Naturalist, Nov/Dec. 1920.* 114.

Holder, F. W. (1924). The white bryony on the Ainsdale sand-dunes *Bryonia dioica* Jacq. *Lancashire and Cheshire Naturalist, 16,* 272.

Holmes, R. A. (1971). Bumble bees recorded for Ainsdale Sand Dunes (On Biological Records card) *NWBFDB.*

Holt, J. (1795). *General View of the Agriculture of the County of Lancaster.* London. LRO 53/B p.84 & p.175.

Horne, S. D. (1979). *The Flora and Fauna of Ainsdale National Nature Reserve.* Merseyside County Museums, Liverpool.

Horrill, A. D. & Livens, F. R. (1987). *Analysis of Natterjack Toads for radionucleides.* Unpublished ITE report to NCC. *ASD 6/5/3/2/2.*

House, S. M & Spellerberg, I. F (1983). Ecology and conservation of the sand lizard (*Lacerta agilis* L.) habitat in southern England. *Journal of Applied Ecology, 20,* 417-437.

Houston, J. A. (1981). *Ainsdale LNR/Birkdale LNR Natterjack Toad Report.* Unpublished report. *ASD 6/5/3/2/2.*

Houston, J. A. (1989). The Sefton Coast Management Scheme in North West England. *Perspectives in Coastal Dune Management* (ed by. F. van der Meulen, P. D. Jungerius & J. Visser) SPB Academic Publishing bv. pp 249 - 253. JCAS database 055 Md 026.

Houston, J. A. (1991). Blowing in the wind. *Landscape Design,* **206,** 25-29.

Houston, J. A. & Jones, C. R. (1987). The Sefton coast management scheme: project and process. *Coastal Management,* **15,** 267-97.

Howard-Davies, C., Stocks, C. & Innes, J.B. (1988). *Peat and the past: a survey and assessment of the prehistory of the lowland wetlands of the North West England.* Lancaster University. Lancaster.

Huddart, D. (1988). *Environmental education on the Sefton coast: its past and current development and possible future management strategies.* Report by Liverpool Polytechnic Science and Outdoor Education Section, I.M. Marsh Campus, commissioned by Sefton Planning Department.

Huddart, D., Tooley, M. J. & Carter, P. A. (1977). The coasts of north-west England. *The Quaternary History of the Irish Sea* (ed. by C. Kidson and M. J. Tooley), Geological Journal Special Issue No.7, Liverpool, Seel House Press, pp. 119-154.

Hughes, E. (1991). *Red squirrel distribution in Formby.* Unpublished. B.Sc. Thesis. Liverpool Polytechnic.

Hydraulics Research Station. (1958). *Radioactive tracers for the study of sand movement, a report on an experiment carried out in Liverpool Bay in 1958.* Hydraulics Research Station Report, Wallingford.

Hydraulics Research Station (1965). *Investigation of Siltation in the Estuary of the River Ribble, July, 1965.* Hydraulics Research Station Report Ex. 281, Wallingford.

Hydraulics Research Station (1968). *Notes on Engineering Works to Reduce Dredging in the Ribble Estuary.* Hydraulics Research Station Report Ex. 391, Wallingford.

Hydraulics Research Station (1969). *The Southwest Lancashire Coastline, a Report of the Sea Defences.* Hydraulics Research Station Report Ex. 450, Wallingford.

Hydraulics Research Station (1977). *Sand Winning at Southport.* Hydraulics Research Station Report Ex. 708, Wallingford.

Hydraulics Research Station (1980). *River Ribble Cessation of Dredging.* Hydraulics Research Station Report Ex. 948, Wallingford.

Indraratne, B. A. (1964). *Nature and activity of fungi in a pine wood soil.* Unpublished. Ph.D. Thesis, University of Liverpool.

Ing, B. (1992). A provisional red data list of British fungi. *The Mycologist,* **6 (3),** 124-128

Innes, J. B. (1983). Notes on the vegetation history of Sefton district, Merseyside. *Sefton Rural Fringes Survey Report,* ed. J. Lewis, Archaeological Survey of Merseyside, Merseyside County Museum.

Innes, J. B. (1986). The history of the Shirdley Hill sand revealed by examination of associated organic deposits. *North of England Soils Discussion Group Proceedings,* **21,** 31-43.

Innes, J. B. & Tomlinson, P. R. (1983). Cultural implications of Holocene landscape evolution in the Merseyside region. *Amateur Geologist,* **10,** 2-17.

Innes, J. B. & Tomlinson, P. R. (1991). Environmental Archaeology. *Journal of the Merseyside Archaeological Society,* **7,** 1-20.

Innes, J. B., Tooley, M. J. & Tomlinson, P. R. (1989). A comparison of the age and palaeoecology of some sub-Shirdley Hill sand peat deposits from Merseyside and south-west Lancashire. *Naturalist,* **114,** 65-69.

JCAS (1990). *A Working Plan for Woodlands on the Sefton Coast.* JCAS database 080 Me 006.

Jackson, H. C. (1976). *Study of the habitat requirements of the Merseyside population of the sand lizard.* Unpublished manuscript, NCC, London.

Jackson, H. C. (1978a). Low May sunshine as a possible factor in the decline of the sand lizard (*Lacerta agilis* L.) in north-west England. *Biological Conservation,* **13,** 1-11.

Jackson, H. C. (1978b). Study of sand lizards. Unpublished. report to NCC. *NCC files Blackwell.*

Jackson, H. C. (1979). The decline of the sand lizard, *Lacerta agilis* L., population on the sand dunes of the Merseyside coast, England. *Biological Conservation,* **16,** 177-193.

Jackson, H. C. & Yalden, D. W. (1977). Study of the habitat requirements of the Merseyside population of the sand lizard. Jan - Oct 1977. Unpublished. report. *ASD 6/5/3/3/2.*

Jackson, H. C. & Yalden, D. W. (1979). *Study of the habitat requirements of the Merseyside population of the sand lizard.* Final report, Contract F3/03/54, NCC.

Jacson, C. (1897). *Formby Reminiscences.* London. *LRO.*

James, P. A. & Wharfe, A. J. (1984). The chemistry of rainwater in a coastal locality of Northwest England. *Catena,* **11,** 219-27.

James, P. A. & Wharfe, A. J. (1989). Timescales of soil development in a coastal sand dune system, Ainsdale, North-West England. *Perspectives in coastal dune management* (Ed. by F. van der Meulen, P. D. Jungerius and J. H. Visser), pp. 287-95. S.P.B. Academic Publishing, The Hague.

James, P. A., Wharfe, A. J., Pegg, R. K. & Clarke, D. (1986). A cation budget analysis for a coastal dune system in North-West England. *Catena,* **13,** 1-10.

James, P. W., Hawksworth, D. L. & Rose, F. (1977). Lichen communities in the British Isles: A preliminary conspectus. *Lichen Ecology* (Ed. by M. R. D. Seaward), pp. 400-2. Academic Press, London.

James, Rev. R. (1636). *Iter Lancastrense,* Chetham Society 1845, Volume 17, (Ed. by T. Corser), pp. 17-85.

Jarvis, R. A., Bendelow, V. C., Bradley, R. I., Carroll, D. M., Furness, R. R., Kilgour, I. N. L. & King, S. J. (1984). Soils and their use in Northern England. *Bulletin of the Soil Survey of Great Britain,* **10.**

Jelgersma, S., Jong, J. de, Zagwijn, W. H. & Regteren Altena, J. F. van (1970a). Holocene sea level changes in the Netherlands. *Mededelingen van de Geologische Stichting,* Serie C. VI - 7, 1-100.

Jelgersma, S., Jong, J. de, Zagwijn, W. H. & Regteren Altena, J. F. van (1970b). The coastal dunes of the western Netherlands; geology, vegetation history and archaeology. *Mededelingen Rijks Geologische Dienst,* **21,** 93-164.

Johnson, C. (1966). List of Coleoptera collected during 1965-1966. Ainsdale. Unpublished report.

Johnson, C. (1976). Nine species of Coleoptera new to Britain. *Entomologists Monthly Magazine,* **111,** 177-183.

Johnson, P. E. (1979). *Nutritional problems associated with the revegetation of eroded sand dunes.* Unpublished Ph.D. Thesis, University of Liverpool.

Jones, J. (1980). *Some aspects of the mineral nutrition of* Salix repens, *with reference to Ainsdale.* Unpublished. B.Sc. Dissertation, University of Liverpool.

Jones, N. P. (1978). *The colonization by invertebrates of recently constructed ponds in Ainsdale National Nature Reserve.* Unpublished. B.Sc. thesis, University of Liverpool.

Jones, P. (1985). The Sefton coast management scheme. *Environmental Education,* 22-23.

Jones, P. S. (1992). *Ecological and hydrological studies of dune slack vegetation in South Wales.* Ph.D. thesis. University of Wales.

Jones, P. S. & Etherington, J. R. (1989). Ecological and physiological studies of dune slack vegetation, Kenfig Pool and Dunes National Nature Reserve, Wales, U. K. *Perspectives in Coastal Dune Management.* (Ed. by F. van der Meulen, P. D. Jungerius and J. H. Visser), pp. 297-303. SPB Academic Publishing, The Hague.

Jones, R. (1967). *The relationship of dune slack plants to soil moisture and chemical conditions.* Unpublished Ph.D. thesis, University of Wales.

Jones, R. & Etherington, J. R. (1971). Comparative studies of plant growth and distribution in relation to waterlogging. IV. The growth of dune and dune slack plants. *Journal of Ecology,* **59,** 793-801.

Jordan, K. (1988). *Ainsdale Sand Dunes, British Mycological Society Day Foray.* Unpublished manuscript. *NWBFDB.*

Jordan, K. (1991). Ainsdale Dune System 1980-1991. Unpublished Species List. Merseyside Naturalists' Association (Fungus Group). *NWBFDB.*

Judd, S. (1986). A checklist of Lancashire and Cheshire Heteroptera. *Annual Report & Proceedings of the Lancashire and Cheshire Entomological Society,* **110,** 60-65.

Kear, B. S. & Wilson, P. (1986). The Shirdley Hill Sand of south-west Lancashire. *North of England Soils Discussion Group Proceedings,* **21,** 21-30.

Keitch, M. L. (1969). Ainsdale National Nature Reserve Collembola of pinewood soils. Unpublished species list.

Kelly, E. (1982). *Viking Village : The Story of Formby.* E. Kelly, Formby.

Kenna, R. J. B. (1986). The Flandrian sequence of North Wirral (N. W. England). *Geological Journal,* **21,** 1-27.

Kennedy, R. J. (1976). The duneland population of Skylarks. *S. W. Lancashire Ringing Group Annual Report.*

Kennedy, R. J. (1977a). Some data from Swift ringing. *S. W. Lancashire Ringing Group Annual Report.*

Kennedy, R. J. (1977b). Greenfinch movements. *S.W. Lancashire Ringing Group Annual Report.*

Kenward, R. E. & Holm, J. L. (1989). What future for British red squirrels? *Biological Journal of the Linnean Society,* **38,** 83-89.

Kibble, R. A. (1966). *Physiological activity in a pinewood soil.* Unpublished. Ph.D. thesis, University of Liverpool, 197pp.

Kirkham, A. J. A. (1978). *The invertebrate fauna of the excavations in the slacks of Ainsdale Sand Dunes National Nature Reserve.* Unpublished report. *E N Blackwell.*

Klijn, J. A. (1990). The Younger Dunes in the Netherlands; Chronology and Causation. *Catena Supplement,* **18,** 89-100.

Lamb, H. H. (1977). *Climate, present, past & future. Vol. II* Methuen, London.

Lamb, H. H. (1982). *Climate, History and the Modern World.* Methuen, London and New York.

Langton, T. (1982). *Sand lizard survey,* Report to NCC.

Lassey, P. A. (1968). *The birds of the South Lancashire dunes and the factors influencing their migrations. Sept. 1964 - May l968.* Unpublished report. *ASD.*

Leach, S. J. & Kinnear, P. K. (1985). Scrub and woodland management, Tentsmuir Point National Nature Reserve: Fife. *Focus on Nature Conservation No. 13. Sand Dunes and their Management.* (Ed. by P. Doody), pp. 239-241. NCC, Peterborough.

Leech, M. J. (1967/68-1969/70). Lepidoptera: from Formby, Lancs. *Annual report and proceedings of the Lancashire and Cheshire Entomological Society,* **91-93,** 17.

Leech, M. L. & Michaelis, H. N. (1957). *The Lepidoptera of Formby.* The Raven Entomological and Natural History Society. pp. 1-38.

Lees, A. M. (1976). *Natural resources, report of survey,* Merseyside Structure Plan. Merseyside County Council.

Lewis, J. (1983). *Sefton Rural Fringes Survey.* Archaeological Survey of Merseyside, Merseyside County Museums, Liverpool. JCAS database. 005 Da 009.

Littledale, E. (1850). Abstract of an Act of Parliament X for draining, improving and preserving the low lands in the parishes of Altcar, Sefton, Halsall and Walton-up-on-the-hill and some facts showing the commencement and progress of the works to the present period. Liverpool.

LNT. (1972). *A report on the conservation of the natterjack toad population in South-West Lancashire.* Unpublished NCC report. *NWBFDB, ASD 6/5/3/2/2.*

Locket, G. A. & Millidge, A. F. (1953). *British Spiders Volume 2.* Ray Society, London.

Londo, G., (1971). *Patroon en proces in duinvalleivegetaties langs een gegraven meer in de Kennermerduinen.* Thesis Nijmegen; Verhandeling nr. 2 Rijksinstituut voor Natuurbeheer, Leersum, 279pp.

Louwe Kooijmans, L. D. (1980). Archaeology and coastal change in the Netherlands. *Archaeology and Coastal Change.* (Ed. by F. H. Thompson), pp. 106-33. The Society of Antiquaries of London Occasional paper (new series) I.

Louwe Kooijmans, L. D. (1987). Neolithic settlement and subsistence in the wetlands of the Rhine/Meuse Delta of the Netherlands. *European Wetlands in Prehistory* (Ed. by J. M. Coles and A.J. Lawson), pp. 227-51. Clarendon Press, Oxford.

Lunn, J. & Wheeler, D. J. (1989). A sand lizard conservation strategy for the Merseyside Coast. Unpublished. NCC report. *ASD 6/5/3/3/2.*

Macdonald, J. (1954). Afforestation of sand dunes. *Advancement of Science,* **11,** 33-7.

Mackie, D. W. (1961-2). Report on spiders. *Lancashire and Cheshire Fauna Society Reports,* **40,** 60-63.

Mackie, D. W. (1967). Spiders and harvestmen of the S. W. Lancashire dune area. *Naturalist,* **92,** 99-103.

Magnusson, M. (1983). Composition and succession of bryophytes and lichens in an outer coastal dune area in Southern Sweden. *Cryptogamie, Bryologie, Lichenologie,* **4,** 335-55.

Malloch, A. J. C. (1985). Plant communities on British sand dunes - the National Vegetation Classification. *Focus on Nature Conservation No. 13. Sand Dunes and their Management.* (Ed. by J. Doody), NCC, Peterborough.

Malloch, A. J. C. (1989). Plant communities of the British sand dunes. *Proceedings of the Royal Society of Edinburgh,* **96B,** 53-74.

Marrat, F. B. (1855). On the musci and hepaticae found within 12 miles of Liverpool and Southport. *Liverpool Literary and Philosophical Society Proceedings,* 9 (supplement).

Marrat, F. B. (1860). On the Hepatics and Lichens of Liverpool and its vicinity. *Liverpool Literary and Philosophical Society Proceedings* **1859-60** Appendix, 1-7.

Marrat, F. B. (1864). The mosses of Southport. *Liverpool Naturalists Scrapbook,* (1863-4).

Marrs, R. (1985). Scrub control. *Focus on Nature Conservation No. 13. Sand Dunes and their Management.* (Ed. by P. Doody), pp. 243-51. NCC, Peterborough.

Marshall, J. K. (1965). *Corynephorus canescens* (L.) P. Beauv. as a model for the *Ammophila* problem. *Journal of Ecology,* **53,** 447-63.

Marshall, W. (1989). *The provision and utilisation of footpath networks and the implication for management on four sites of the Sefton coast sand dune system.* Unpublished. thesis. Liverpool Institute of Higher Education.

Martin, W. E. (1959). The vegetation of Island Beach State Park, New Jersey. *Ecological Monographs,* **29,** 1-46.

Martyr, R. (1968). *Some observations on soil development on the sand dunes at Freshfield, South Lancashire, especially under plantations of Corsican pine.* Unpublished. thesis, University of Lancaster.

Massey, J. D. (1937). Notes and Records. *North West Naturalist*

Mathias, J.H. (1971). *The Comparitve Ecologies of Two Species of Amphibia* (Bufo bufo) *and* (Bufo calamita) *on the Ainsdale Sand Dunes National Nature Reserve.* Unpublished Ph.D. thesis, University of Manchester. *ASD 6/5/3/2/2.*

McDowell, D. M. & O'Connor, B. A. (1987). *The Hydraulic Behaviour of Estuaries.* Macmillan, London.

McKinnell, S. A. (1990) *A Study of the distribution of* Juncus balticus *Willd. in the Merseyside sand-dune system.* Unpublished B.Sc.(Hons) Project Report, School of Natural Sciences, The Liverpool Polytechnic.

McLardy, S. G. (1987). *Cabin Hill birds* Unpublished letter. *CH* files.

McMillan, N. F. (1969). *Ainsdale Sand Dunes National Nature Reserve: Mollusca - snails and slugs.* Unpublished list. *ASD 6/6/3.*

McNaught, J. K. (1973). *A Study of the Use of Coastal Resources on the South West Lancashire Coast from Marshside Sands to Formby Point.* Unpublished M.Sc thesis, University of Salford. *JCAS database.*

Mcleod, R. G. (1866). Microscopic fungi of the district around Liverpool. *Historic Society of Lancashire and Cheshire Transactions 1865-66,* New Series,**6,** 127-36.

Megaw, J. V. S. & Simpson D. D. A. (1979). *Introduction to British Prehistory.* Leicester University Press, Leicester.

Meikle, R.D. (1977). Salix hybrids - letters. *ASD 34/21.*

Meikle, R. D. (1984). *BSBI Handbook No 4. Willows and Poplars of Great Britain and Ireland.* Botanical Society of the British Isles, London.

Mennema, J., Quene-Boterenbrood, A. J. & Plate, C. L. (1985). *Atlas van de Nederlandse Flora. Part 2.* Bohn, Scheltema and Holkema, Utrecht.

Merchant Taylors Field Club (1968). *Ainsdale Sand Dunes National Nature Reserve ornithological report.* Unpublished report. *E N, Blackwell.*

Merseyside County Council (1977a). Management Scheme for the Sefton Coast between Hightown and Birkdale. CPO/56/77. *JCAS database.*

Merseyside County Council (1977b). *Report of survey of the National Trust Land at Formby Point* Unpublished report, 22 pp. *JCAS database. 055 Ma 007/075 Da 016.*

Merseyside County Council (1978). *Report of Survey, The Dune System at Lifeboat Road, Formby* Unpublished report, 20 pp. *JCAS database. 055 Ma 006/075 Da 018.*

Michaelis, H. N. (1957). The lepidoptera of Formby. *Raven Entomological and Natural History Society,* 11-38.

Mills, D. (1976). *The Place Names of Lancashire.* B. T. Batsford, London.

Minton, C. L. (1985). *The relative importance of the input of cations into the Ainsdale sand dune system from mineral weathering.* Unpublished. B.Sc. thesis, University of Liverpool. 97 pp.

Mitchell, F. S. (1885). *The Birds of Lancashire.* Edition 1. Gurney & Jackson, London.

Mitchell, F. S. (1892). *The Birds of Lancashire.* Edition 2. Gurney & Jackson, London.

Mitchell, J. R., Moser, M. E., & Kirby, J. S. (1988). Declines in mid-winter counts of wader roosts on the Dee estuary. *Bird Study,* **35,** 191-198.

Moore, J. A. (1986). *BSBI Handbook No 5. Charophytes of Great Britain and Ireland.* Botanical Society of the British Isles, London.

Moorhouse, S. (1950). Asparagus from the Lancashire Sands. *'Esso' Farmer,* **2.**

Moriarty, D. E. M. (1978). *Acidification and podzolization under pinewoods on the sand dunes at Ainsdale, S. W. Lancashire.* Unpublished. thesis, University of Liverpool.

Murthy, T. K. S. & Cook, J. (1962). *Maximum wave heights in Liverpool Bay,* Vickers Armstrong, Department of Design, Report No V3031/HYDRO/04.

Musgrave, M. (1974). *Ainsdale Sand Dunes National Nature Reserve. Vertebrates: Amphibians, Reptiles, Mammals 1966-74.* Unpublished. *ASD 6/5/1/2.*

Musgrave, M. (1975). *Ainsdale Sand Dunes NNR. Mosses and liver-worts checklist, 1975.* Unpublished. *ASD.*

National Curriculum Council. (1990). Environmental Education, Curriculum Guidance 7, 49pp, NCC Peterborough.

National Foundation for Educational Research. (1991). *Charging for School Activities.* NFER.

National Trust. (1988). *Woodland plan of operations. Unpublished. report National Trust.* National Trust Reg. Office, Attingham Park.

NC Warden (1967). *Ainsdale National Nature Reserve, Warden's natural history report, April & May* (amphibians). Unpublished. *ASD 6/5/3/2/2.*

NC Warden (1971). *Ainsdale National Nature Reserve. Warden's Natural History Report, Natterjack Section.* Unpublished. *ASD 6/5/3/2/2.*

Nature Conservancy (1971). *The management of sea buckthorn* Hippophae rhamnoides *in National Nature Reserves and SSSIs.* Unpublished report Coastal Habitat Team, *Hippophae* Study Group. Held at EN, Blackwell.

NCC (1983). *The Ecology and Conservation of Amphibian and Reptile Species Endangered in Britain*, NCC, Peterborough.

NCC Wardens (undated). Glass vivarium, sand lizard breeding programme. Initial Development. Ainsdale National Nature Reserve *ASD 2/6/2/2/4.*

NCC Wardens (undated). Conservation Transplants, *Scirpus americanus, Potamogeton gramineus* and *Juncus balticus* and hybrids x *effusus*, x *inflexus*. *ASD 2/6/1/8.*

NCC Wardens (undated). Island Vivarium, Ainsdale National Nature Reserve *ASD 2/6/2/2/3.*

NCC Wardens (undated). Large pond and long slack excavation. *ASD 2/6/2/3/4.*

NCC Wardens (undated). Natterjack Toads, plastic breeding pools. *ASD 2/6/2/3/5.*

NCC Wardens (undated). Slack excavations, Ainsdale National Nature Reserve 1976-1977. *ASD 2/6/2/3/2.*

NCC Wardens (undated). Vivarian Management papers. *ASD 2/6/2//2/1 & 2.*

NC/NCC Wardens (1972-75). *Ainsdale National Nature Reserve. Warden's natural history reports, amphibians section. Ainsdale National Nature Reserve & LNR frontal strip.* Unpublished. *ASD 6/5/3/2/2.*

NCC Wardens (1976a). *Some Notes on the Natterjack Toad at Ainsdale National Nature Reserve 1976.* Unpublished report. *ASD 6/5/3/2/2.*

NCC Wardens (1976b). *Natterjack Toad Breeding Survey 1976. Summary up to 11/6/76. Ainsdale National Nature Reserve and LNR Frontal Strip.* Unpublished report. *ASD 6/5/3/2/2.*

NCC Wardens (1977-90). *Amphibian Breeding Surveys, Ainsdale* [1977-83 includes LNR frontal strip + National Nature Reserve l984-90 covers only National Nature Reserve. l984 includes Cabin Hill]. Unpublished annual reports. *ASD 6/5/3/2/2.*

NCC Wardens (1978-88). *Sand Lizard Captive Breeding Programme Vivarium Reports.* Ainsdale Sand Dunes National Nature Reserve unpublished annual reports. *ASD.*

NCC Wardens (1981). *First Four Years of the Sand Lizard Captive Breeding Programme, 1978-1981.* Ainsdale Sand dunes National Nature Reserve unpublished report. *ASD.*

NCC Wardens (1985a-90a). Amphibian breeding survey reports Cabin Hill National Nature Reserve and Altcar Rifle Range. Unpublished annual reports. *ASD 6/5/3/2/2.*

Nesbitt, A. (1981). *The distribution and abundance of sea buckthorn at Ainsdale and Birkdale LNR.* Unpublished B.Sc. Dissertation, Liverpool Polytechnic. *JCAS 75 Db 8.*

Newlands, C. D., Thompson, S. P. & Robinson, N. A. (1987). Ainsdale Sand Dunes NNR air photo. interpretation: spread of deciduous scrub and woodlands 1968 - 1983. Unpublished report to NCC. *ASD 6/4/1.*

Nicolle, P. D. (1988). *Environmental physiologies of natterjack and common toad tadpoles.* Unpublished report to NCC, Liverpool Polytechnic. *ASD 6/5/3/2/2.*

Nissenbaum, D. A. (1986). *Buckthorn control programme 1984/86.* Unpublished report Sefton Council.

Nissenbaum, D. A. (1988a). *National Trust, Formby Point sand lizard survey 1988.* Unpublished report to National Trust.

Nissenbaum, D. A. (1988b). *Merseyside sand lizard survey 1988.* Unpublished report to NCC. *ASD 6/5/3/3/2.*

Nissenbaum, D. A. (1989). *Merseyside sand lizard survey 1989.* Unpublished report to NCC. *ASD 6/5/3/3/2.*

Nissenbaum, D. A. (1990). *Merseyside sand lizard survey 1990.* Unpublished report to NCC. *ASD 6/5/3/3/2.*

Nissenbaum, D. A. & Hall, R. A. (1988). *Merseyside Sand Lizard Survey 1988.* Unpublished report to NCC.

Nykvist, N. (1959). Leaching and decomposition of litter. II: Experiments on needle litter of *Pinus sylvestris. Oikos,* **10,** 212-223.

O'Connor, B. A. (1987). Short and long term changes in estuary capacity. *Journal of the Geological Society of London,* **144,** 187-195.

O'Garra, A. (1976). *Dune slack systems - vegetation and morphological development at Ainsdale.* Unpublished thesis, Department of Geography, University of Liverpool.

O'Toole, C. (1974). A new subspecies of the vernal bee *Colletes cunicularius* (L.). Hymenoptera: Colletidae). *Journal of Entomology (B)* **42,** 163-169.

O'Toole, C. (1989). Profile of *Colletes cunicularius* (L.). in the British Isles (Hymenoptera: Colletidae). *Bees, Wasps and Ants Recording Scheme Newsletter, Spring 1989,* 3-7.

Oakes, C. (1953). *The Birds of Lancashire.* Oliver and Boyd, Edinburgh.

Oosterveld, P. (1985). Grazing in dune areas: the objectives of nature conservation and aims of research for nature conservation management. *Focus on Nature Conservation No 13. Sand Dunes and their Management* (Ed. by P. Doody), pp.187-203. NCC, Peterborough.

Page, C. N. (1982). *The Ferns of Britain and Ireland.* Cambridge University Press, Cambridge.

Page, W. (ed.). (1911). *Victoria history of the counties of England. A history of the County of Lancashire.* Constable, London.

Palmer, C. (1988). Some notes on the hoverflies of the north Merseyside coastal dune system. *Diperists' Digest,* **1,** 41-42.

Parker, W. R. (1971). *Aspects of the marine environment at Formby Point, Lancashire.* Unpublished Ph.D. Thesis, University of Liverpool.

Parker, W. R. (1974). Sand transport and coastal stability, Lancashire, U.K. *Proceedings of the 14th Conference on Coastal Engineering,* 828-50.

Parker, W. R. (1975). Sediment mobility and erosion on a multi-barred foreshore (south-west Lancashire, U.K.). *Nearshore Sediment Dynamics and Sedimentation* (Ed. by J. R. Hails and A. P. Carr), pp. 151-77. Wiley, London.

Parkinson, D. & Balasooriya, I. (1967). Studies on fungi in a pine-wood soil I. Nature and distribution of fungi in the different soil horizons. *Revue d'Ecologie et du Biologie du Sol,* **4,** 63-478.

Parkinson, D. & Balasooriya, I. (1969). Studies on fungi in a pine-wood soil IV. Seasonal and spatial variations in the fungal populations. *Revue d'Ecologie et du Biologie du Sol,* **6,** 147-53.

Parkinson, D. & Crouch, R. (1969). Studies on fungi in a pine-wood soil V. Root mycofloras of seedlings of *Pinus nigra* var. *laricio. Revue d'Ecologie et du Biologie du Sol,* **6,** 263-75.

Parsons, M. (1987a). *Invertebrate Site Register. 96: 1 & 2 Merseyside and Greater Manchester.* NCC, Peterborough.

Parsons, M. (1987b). Unpublished letter and list of lepidoptera caught at a light trap at Cabin Hill NNR, 21/4/87. *ASD.*

Paull, L. (1984). *Ainsdale LNR natterjack toad survey spring/summer 1984.* Unpublished report. *ASD 6/5/3/2/2.*

Payne, K. R. (1976a). *The Odonata of Ainsdale Sand Dunes National Nature Reserve: An Appraisal of Past Records and Distribution in 1976.* Unpublished file note. *ASD.*

Payne, K. R. (1976b). Crassula *sp. at Ainsdale National Nature Reserve.* Unpublished note. *ASD 6/2/2.*

Payne, K. R. (1977). Salix *hybrids - Ainsdale* Unpublished. letter *ASD 34/21.*

Payne, K. R. (1978a) *The* Crassula helmsii *in the large pond.* Unpublished note. *ASD 6/2/2.*

Payne, K. R. (1978b). *A review of the insect records for Ainsdale Sand Dunes National Nature Reserve, autumn 1978.* Unpublished report. *ASD.*

Payne, K. R. (1978c). Untitled letter regarding various species on the National Nature Reserve including a map. *ASD 6/2/2.*

Payne, K.R. (1978d). *Fox Deaths in the Ainsdale Sand Dunes, December 1977-February 1978.* Unpublished note. *ASD 6/5/1/2.*

Payne, K. R. (1979a). Unpublished *Auchenorhynca* species list for Raven Meols Hills (On Biological Records Card). *NWBFDB.* ·

Payne, K. R. (1979b). *Observations on the distribution of and food-plants of Cercopidae nymphs (Homoptera:* Auchenorhynca*) on Ainsdale Sand Dunes National Nature Reserve, Merseyside.* Unpublished draft. *ASD 6/9.*

Payne, K. R. (1979c). *To monitor the colonisation and vegetation development within firebreaks and within the pinewoods on the National Nature Reserve.* Unpublished internal file NCC.

Payne, K. R. (1980a). Rabbit grazing and *Salix repens* growth in the dunes of Ainsdale Sand Dunes N. N. R. Internal N. C. C. report ASD 6/4/6.

Payne, K. R. (1980b).. Unpublished Auchenorhynca species list for Ainsdale Sand Dunes National Nature Reserve, 1976-80 (On Biological Records Card). *NWBFDB.*

Payne, K. R. (ca.1980). *The distribution and inter-relationships of the* Salix*-feeding leafhoppers (Homoptera:* Auchenorhynca*) on the Ainsdale Sand Dunes National Nature Reserve, Merseyside: With special reference to those on* S. repens. Unpublished draft *ASD 6/9.*

Payne, K. R. (1981a). The Life-history and host-plant relationships of *Eupteryx notato* Curtis (Homoptera: Cicadellidae). *Entomologists' Monthly Magazine,* **117,** 167-173.

Payne, K. R. (1981b). Comparison of the catches of Auchenorhynca (Homoptera) obtained from sweep netting and pitfall trapping. *Entomologists' Monthly Magazine,* **117,** 215-223.

Payne, K. R. (1982a). *Invertebrate species of interest at Cabin Hills 1982.* Unpublished list SD 20/3 Sc. *NWBFDB, file SD/20/85, Cabin Hill.*

Payne, K. R. (1982b). *Ainsdale Sand Dunes National Nature Reserve vascular plant species list (1982 revision)* Unpublished list *ASD 6/2/2.*

Payne, K. R. (1983a). The Vegetation of Ainsdale Dunes. Unpublished report NCC. *ASD.*

Payne, K. R. (1983b). Ainsdale Sand Dunes National Nature Reserve frontal dunes - management review. Unpublished file note. *ASD.*

Payne, K. R. & Singleton, P. (1978). *Notes on natterjack toad and sand lizard conservation at Ainsdale National Nature Reserve for BTCV handbook on coastal conservation.* Unpublished. paper. *ASD 6/5/3/2/1.*

Peace, D. M. (1977). *The breeding bird community of Royal Birkdale golf course.* Unpublished B.Sc.(Hons.) Project report. Department of Biology Liverpool Polytechnic.

Pearsall, W. H. (1934). North Lancashire sand dunes. *The Naturalist,* 201-5.

Pearson, G. W. & Stuiver, M. (1986). High precision calibration of the radiocarbon timescale, 500-2500 BC. *Radiocarbon,* **28,** 839-62.

Penman, H. L. (1948). Natural evaporation from open water, bare soil and grass. *Proceedings of the Royal Society of London* Series A. **193,** 120-45.

Pennington, M. J. (1986). Migration and biometrics of blackcaps caught in S. W. Lancs. *S. W. Lancashire Ringing Group Annual Report.*

Pennington, M. J. (1987). Passage of warblers in S. W. Lancs. as demonstrated by ringing data. *S.W. Lancashire Ringing Group Annual Report.*

Perring, F. N. & Farrell, L. (1977). *British Red Data Books: 1. Vascular Plants.* The Society for the Promotion of Nature Conservation, Lincoln.

Picton, J. A. (1849). The changes of sea-levels on the west coast of England during the historic period. *Proceedings of the Literary and Philosophical Society of Liverpool,* **5,** 113-115.

Pierce, J. (1989). The effect of climate on the breeding activity of the natterjack toad *Bufo calamita* on the Sefton Coast. (with a summary by P. H. Smith.) Unpublished. B.Sc. (Hons.) Project report Liverpool Polytechnic. *ASD 6/5/3/2/2.*

Pollard, E., Hall, M. L. & Bibby, T. J. (1986). *Monitoring the abundance of butterflies 1976-1985.* NCC, Peterborough.

Poole, R. (1987). *Ainsdale National Nature Reserve, additions to mycological species list, March 1986 - March 1987.* Unpublished manuscript, Merseyside Naturalists' Association. *NWBFDB.*

Poole, R. & Jordan, K. (1986). *Ainsdale Sand Dunes National Nature Reserve, mycological records to 1986.* Unpublished manuscript, Merseyside Naturalists Association. *NWBFDB.*

Prestt, I., Cooke, A. S. & Corbett, K. (1974). British amphibians and reptiles. *The changing flora and fauna of Britain* (Ed. by D. L. Hawksworth). pp. 229-254. Academic Press, London and New York.

Price, W. A. & Kendrick, M. P. (1963). Field and model investigations into the reasons for siltation in the Mersey estuary. *Journal of the Institution of Civil Engineers,* **24,** 473-517.

Pye, K. (1990). Physical and human influences on coastal dune development between the Ribble and Mersey estuaries, northwest England. *Coastal dunes: form and process.* (Ed. by K. F. Nordstrom, N. Psuty, and R. W. G. Carter), pp. 339-59. John Wiley and Sons, Chichester.

Pye, K. (1991). Beach deflation and backshore dune formation following erosion under storm surge conditions: an example from Northwest England. *Sand, Dust & Soil in their Relation to Aeolian and Littoral Processes.* (Ed. by O. E. Barndorff-Nielsen and B. B. Willetts), *Acta Mechanica, Supplementum 2.*

Pye, K. (1992). Coastal dune erosion at Formby Point, north-west England: causes and consequences. *Marine Geology,* (in press).

Pye, K. & Neal, A. (1992). Late Holocene sedimentation on the Sefton dune coast, north-west England: response to changes in sea level and wind/wave climate. *The Dynamics and Environmental Context of Aeolian Sedimentary Systems.* (Ed. by K. Pye) Geological Society Publishing House, Bristol, (in press).

Pye, K. & Smith, A. J. (1988). Beach and dune erosion and accretion on the Sefton Coast, Northwest England. *Journal of Coastal Research Special Issue,* **3,** 33-6.

Rackham, O. (1986). *The History of the Countryside.* J.M. Dent, London.

Rance, C. E. de (1869). The Geology of the country between Liverpool and Southport. Explanation of Quarter Sheet 90SE of the 1 inch Geological Survey Map of England and Wales. *Memoirs of the Geological Survey of the U.K.,* HMSO, London.

Rance, C. E. de (1872). Geology of the country around Southport, Lytham Southshore. Explanation of the Quarter Sheet 90NE. *Memoirs of the Geological Survey of the U.K.,* HMSO, London.

Rance, C. E. de (1877). The Superficial Geology of the country adjoining the coast of south-west Lancashire. *Memoirs of the Geological Survey of the U.K.,* HMSO, London.

Rance, C. E. de (1878). Geology of the country around Preston, Blackburn and Burnley. Explanation of the Quarter Sheet 89NW of the 1 inch Geological Survey Map of England and Wales. *Memoirs of the Geological Survey of the U.K.,* HMSO, London.

Ranwell, D. S. (1958). Movement of vegetated sand dunes at Newborough Warren, Anglesey. *Journal of Ecology,* **46,** 83-100.

Ranwell, D. S. (1959). Newborough Warren, Anglesey. I. The dune system and dune slack habitat. *Journal of Ecology,* **47,** 571-601.

Ranwell, D. S. (1960). Newborough Warren, Anglesey. II. Plant associes and succession cycles of the sand dune and dune slack vegetation. *Journal of Ecology,* **48,** 117-41.

Ranwell, D. S. (1972a). *Ecology of Salt Marshes and Sand Dunes.* Chapman and Hall, London.

Ranwell, D. S. (1972b). *The management of sea buckthorn on selected sites in GB.* Report of the *Hippophae* Study Group. Nature Conservancy. *JCAS 75 Ma 46.*

Ranwell, D. S. & Boar, R. (1986). *Coast Dune Management Guide* Institute of Terrestial Ecology, Huntingdon.

Ratcliffe, D. A. (1977). *A Nature Conservation Review Vols 1 & 2.* Cambridge University Press, Cambridge.

Reade, T. M. (1871). The geology and physics of the post-glacial period, as shown in deposits and organic remains in Lancashire and Cheshire. *Proceedings of the Liverpool Geological Society,* **2,** 36-88.

Reade, T. M. (1872). The post-glacial geology and physiography of west Lancashire and the Mersey estuary. *Geological Magazine,* **9**(93), 111-9.

Reade, T. M. (1881a). On a section of the Formby and Leasowe marine beds, and superior peat bed, disclosed by cuttings for the outlet sewer at Hightown. *Proceedings of the Liverpool Geological Society,* **4**(4), 269-77.

Reade, T. M. (1881b). The date of the last change of level in Lancashire. *Quarterly Journal of the Geological Society of London,* **37,** 436-9.

Reade, T. M. (1902). Glacial and post-glacial features of the lower valley of the River Lune and its estuary. *Proceedings of the Liverpool Geological Society,* **9**(2), 163-93.

Reade, T. M. (1908a). A Prehistoric Forest at Waterloo. *Waterloo Herald,* 31.10.08.

Reade, T. M. (1908b). Post-glacial beds at Great Crosby as disclosed by the new outfall sewer. *Proceedings of the Liverpool Geological Society,* **10**(4), 249-61.

Rechinger, K.H. (1964) *Salix* L. *Flora Europaea* (Ed. by T.G. Tutin, V.H. Heywood, N.A. Burges, D.H. Valentine, S.M. Walters and D.A. Webb), pp 45-54. Cambridge University Press, Cambridge.

Rice-Oxley, S. B. (1991). *Caching behaviour of protected red squirrels* (Sciurus vulgaris) *under conditions of high food availability.* Unpublished M.Sc thesis, University of Liverpool.

Riley, S. J. (1983). *A guide to birds and birdwatching in the Southport area.*

Rimmer, J. (1986). *The decline of* Asparagus *farming on the Formby coast - Merseyside.* Unpublished thesis, Open University. *ASD, JCAS.*

Roberts, J. M. (1981). *A study of the natterjack toad at an atypical but productive breeding site - Formby Point denatured tobacco waste dump in Lancashire.* Unpublished report. *ASD 6/5/3/2/2.*

Robinson, N.A. (1972). *Short History of Squirrels in the Pinewoods.* Letter to Pedlar. *ASD 6/5/1/2.*

Robinson, N. A. (1973). *Juniper at Ainsdale Sand Dunes National Nature Reserve* Unpublished letter. *ASD 6/3*.

Robinson, N. A. (1975). Alder Wood by Fishermans path, Ainsdale Sand Dunes National Nature Reserve. Unpublished letter. *ASD 6/2/2*.

Robinson, N. A. (1977). *Merseyside dunes. Natterjack breeding survey 1977 by NCC and LNT (Summary).* Unpublished report. *ASD 6/5/3/2/2*.

Robinson, N.A. (1985). Unpublished letter to C. Gillham, referring to badgers. *ASD 6/5/1/2*.

Robinson, N. A. (1989). Southport Sand Dunes and Foreshore SSSI - site quality monitoring. Air photo interpretation: Ainsdale Hills 1988, Birkdale frontal dunes 1988. NCC Reports.

Rodwell, J. (undated). National Vegetation Classification Volumes : - Calcifugous Grasslands, Heaths, Mesotrophic Grasslands, Shingle, Strandline and Sand-Dune vegetation. Unpublished manuscripts. NCC/University of Lancaster.

Rolfe, C. W. (1989). *Formby Point management plan, Part A.* Unpublished report. National Trust. *Held at National Trust, Mercia Regional Office, Attingham Park, Shrewsbury.*

Rooney, P. J. (1987). *Analysis of visitor distribution at Lifeboat Road, Formby.* Unpublished thesis. Liverpool Institute of Higher Education.

Rose, F. (1989). *Grasses, Sedges, Rushes and Ferns of the British Isles and North-Western Europe.* Viking, London.

Rostanski, K. (1982). The species of *Oenothera* L. in Britain. *Watsonia*, **14**, 1-34.

Rothwell, P. (1985). Management problems on Ainsdale Sand Dunes National Nature Reserve. *Focus on Nature Conservation No 13. Sand Dunes and their Management.* (Ed. by P. Doody), pp. 151-58. NCC, Peterborough.

SMBC (1983). *Coast Management Scheme : Plan for Coastal Management between Hightown and Birkdale.* Sefton Coast Management Scheme Steering Group. 26pp. JCAS database. 055 Ma 008.

SMBC (1989a). *Coast Management Plan Review.* Sefton Coast Management Scheme Steering Group. 27pp. JCAS database. 055 Ma 022.

SMBC (undated). *Ainsdale and Birkdale Hills Local Nature Reserve : Descriptive Plan.* Metropolitan Borough of Sefton. JCAS database 075 Mb 001.

SMBC, Borough Planning Officer. (1989b). Sefton Coast Interpretive Plan, Sefton Council.

SMBC, Borough Planning Officer. (1991). Sefton Coast Interpretive Plan, first review, Sefton Council.

SMBC, Sefton Coast Education Project. (1991). Management Plan, draft copy, 11pp.

SMBC, Sefton Coast Management Scheme (1987-90). *Natterjack Reports* Unpublished annual reports. *ASD 6/5/3/2/2*.

SMBC, Sefton Ranger Service (1985). *Natterjack Toads at Hightown.* Unpublished report. *ASD 6/5/3/2/2*.

SMBC, Sefton Ranger Service (1985-90). *Natterjack Toad Reports, Ainsdale and Birkdale LNR.* Unpublished annual reports *ASD 6/5/3/2/2*.

SMBC, Sefton Ranger Service (1987). *Amphibian Breeding Survey Report, Hightown.* Unpublished report. *ASD 6/5/3/2/2*.

SMBC, Sefton Ranger Service (1990). *Natterjack Report 1990. Formby* (Lifeboat Rd.) Ravenmeols and Hightown. Unpublished report. *ASD 6/5/3/2/2*.

Salisbury, E. J. (1920). Note on the edaphic succession in some dune soils with special reference to the time factor. *Journal of Ecology,* **8**, 322-328.

Salisbury, E. J. (1925). Note on the edaphic succession in sand dune soils with special reference to the time factor. *Journal of Ecology,* **13**, 322-328.

Salisbury, E. J. (1952). *Downs and Dunes. Their Plant Life and Its Environment.* G. Bell & Sons, London.

Salisbury, G. (1950). The genus *Thelocarpon* in Britain. *North West Naturalist* (New Series), **1**, 27-38.

Savidge, J. P., Heywood, V. H. & Gordon, V. (1963). *Travis's Flora of South Lancashire.* Liverpool Botanical Society, Liverpool.

Schumacker, R. (1990). *Preliminary Lists of Threatened (Ex, E, V, R sensu IUCN) Bryophytes in EEC-Countries including Macaronesia (version 2, April 1990).* Unpublished report, EEC.

Sephton, M. A. (1989). *Sefton Coast Rangers' Odonata Report.* Sefton Metropolitan Borough Council.

Sheail, J. (1976). *Nature in Trust, A History of Nature Conservation in Great Britain.* Blackie, Glasgow.

Shennan, I. (1989). Holocene crustal movements and sea-level changes in Great Britain. *Journal of Quaternary Science,* **4**, 77-89.

Shirt, D.B. (ed.) (1987). *British Red Data Book Number 2, Insects.* Nature Conservancy Council.

Simms, C. (1963). *Interim Report of an Investigation of the Winter Avifauna of Coastal Pinewoods in Lancashire.* Unpublished report. *EN Blackwell.*

Simms, C. (1966). The status of amphibians and reptiles in the dunes of south west Lancashire 1961-l964. *Lancashire and Cheshire Fauna Society,* **36**, 7-10.

Simms, C. (1968). Terrestrial mammals in the dunes of South West Lancashire 1961-1964. *Lancashire and Cheshire Fauna Society,* **53**.

Simms, C. (1969). The sand lizard in north west Britain. *Naturalist,* **94**, 119-122.

Simpson, D. E. (1989a). *Green-winged orchid (*Orchis morio) *and cowslip (*Primulus veris) *on Altcar Firing Range 1989.* ASD CH 6/12/1.

Simpson, D. E. (1989b). *Cabin Hill National Nature Reserve: Meadow Management Project Plan 1990-1991.* Unpublished report. NCC. *ASD CH 2/6/1/9.*

Simpson, D. E. (1989c). *The Status of Commoner Amphibians and Reptiles,* NCC, sheet for Sefton Coast. *ASD.*

Simpson, D. E. (1990a). Final summary report on the clearance of sea buckthorn, Ainsdale National Nature Reserve. Unpublished report NCC. *ASD 6/4/3.*

Simpson, D. E. (1990b). *Change in Status of the Common Amphibians and Reptiles 1980-1990.* Sefton Coast records for National NCC survey by Leicester Polytechnic. Unpublished site summaries.

Simpson, D. E. (1990c). Interim report No 1: Monitoring the vegetation response to slack mowing. Unpublished report NCC. *ASD 2/6/1/5.*

Simpson, D. E. (1990d). Final Summary Report: Ainsdale Vegetation Surveys 1960/1971/1976. Unpublished report NCC. *ASD 6/4/1 & 6/4/8.*

Simpson, D. E. (1990e). *Interim report No 1. Monitoring the vegetational response to sheep grazing at Ainsdale Sand Dunes National Nature Reserve.* Unpublished report, NCC. *ASD 2/6/1/9.*

Simpson, D. E. (1990f). *Summary report of monitoring development of vegetation at excavations made to recreate wet slack habitat, Ainsdale Sand Dunes National Nature Reserve.* Unpublished report, NCC. *ASD 6/4/2.*

Simpson, D. E. (1990g). *Cabin Hill National Nature Reserve. Management plan. Prescriptive sections, natterjack toads & sand lizard.* Unpublished report. NCC. *ASD CH 2/1.*

Simpson, D. E. (1990h). *Project plan - The conservation of* Scirpus americanus (Schoenoplectus pungens) *on the Sefton Coast: The introduction of the species to Taggs Island.* Unpublished report. NCC. *ASD 2/6/1/8.*

Simpson, D. E. (1990i). *First interim report on the introduction of* Schoenoplectus pungens *to the Taggs Island area of Birkdale LNR.* Unpublished NCC report. *ASD 2/6/1/8.*

Simpson, D. E. (1990j). *Vegetation monitoring at Altcar Rifle Ranges: 'I' Range.* Unpublished report, NCC. *ASD CH 6/12/1.*

Simpson, D. E. (1990k). *Green-winged orchid (*Orchis morio*) and cowslip (*Primulus veris*) on Altcar Firing Range 1990.* Unpublished report. NCC, *ASD CH 6/12/1.*

Simpson, D. E. (1990l). *Final summary report of the response of ground vegetation to thinning. Ainsdale Sand Dunes National Nature Reserve.* Unpublished report NCC. *ASD 6/4/5.*

Simpson, D. E. (1990m). *Interim report on the response of vegetation to the removal of* Pinus contorta, *Ainsdale Sand Dunes National Nature Reserve.* Unpublished report NCC. *ASD 6/4/4.*

Simpson, D. E. (1990n). *Natterjack toad management: Altcar Rifle Range.* Unpublished report, nature Conservancy Council. *ASD CH 6/12/1.*

Simpson, D. E. (1991a). *Cabin Hill National Nature Reserve Project Plan: Grazing management period 1991-1996.* Unpublished report English Nature *CH 2/6/1/10.*

Simpson, D. E. (1991b). *Interim report No. 2. Monitoring the vegetational response to sheep grazing at Ainsdale Sand Dunes National Nature Reserve.* Unpublished report, English Nature. *ASD 2/6/1/9.*

Slatter, R. J. (1978). Ecological effects of trampling on sand dune vegetation. *Journal of Biological. Education,* **12** (2) 89-96.

Sly, P. G. (1966). *Marine geological studies in the eastern Irish Sea and adjacent estuaries, with special reference to sedimentation in Liverpool Bay and the River Mersey.* Unpublished Ph.D. thesis, University of Liverpool.

Smith, A. J. E. (1978). Distribution maps of Bryophytes in Britain and Ireland. *Journal of Bryology,* **10,** 73-81.

Smith, M. (1952). The climate of the British Isles and its influence on the habitats and distribution of amphibians and reptiles. *British Journal of Herpetology,* **1,** 103-112.

Smith, M. (1973). *The British Amphibians and Reptiles.* Collins, London.

Smith, P. H. (1975). *The Natural Resources of the Sefton Metropolitan District Coast.* Unpublished report Lancashire Naturalists' Trust. JCAS database.

Smith, P. H. (1976). *The use by natterjack toads of the Formby Point denatured tobacco waste depositing area 1972-1976.* Unpublished report. *ASD 6/5/3/2/2.*

Smith, P. H. (1977). *Transplanting of endangered* Juncus balticus *x* effusus *at Hightown.* Unpublished report. *CH 6/12/1.*

Smith, P. H. (1977-1980). *Natterjack toad reports, Cabin Hill and Altcar Rifle Range.* Unpublished reports. *ASD 6/5/3/2/2.*

Smith, P. H. (1978). The Ecological Evaluation of Wetland Habitats in the North-Merseyside Sand-dune System. Report to Merseyside County Council. JCAS database 075 Da 071.

Smith, P. H. (1979-90). *Natterjack toad reports, Formby Point and Ravenmeols Hills.* Unpublished reports *ASD 6/5/3/2/2.*

Smith, P. H. (1980). *An Ecological Survey of Ravenmeols Sandhills and Foreshore, Formby Point.* Unpublished report, Merseyside County Council by Lancashire Trust for Nature Conservation. *NWBFDB.*

Smith, P. H. (1982a). *The Ecological Evaluation of Trust Sites in Sefton.* Unpublished report, Lancashire Trust for Nature Conservation.

Smith, P. H. (1982b). *A Report on yellow bartsia at Cabin Hill.* Unpublished report, Lancashire Trust for Nature Conservation. *NWBFDB 34/20/84.*

Smith, P. H. (1983a). *Ecology and management of Birkdale frontal dunes, Merseyside.* Unpublished report for Sefton Metropolitan Borough Council. Lancashire Trust for Nature Conservation. *JCAS 75 Da 74.*

Smith, P. H. (1983b). *The Ainsdale buffer strip: a preliminary report on its ecological interest.* Unpublished report, Lancashire Trust for Nature Conservation.

Smith, P. H. (1983c). *Status of Birds at Cabin Hill.* Unpublished provisional notes.

Smith, P. H. (1984a). *A strategy for the conservation of the natterjack toad in the north Merseyside sand dune system.* Unpublished report, Lancashire Trust for Nature Conservation. *ASD 6/5/3/2/2.*

Smith, P. H. (1984b). The distribution, status and conservation of *Juncus balticus* Wild. in England. *Watsonia,* **15,** 15-26.

Smith, P. H. (1984c). *The special plants of Hightown sand dunes and salt marsh.* Unpublished report, Lancashire Trust for Nature Conservation. *NWBFDB 34/20/94.*

Smith, P. H. (1989). Natterjacks at Altcar, Merseyside. *Ministry of Defence Conservation Journal,* 1989. *CH 6/12/1.*

Smith, P. H. (1990). Size differences of natterjack toads breeding in the North Merseyside Sand dunes. *Herpetological Journal,* l, 493-498.

Smith, P. H. & Bownes, C. F. (1978). *The use of artificial breeding pools by adult natterjack toads in Ainsdale Sand Dunes National Nature Reserve in 1978.* Unpublished report. *ASD 6/5/3/2/2.*

Smith, P. H., Harris, J. I. & Hancock, E. G. (1972). The natterjack toad in south-west Lancashire. 1972. *Nature in Lancashire,* **4,** 44-48 (1973-4).

Smith, P. H. & Flynn, D. H. (1977). *A population census of adult natterjack toads* (Bufo calamita) *at excavated breeding sites on Ainsdale Sand Dunes National Nature Reserve, Merseyside.* Unpublished report. *ASD 6/5/3/2/2.*

Smith, P.H. & Hall, R.A. (1991). The Isle of Man Cabbage in South Lancashire. *Lancashire Wildlife Journal,* **1,** 40-41.

Smith, P. H. & Payne, K. R. (1980). A survey of natterjack toad (*Bufo calamita*) distribution and breeding success in the north Merseyside sand dune system, England. *Biological Conservation,* **19,** 27-39.

Smith, R. H. (1957). *Freshfield to Ainsdale Ornithological Report.* Unpublished report. *EN, Blackwell.*

Smith, R. H. (1967). *The Breeding Birds of the Formby District 1954-63. Part 2.* Unpublished species list. *EN, Blackwell.*

Smith, R. H. & Henderson, M. (1955). *Ornithological Survey of Nature Reserves (1955); Ainsdale Dunes, Lancashire ASD.*

Smith, S. H. (1974a). *The National Nature Reserve, Ainsdale and adjoining lands, South-west Lancashire.* Unpublished report. *ASD 6/5/3/2/2.*

Smith, S. H. (1974b). *Hybridisation in the two species of amphibian* (Bufo bufo *and* Bufo calamita) *in controlled conditions and in the wild at Ainsdale, South-west Lancashire.* Unpublished M.Sc. thesis, University of Lancaster. *ASD 6/5/3/2/2.*

Smith, S. H. & Lambert, M. R. K. (1973). *The situation of breeding amphibians in sites between Southport and Formby, S. W. Lancashire, with special reference to the natterjack.* Unpublished report. *NWBFDB.*

Smyth, J. C. (1985). *Learning for Living: Environmental Education in Scotland.* Scottish Environmental Education Council.

Southport Visiter (1972). 250,000 toads being bred in back garden. *Southport Visitor, 29/4/72.*

Spellerberg, I. F. (1988). Ecology and management of *Lacerta agilis* L. populations in England. *Mertensiella,* **1,** 113-121.

Spencer, K. G. (1973). *The Status and Distribution of Birds in Lancashire.* Private Print, Burnley.

Staaf, H. & Berg, B. (1982). Accumulation and release of plant nutrients in decomposing Scots Pine needle litter. Long term decomposition in a Scots Pine forest II. *Canadian Journal of Botany,* **60,** 1561-1568.

Stace, C. A. (1970). Unique *Juncus* hybrids in Lancashire *Nature,* **226,** 180.

Stace, C. A. (1972). The history and occurrence in Britain of hybrids in *Juncus* subgenus *Genuini. Watsonia,* **9,** 1-11.

Stace, C. A. (1991). *New Flora of the British Isles.* Cambridge University Press, Cambridge.

Stansfield, H. (1936). The broad-leaved centaury *Centaurium latifolium* Druce (*Erythraea latifolia* Smith) *North Western Naturalist* **11,** 245-247.

Stewart, N. F. (1991). *Conservation Requirements of Threatened Lower Plants.* NCC CSD Contract report. **No. 1227.**

Stoney, R. E. (1988). *Environmental change and coastal development in south-west Lancashire.* Unpublished dissertation. Department of Geography, University of Durham.

Stuiver, M., Kromer, B., Becher, B. & Ferguson, C. W. (1986). Radiocarbon age calibration back to 13,300 years BP and the 14C age matching of the German oak and US Bristlecone Pine chronologies. *Radiocarbon,* **28,** 969-979.

Stuiver, M. & Reimer, P. J. (1986). A computer program for radiocarbon age calibration. *Radiocarbon,* **28,** 1022-1030.

Sturgess, P. W. (1988). Taggs Island, a survey. Unpublished report, Sefton Metropolitan Borough Council.

Sturgess, P. W. (1989a). Pine Plantations: Irreversible Damage to the Dune Ecosystem ? A Study of three British Nature Reserves. Unpublished paper. Dept. of Environmental and Evolutionary Biology, University of Liverpool. *ASD 2/2/1.*

Sturgess, P. W. (1989b). An Experimental Technique for the Creation of Dune Heath on the Sefton Coast. Unpublished paper. Liverpool University. *ASD files.*

Sturgess, P. W. (1990). The Ecological Impact of Clear-felling Dune Woodland. Interim Report: Ainsdale March 23rd 1990. Unpublished report. Dept. of Environmental and Evolutionary Biology, University of Liverpool.

Sturgess, P. W. (1991). *Post-felling vegetation changes on three afforested sand dune systems* Unpublished. Ph.D. thesis, University of Liverpool.

Sturgess, P. W. (in press). Sand dune plantations: Irreversible damage? *Proceedings of the 2nd European Coastal Dune Congress,* 1989. Seville.

Sumner, D. P. (1985). The geographical and seasonal distribution of the dragonflies of Lancashire and Cheshire, 1985. *108th Annual Report and Proceedings of the Lancashire and Cheshire Entomological Society 1984-85,* 177-194.

Sutton, R. D. (1982). *The Ecology of Three Species of Psyllid* (Homoptera: Psylloidea) *Living on Hawthorn* (Crataegus monogyna Jacq). Unpublished Ph.D. thesis, Liverpool Polytechnic.

Swinscow, T. D. V. (1965). Pyrenocarpous Lichens: 9. *Lichenologist* **3(1),** 72-83.

Taylor, C. (1983). *Village and Farmstead: a History of Rural Settlement in England.* George Phillip, London.

Terret, I. B. (1962). Lancashire. *The Domesday Geography of Northern England* (Ed by H.C. Derby & I.S. Maxwell). Cambridge University Press, Cambridge.

Thomas, A. (1989). Has fieldwork a future ? The Times Educational Supplement, 23rd June.

Thomas, S. K. (1973). Wintering siskins from an alder wood. *S. W. Lancashire Ringing Group Annual Report.*

Todd, D. K. (1959). *Groundwater Hydrology.* Wiley, New York

Tooley, M. J. (1969). *Sea-level Changes and the Development of Coastal Plant Communities during the Flandrian in Lancashire and adjacent areas.* Ph.D. Thesis, University of Lancaster.

Tooley, M. J. (1970). The peat beds of the South-west Lancashire coast. *Nature in Lancashire,* 1, 19-26.

Tooley, M. J. (1971). *Changes in sea-level and the implications for coastal development.* Association of River Authorities Yearbook, London, 220-225.

Tooley, M. J. (1973). Flandrian sea-level changes in north-west England and pan-North-west European correlations. *Internation Union of Quaternary Research 9th Congress,* Christchurch, New Zealand, 373-374.

Tooley, M. J. (1974). Sea-level changes during the last 9000 years of north-west England. *Geographical Journal,* 140, 18-42.

Tooley, M. J. (1976). Flandrian sea-level changes in west Lancashire and their implications for the 'Hillhouse coastline'. *Geological Journal,* 11(2), 37-52.

Tooley, M. J. (1977a). *The Isle of Man, Lancashire Coast and Lake District* (Ed. by D. Q. Bowen), Guidebook for Excursion A4, X INQUA Congress, Geoabstracts, Norwich.

Tooley, M. J. (1977b). The Quaternary of north-west England and the Isle of Man. *The Isle of Man, Lancashire Coast and Lake District* (Ed. by D. Q. Bowen), Guidebook for Excursion A4, X INQUA Congress, Geoabstracts, Norwich, 5-7.

Tooley, M. J. (1978a). *Sea-Level Changes in north-west England during the Flandrian Stage,* Oxford Research Studies in Geography, Clarendon Press, Oxford.

Tooley, M. J. (1978b). Interpretation of Holocene sea-level changes. *Geologiska Foreningens i Stockholm Forhandlingar,* 100(2), 203-212.

Tooley, M. J. (1979). Sea-level changes during the Flandrian Stage and the implications for coastal development. *Proceedings of the 1978 Symposium on Coastal Evolution in the Quaternary* (Ed. by K. Suguio et al), Universidade de Sao Paulo, Sao Paulo, Brazil, 502-533.

Tooley, M. J. (1980). Theories of coastal change in north-west England. *Archaeology and Coastal Change* (Ed. by F. H. Thompson), Society of Antiquaries, London, 74-86.

Tooley, M. J. (1982). Sea-level changes in northern England. *Proceedings of the Geologists' Association* 93(1), 43-51.

Tooley, M. J. (1985a). Sea level changes and coastal morphology in north-west England. *The geomorphology of north-west England* (ed. by R. H. Johnson), Manchester University Press, 94-121.

Tooley, M. J. (1985b). Climate, sea-level and coastal changes. *The Climatic Scene* (ed. by M. J. Tooley and G. M. Sheail), George Allen and Unwin, London, 206-234.

Tooley, M. J. (1990). The chronology of coastal dune development in the United Kingdom. *Catena Supplement* 18, 81-88.

Tooley, M. J. & Kear, B. (1977). Shirdley Hill Sand Formation. *The Isle of Man, Lancashire Coast and Lake District* (ed. by D. Q. Bowen), Guidebook for Excursion A4, X INQUA Congress, Geoabstracts, Norwich, 9-12.

Travis, C. B. (1926). The peat and forest bed of the south-west Lancashire coast. *Proceedings of the Liverpool Geological Society,* 14, 263-277.

Travis, C. B. (1929). The peat and forest beds of Leasowe, Cheshire. *Proceedings of the Liverpool Geological Society,* 15, 157-178.

Travis, W. G. (1908). On Plant Remains in Peat in the Shirdley Hill Sand at Aintree, South Lancashire. *Transactions of the Liverpool Botanical Society,* 1, 47-52.

Travis, W. G. (1915). Marram grass and dune formation on the Lancashire Coast. *Lancashire and Cheshire Naturalist,* 8, 313-320.

Travis, W. G. (1922a). On peaty beds in the Wallasey Sand-Hills. *Proceedings of the Liverpool Geological Society,* 13(3), 207-214.

Travis, W. G. (1922b).. Some south Lancashire myxomycetes. *Lancashire and Cheshire Naturalist,* 17(2), 187.

Travis, W. G. (1929). *Scirpus americanus Pers.* and *Weingaertneria canescens Bernh.* in Lancashire, *North Western Naturalist,* 4, 175-177.

Travis, W. G. (1943). *Epipactis vectensis* (Steph.) Brooke & Rose in Lancashire, *North Western Naturalist,* 18, 326.

Travis, W. G. (1947). A new British lichen. *North Western Naturalist,* 22, 240-1.

Trees, H. (1981). Analysis of the Formby Point visitor survey, 5th July 1981, Unpublished Outdoor Education project, Liverpool Polytechnic.

Tucker, M. J. (1963). Analysis of records of sea waves. *Proceedings of the Institution of Civil Engineers,* 26, 304-316.

Turner, A. (1934). South Lancashire Bryophyta. *North Western Naturalist,* 9, 160.

Turner, D. A. (1984). *A guide to the Sefton Coast Data Base.* Metropolitan Borough of Sefton, Engineer's Department. Sefton Coast Data Base.

Tuscon, J. (1989). Possible environmental impact of the proposed Mersey Barrage, with reference to the development of *Spartina anglica* at Hightown saltmarsh. Undergraduate dissertation, North East Wales Institute (JCAS database) 75 Db 3.

University of Liverpool. (1976). *Rehabilitation of Sand Dunes - Formby Point.* 10 pp. Environmental Rehabilitation Unit, Department of Botany. JCAS database. 055 Ma 001 / 075 Ma 056.

University of Liverpool. (1978). *Landscape Restoration at Victoria Road, Formby Point. Survey of water Table Depth, Soil and Water Chemistry.* 23 pp. Environmental Advisory Service, Department of Botany. *JCAS 055 Ma 009.*

VCH III. (1907). *The Victoria History of the Counties of England.* Archibald Constable, London. LRO.

Van Dijk, H. W. J. (1989). Ecological impact of drinking-water production in Dutch coastal dunes. *Perspectives in Coastal Dune Management.* F. van der Meulen, P. D. Jungerius and J. H. Visser, pp.163-182. SPB Academic Publishing, The Hague.

Van Huis, J. (1989). European dunes, climate and climatic change, with case studies of the Coto Donana (Spain) and The Slowinski (Poland) national parks. (*Perspectives in Coastal Dune Management.*) F. van der Meulen, P. D. Jungerius and J.H. Visser, pp. 313-326. SPB Academic Publishing, The Hague.

Van Zadelhoff, F. J. (1981). Nederlandse Kustduinen: Geobotanie. Pudoc, Wageningen.

Van der Laan, D. (1979). Spatial and temporal changes in the vegetation of dune slacks in relation to the groundwater regime. *Vegetatio,* **39,** 43-51.

Van der Laan, D. (1985). Changes in the flora and vegetation of the coastal dunes of Voorne (The Netherlands) in relation to environmental changes. *Vegetatio,* **61,** 87-95.

Van der Maarel, E. (1979). Environmental management of coastal dunes in The Netherlands. *Ecological processes in coastal environments.* (R. L. Jefferies and A. J. Davy). Blackwell Scientific Publications, London. pp. 543-570.

Van der Meulen, F. (1990). Landscape ecological impact on coastal dunes of Europe. *Eurodunes,* **2,** 47-54.

Van der Meulen, F., Jungerius, P. D. & De Groot, R. S. (1989). *Landscape Ecological Impact of Climatic Change on Coastal Dunes in Europe.* Discussion report prepared for the European Conference on Landscape Ecological Impact of Climatic Change, Lunteren, The Netherlands, December 1989. Universities of Wageningen, Utrecht and Amsterdam.

Van der Zande, A. N., (1989). Outdoor Recreation and Dune Conservation in the Netherlands. *Perspectives in Coastal Dune Management.* (Ed F. van der Meulen *et al.*) pp. 207-215.

Venner, J. (1977). The eradication of *Hippophae rhamnoides L* from the Braunton Burrows sand dune system. Unpublished report NCC.

Vitousek, P. M. (1981). Clear-cutting and the nitrogen cycle. *Terrestrial Nitrogen Cycles. Ecological Bulletin.* **33,** 631-642.

Waddington, W. (1938). Diatoms found in Southport. *Report of the Southport Scientific Society for 1937-38,* 195-197.

Waddington, W. (1939). Diatoms found in Southport, first supplementary list. *Report of the Southport Scientific Society for 1938-39,* 215-218.

Wagstaffe, R. (1932). Birds of the south west Lancashire coast. *23rd Report, Southport Society of Natural Science* pp. 15-16.

Wagstaffe, R. (1934). The birds of Southport and district with notes on their distribution and status. *Report of The Southport Scientific Society* **4**.

Wagstaffe, R. (1935). Ornithology *26th Report Southport Society of Natural Science* pp. 26-27.

Wall, R. (1985). *Competition and the Individual: Intraspecific Competition in the Common Field Grasshopper* Chorthippus brunneus, *Thunberg (Orthoptera: Acrididae).* Unpublished Ph.D. thesis, University of Liverpool.

Wallace, I. D. (1981). Ainsdale National Nature Reserve, Moth Night 8th July 1981. Unpublished list.

Warrick, R. & Farmer, G. (1990). The greenhouse effect, climatic change and rising sea level: implications for development. *Transactions of the Institute of British Geographers,* New Series **15,** 5-20.

Watling, R. & Rotheroe, M. (1989) Macrofungi of sand dunes. *Proceedings of the Royal Society of Edinburgh,* **96B,** 111-126.

Waughman, G. J. (1972). Acetylene reduction assay for nitrogen fixation in sand dunes. *Oikos,* **23,** 206-212.

Westhoff, V. (1947). *The vegetation of dunes and saltmarshes on the Dutch islands of Terschelling, Vlieland and Texel.* Thesis. C. J. van der Horst, The Hague.

Whalley Coucher (1847). *The Coucher Book or Chartulary of Whalley Abbey* (ed. W.A. Hulton). Chetham Society. **Vol I.** pp 489-531.

Wharfe, A. J. & James, P. A. (1985). Atmospheric sulphur dioxide and rainwater pH at a coastal locality in N. W. England. *Water, Air and Soil Pollution,* **25,** 237-242.

Wharfe, A. J. (1984). *Towards a cation budget for a coastal sand dune system.* Unpublished Ph.D. thesis, University of Liverpool. 372 pp.

Wheeler, D. J. & Carty, P. (1985). *Status and Ecology of Crested Newt Triturus cristatus.* Ainsdale records for NCC-commissioned Leicester Polytechnic project. Unpublished survey recording forms. *ASD 6/5/3/2/2.*

Wheeler, D. J. (1984a). Survey of artificial ponds dug for natterjack toads. Ainsdale National Nature Reserve records for national survey by T. Beebee, Sussex Univ. Unpublished survey recording forms. *6/5/3/2/2.*

Wheeler, D. J. (1984b). Ainsdale National Nature Reserve, Management Proposals for Erosion Control on Frontal Dunes. Unpublished report NCC. *ASD 2/3/1.*

Wheeler, D. J. (1986a). Ainsdale National Nature Reserve: Management Plan. Prescriptive section including natterjack toad, sand lizard, great-crested newt and red squirrel 1986. Unpublished NCC. *ASD 2/1.*

Wheeler, D. J. (1986b). Status and ecology of crested newt, *Triturus cristatus.* Ainsdale records for NCC commissioned Leicester Polytechnic project. Unpublished survey recording forms. *ASD 6/5/3/2/2.*

Wheeler, D. J. (1986c). Ainsdale Sand Dunes National Nature Reserve. Management Plan Part 2 Evaluation and Objectives. Unpublished paper NCC.

Wheeler, D. J. (1987). *Ainsdale Sand Dunes National Nature Reserve, Sand Lizard Vivarium Report 1985.* Unpublished report in file ASD 2/6/2/2/2.

Wheeler, D. J. (1988). Ainsdale Sand Dunes National Nature Reserve - Coastal Erosion Control, Mid-Term Assessment. Unpublished report NCC. *ASD 2/3/1.*

Wheeler, D. J. (1989). Ainsdale Sand Dunes National Nature Reserve Dune Grazing Project. Project Plan. Unpublished report NCC. *ASD 2/6/1/9.*

Wheeler, D. J. (1990). Ainsdale Sand Dunes National Nature Reserve. Recreation of open Yellow Dunes. Unpublished report NCC. *ASD 2/2/5.*

Wheldon, H. J. (1914). The fungi of the sand dune formation of the Lancashire coast. *Lancashire and Cheshire Naturalists* **7** 5-10, 61-64, 88-91, 131-134, 193-196, 217-219.

Wheldon, J. A. (1898). The mosses of South Lancashire. *Journal of Botany,* **36,** 133-40.

Wheldon, J. A. (1899). The mosses of South Lancashire. *Journal of Botany,* **37,** 11-16.

Wheldon, J. A. (1903). Mosses and Hepatics. *British Association Handbook to Southport.*

Wheldon, J. A. (1910). New Lancashire Lichens. *Lancashire Naturalist*, **3**, 192-4.

Wheldon, J. A. (1911). Curious Lancashire Fungi. *Lancashire Naturalist*, **4**, 55-60.

Wheldon, J. A. (1912). Lancashire Ascomycetes. *Journal of Botany*, **50** 182-193.

Wheldon, J. A. (1913a). The dry dune flora in June. *Lancashire Naturalist*, **6**, 110.

Wheldon, J. A. (1913b). The *Oenothera* of the South Lancashire Coast *Lancashire Naturalist*, **6**, 205-210.

Wheldon, J. A. (1914). On the older sand dunes at Ainsdale. *Lancashire and Cheshire Naturalist*, **7**, 149-150.

Wheldon, J. A. (1915a). On the sand dunes at Ainsdale. *Lancashire and Cheshire Naturalist*, **8**, 123-124.

Wheldon, J. A. (1915b). *Bidens minima* Huds. *Lancashire and Cheshire Naturalist*, **8**, 224.

Wheldon, J. A. (1918). The fungus flora of Lancashire. *Lancashire and Cheshire Naturalist*, **11(124)**, 103-8; **(125)**, 139-43; **(126)**, 166-9; **(127)**, 181; **(131)**, 281-312.

Wheldon, J. A. & Travis, W. G. (1915). The Lichens of South Lancashire. *Journal of the Linnean Society (Botany)*, **43**, 87-136.

Whitehead, P. (1985). Letter to P. J. Knights, R.O. Blackrod. Unpublished. *ASD 6/6/1/57*.

Whittaker, J. B. (1965). Some homoptera, Auchenorrhynca, from the Ainsdale Sand Dunes National Reserve, Lancashire. *Entomologists Monthly Magazine*, **101**, 124.

Whittaker, O. (1906). A preliminary catalogue of the Hemiptera - Heteroptera of Lancashire and Cheshire. *Proceedings of the Lancashire and Cheshire Entomological Society*, **30**, 32-45.

Whitticase, K. M. (1985). *An Investigation of the Small Mammal Population of Adjacent Coniferous and Dune Slack Habitats*. Unpublished thesis. *ASD*.

Wilkinson, H. R., Monkhouse, F. J. & Smith, W. (1953). *A Scientific Survey of Merseyside*. British Association, University Press. Liverpool.

Williams, B. L. (1972). Nitrogen mineralisation and organic matter decomposition in Scots Pine humus. *Forestry*, **45**,177-188.

Williams, D. R. (1974). *Sites of Ornithological Importance near Formby. NWBFDB*.

Williams, D. R. (1977). The autumn migration seasons of warblers through S. W. Lancs. 1971-76. *S. W. Lancashire Ringing Group Annual Report*.

Williams, D. R. (1978). Ringing at Cabin Hill, Formby. *S. W. Lancashire Ringing Group Annual Report*.

Williams, T. S. (1936). *Bird Life round Formby. Observations on Wild Duck*. Unpublished Report. *NWBFDB*.

Williams, T. S. (1939). *Our Bird Population*. Formby Lancs. RSPB gold medal. *NWBFDB*.

Williams, T. S. (1942). Bird Life of the Formby District. *North Western Naturalist*, **17**. *NWBFDB*.

Willis, A. J., Folkes, B. F., Hope-Simpson, J. F. and Yemm, E. W. (1959). Braunton Burrows: The dune system and its vegetation. Parts I and II. *Journal of Ecology*, **47**, 1-24, 249-288.

Wilson, J. C. (1912). New and rare mosses in Lancashire. *Lancashire Naturalist*, **5**, 102, 260, 391.

Wilson, P. (1985). The Mere Sands of Lancashire - a forgotten Flandrian deposit. *Quaternary Newsletter*, **45**, 23-26.

Wilson, P., Bateman, R. M. & Catt, J. A. (1981). Petrography, origin and environment of deposition of the Shirdley Hill Sand of South-west Lancashire. *Proceedings of the Geologists' Association*, **92**, 211-229.

Wolfenden, I. H. (1973). Results from ringing greenfinches. *S. W. Lancashire Ringing Group Annual Report*.

Wolfenden, I. H. (1978). A study of breeding skylarks in 1978. *S. W. Lancashire Ringing Group Annual Report*.

Wolfenden, I. H. (1979a). The reed bunting (*Emberiza schoeniclus*) in Sefton-Merseyside. *S. W. Lancashire Ringing Group Annual Report*.

Wolfenden, I. H. (1979b). Colour-ringed skylarks. *S. W. Lancashire Ringing Group Annual Report*.

Wolfenden, I. H. (1980). The birds of the Crosby-Hightown dunes. *S. W. Lancashire Ringing Group Annual Report*.

Wolfenden, I. H. (1984). A study of colour-ringed skylarks: some initial results. *S. W. Lancashire Ringing Group Annual Report*.

Wolfenden, I. H. (1985). Some information from nest-recording and pulli-ringing. *S. W. Lancashire Ringing Group Annual Report*.

Wolfenden, I. H. (1986). *Ringing at Altcar Rifle Range*. Unpublished report. *ASD*.

Wolfenden, I. H. (1989). Some results from a skylark colour-ringing project. *S. W. Lancashire Ringing Group Annual Report*.

Wood, K. W. (1978). *Magpie Study* Unpublished report. *ASD*.

Wood, K. W. (1982-84). *Ainsdale Winter Atlas Records by Habitat*. Unpublished annual records. *ASD*.

Wood, K. W. (1984-86) *Cabin Hill Bird Notes and Related Weather Notes*. Unpublished. *CH*.

Wood, K. W. (undated). *Ainsdale Winter Bird Survey Records*. Unpublished. *ASD*.

Wood, P. (1980). *Merseyside Structure Plan. Written Statement*. Merseyside County Council.

Wood, P. (1985). *Sefton Coast Management Scheme, Dune Restoration at Formby Point. Report of Environmental Improvement Works carried out by Merseyside County Council 1977-1985*. Unpublished report, 17pp. Merseyside County Council, Liverpool. *JCAS database 055 Ma 005*

Wray, D. A. & Cope, F. W. (1948). Geology of Southport and Formby. One Inch Geological Sheets 74 and 83. *Memoirs of the Geological Survey of the UK.*, HMSO, London.

Wright, A. E. (1941). Lepidoptera and Diptera from Formby, Lancashire. *Northwestern Naturalist* **16**, 87-88.

Wright, J. E., Hull, J. H., McQuillin, R & Arnold, S. E. (1971). Irish Sea Investigations 1969-71, *Institute of Geological Sciences Report 71/19*, HMSO, London.

Wright, P. (1976). *The morphology, sedimentary structures and processes of the foreshore at Ainsdale, Merseyside, England.* Ph.D. Thesis, University of Reading.

Wright, S. & Cooke, A. S. (1982). *Map of Lizard Area at Big Balls Hill.* Note in NCC files.

Wright, W. B. (1914). *The Quaternary Ice Age*, Macmillan, London.

Wrigley, J. (1893). *Notes on the bird life of Formby 1892.* Privately published.

Yalden, D. W. (1980a). A reply. letters to the editor, *British Journal of Herpetology,* **5,** 105-106.

Yalden, D. W. (1980b). An alternative explanation of the distribution of the rare herpetiles in Britain. *British Journal of Herpetology,* **6,** 37-40.

Young, J. O. & Williams, T. R. (1968). *List of Invertebrates Collected in Massam's slack ditch with course-mesh Freshwater Biological Association hand-net on 29/8/68.* Unpublished list. *NWBFDB.*

Zeevalking, H. J. & Fresco, L. F. M (1977). Rabbit grazing and species diversity in a dune area. *Vegetatio,* **35,** 193-196.

INDEX